The
Princess Alice M

Hospital
Eastbourne

and other Eastbourne hospitals

John Surtees

Foreword by HRH The Prince Philip Duke of Edinburgh

Published
by the
Eastbourne Local History Society
1994

ISBN 0 9504560 5 5 (Pbk)

by the same author
The House Physician's Handbook (jointly)
Barracks workhouse and hospital, St Mary's Eastbourne 1794-1990

Cover illustrations:-

Front: Water-colour of the Princess Alice Memorial Hospital c. 1900.
Back:
    -Upper left: Downside Hospital, Nurses' Home and Lodge. For Sale 1980.
    -Upper right: Gildredge Hospital. Kitchen and Nurses' Home in front,
                patients' cubicles in background, 1976.
    -Lower left: 1-3 Marine Road, the Leaf Homoeopathic Hospital 1888-1934.
    -Lower right: The Maternity Home, 1920-76, from Southfields Road.
Spine: Nurses' badge of the Princess Alice Memorial Hospital.

Printed in Great Britain
by
Sumfield & Day Ltd
Eastbourne BN21 4RQ
Tel 0323 720455   Fax 0323 411230

CONTENTS

~

ILLUSTRATIONS

ILLUSTRATIONS (continued)

ACKNOWLEDGMENTS

Thanks are due to all contributors, with especial appreciation for the help from Mrs Doris M. Bates, Miss Elizabeth Brockhurst, Mr H.N. Brook, Brigadier A. Crook *MC,* Miss Jean Dowden, Mr R.A. Elliston, Mrs E. Field, Miss B.E. Halsall, Miss Vera Hodsoll, Miss Marie Lewis, Mr P.G. Jenkins, Brigadier Miles Hunt-Davis CBE, Mrs A. Reed, Mr L.T. Spearing, Mr Harold Spears, Mrs E.R. Tucker, Mr H. Weavers, Mrs H.J. Wells, and Mr John Cant for the cover design.

For photographs thanks are due to Mrs R. Flude, Mrs C. Foord, Mrs W.G. Harriott, Mrs M. Hastings, Miss V. Kendrick, Mrs D. Kingsford, Mrs A. Ledgerwood, Mrs K.M. Partington, Miss M.E. Quick and Mrs M.E. Spearing.

I have received invaluable support from my wife, Sheila, and from Stephen K. Bangert, Sir Brian McGrath KCVO, John D. O'Connor, Noel Primrose and Nicholas R. Taylor, as well as Liz Oliver-Taylor of the Eastbourne Postgraduate Medical Centre, the Central Library, Eastbourne, the County Record Office, Lewes, and Penelope Johnson and Catherine Tonge, Curator and Assistant Curator at the Towner Art Gallery and Local History Museum, Eastbourne.

Acknowledgments are due to the *Daily Express, Eastbourne Herald, Gazette, Echo,* the *Eastbourne Medical Gazette,* the Brighton *Evening Argus,* the *Nursing Mirror, Eastbourne, A Pictorial History,* D.R. Elleray (Phillimore, Chichester 1978), Harry C. Deal, press photographer, and reporters: Mollie Leach, Gary Noakes, Janette Rapley, Jeannine Williamson.

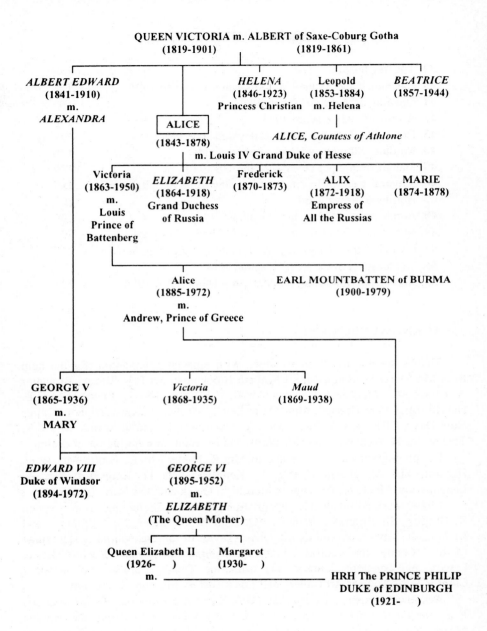

1. Relevant Genealogical Table. Members of the Princess Alice's family mentioned in the book are in capital letters; those in italics visited the hospital.

6

FOREWORD

by

HRH The Prince Philip Duke of Edinburgh KG, KT

BUCKINGHAM PALACE

Local history is not just something of academic interest, it is part of the fabric of a local community. It reflects the changes in customs and attitudes and explains why things are the way they are today.

There is a Princess Alice Memorial Hospital in Eastbourne, but the question is why should it be there? Why should the wife of the ruler of a Grand Duchy in Germany be commemorated in Eastbourne by the building of a hospital funded by public subscription? Those are the questions that John Surtees answers in this little book.

It might also be asked why am I writing a foreword to this book. It so happens that Princess Alice was Queen Victoria's second daughter and my great grandmother. I know the places where she lived in Hesse and as a boy I stayed with her son, my great uncle, then the Grand Duke of Hesse. The family connection was made even closer when my third sister married his eldest son.

I am naturally delighted that Dr. Surtees and the Eastbourne Local History Society have compiled and published this interesting account of a piece of Eastbourne's history.

2. HRH Princess Alice, Grand Duchess of Hesse, 1878 {Towner
Art Gallery and Local History Museum, Eastbourne}.

PREFACE

When Mrs Hilda Wells (née de Pinto), a former matron of the Princess Alice Memorial Hospital, read the St Mary's Hospital book and wrote to say that Eastbourne's other hospitals deserved a book as well, I doubted whether there was enough material for an Eastbourne Local History Society publication. There were no barracks or workhouse - in the case of the Princess Alice just 110 years of an average, provincial hospital.

Yet as Chesterton said, 'Nothing is real unless it is local'. I soon realised that the Princess Alice was exactly that, a microcosm of the Victorian Voluntary Hospital. It was the other side of the coin to the St Mary's account: instead of the stench of pauperism and a successful struggle to overcome extremes of tyranny and poverty, it typified gentilism, "select Eastbourne"; patients even thought of it as a "home from home", and intense pride was generated in "our hospital".

As such, it represented a rich seam of changing social attitudes and the local impact of medical and nursing developments. There was the surgeon who, having stated in 1888 that there was no place for operation in appendicitis, by 1902 was saying that early operation was the best treatment. There was the hospital report that a patient was "not a fit case" and should be sent to the Union Infirmary instead. The fashions of the day are reflected in the response to the discovery of X-rays, insulin, antibiotics and other advances.

The hospital fabric could always be improved, but not the human fibre. Personalities strode the wards, representing the church, business, the doctors and nurses. Especially the nurses, for these hospitals encapsulate the days of the single woman married to her nursing profession, dedicated to her ward, and devoted to her patients. She took no time off, she was first on the ward of a morning, she made everyone else look as if they were standing still, she always found a job for anyone who put in an appearance, and she tucked-in each and every patient and bid them good-night before she retired at the end of her long day. Their hey-day was 1890 to 1950, and although their like is gone, they are not forgotten: Miss Lancaster, Miss Coggan, Miss Clark - and Miss Bailey, matron of "Downside" Fever Hospital for over 40 years, who hardly ever left the place and who died in harness. Such service was found in all the staff. Mr Crook started as a surgeon in 1914 and when he reached the time limit in 1937 switched jobs, so that he could continue for another 14 years. Mr Pumfrey was hospital secretary 1935-1975, Miss Wortley a domestic 1934-1975, and Mr Pilbeam a porter 1939-1970. It was not so much a job for life as a life for the job.

This is their story. All I have done, however imperfectly, is to set down the record.

Eastbourne 1993.

3. The front of the Princess Alice Hospital in the 1880s (top) and 1990s, both from the area of Hartfield Road. The half timbering of the centre gables has been lost, but the four gable ends, altered over the years are recognisable - as is the bicyclist in front of the hospital.

Chapter 1

Princess Alice, an end to the beginning

To die in your thirties, or younger, was commonplace in Victorian times. Dr A.C. Tait, later Archbishop of Canterbury, lost five children from scarlet fever over a month in 1856. Even a princess might die of diphtheria, for in Britain over 3000 children died every year of the disease, until the immunisation campaigns of the 1940s. So while Princess Alice's death from diphtheria at the age of 35 was sad, it was far from a surprise.

Princess Alice was born on April 25th 1843, the third child and second daughter of Queen Victoria, inheriting her father's ability and ideals. She married Prince Louis, Grand Duke of Hesse, who was described as "good, kind and courageous" but no intellectual match for her, and had seven children.[1] The Earl Mountbatten of Burma was a grandson, and she was the great-grandmother of His Royal Highness, the Prince Philip, Duke of Edinburgh.

She had her full share of tragedy. As a young girl, in 1861, she took the brunt of Queen Victoria's grief, when Prince Albert died of typhoid fever, and in 1873 her second son, who was a haemophiliac, died at the age of three, having fallen from his mother's bedroom window. She was also the mother of Princess Alix, who was to be assassinated, in 1918, by the Bolsheviks along with her husband, the Tsar, and all their family.[2]

In September 1878 Princess Alice spent a holiday in Eastbourne, with the Grand Duke and their children. While in the town she made her usual good impression, opening fêtes, patronising events and taking a deep interest in the various institutions of the town, particularly those which ministered to people in trouble. G.F. Chambers wrote, "...This visit was a great 'lift' for the Bazaar, which yielded £720".[3]

In such ways she endeared herself to all Eastbournians. Even those who were not closely associated with her could not fail to be aware of her name when, during her stay, a paddle steamer, the *Princess Alice,* on an excursion from Sheerness to Woolwich, collided with the collier, *Bywell Castle,* and sank in five minutes with the loss of 600 lives - still the greatest peace-time disaster of the River Thames.

After the sojourn in Eastbourne Princess Alice returned to her German court. In the November, however, her children developed diphtheria and Marie, her beloved youngest daughter, died of the disease. She nursed them all, and just when it was clear that her youngest son would recover, Princess Alice went down with the illness and died a few days later.

The people of Eastbourne were shocked when news of the tragedy reached them, and they determined to commemorate her good deeds and her pleasant, popular personality, and to ensure some good would arise from the tragedy.

The town already had the Princess Alice Tree [cut down for the War Memorial in 1920], and Christ Church, Seaside, where Princess Alice had worshipped during her stay, installed a memorial window,[4] but something more was required and the obvious response was a clock tower - a popular manifestation of affection in the days when most domestic clocks were not good time-keepers, when great store was kept on punctuality and when to own a personal watch, on a waistcoat chain, was a mark of the establishment.

A fund was set up and it was soon evident that the princess's place in the hearts of Eastbournians was such that, with the money collected, the town could have become a little Switzerland of clocks, and the alternative proposal of a drinking fountain was similarly oversubscribed. A Mr Percival of Bolton Road made the suggestion that, if real benefit were to come out of tragedy, a hospital would be a fitting memorial to the noble life and kindly recollections of Princess Alice. There is no doubt that her life had been devoted to the care of those in pain and need, and she was especially renowned for her interest in nursing, having tended the wounded in the 1866 Austro-Prussian war. She had also corresponded with Florence Nightingale, created nursing associations in Germany, one of which, the *Alice Frauenverein,* celebrated its centenary in 1967, and Sir Brian McGrath has reminded me that she founded a hospital in Darmstadt which still goes under her name to-day.

Orchestrated by the Revd Thomas Pitman, Vicar of Eastbourne, there had been correspondence in the local newspapers for some years on the need for a voluntary hospital in Eastbourne, so Mr Percival's suggestion was greeted with enthusiasm.

At a public meeting held on 19th April 1879, a committee was formed with the Vicar of Eastbourne as chairman. The committee was entrusted with the erection of a Cottage Hospital as a suitable memorial to the late Princess Alice of Great Britain, Grand Duchess of Hesse, and to obtain subscriptions. It was decided that the proposed hospital be called the "Princess Alice Memorial Hospital" and that it should provide not less than 12 beds, this being considered a suitable number to serve a population of 25000.

Three medical men, Drs Robert Colgate, George Mundie and Bransby Roberts, reported that it was desirable to build a hospital, capable of extension, on a site of about two acres, which combined the elements of plenty of sunlight and fresh air. "No time should be lost ... as owing to the rapid spread of the town, we fear that all the available situations will in a short time be built over".[5]

Plans were prepared by Mr T.W. Cutler, and the tender of Mr William Gregar amounting to £4357 was accepted.

Later there was disagreement over the choice of site. So heated was the discussion that most members of the original committee, including the chairman, resigned. The Duke of Devonshire had offered two sites. One, in Beachy Head Road, was considered to be too far from the centre of the town, while the other site, which adjoined Ocklynge Cemetery, received no support whatsoever.

As a result an approach was made to Eastbourne's other great landowner, Mr Carew Davies Gilbert, who gave the committee a site in St Leonard's Road, close to the Cavendish railway bridge. All looked well until it was ascertained that the railway company intended to build a "Goods Yard" adjoining the hospital site, when the in-fighting began again: "the site was too near the railway line for smuts" and "the shunting yards would keep patients awake at night"; arguments perhaps not unreasonable in the days of steam and sulphuretted smoke.

It was only a few days before the date fixed for commencing work that this site was abandoned. Mr Davies Gilbert then gave the present site at the end of Hartfield Road.[6]

The Duke of Devonshire took it all in good part and gave £400 towards the hospital in lieu of providing the site.

All these negotiations wasted time and it was not until 1882 that building started and the foundation stone was laid on 5th July by HRH Princess Christian, a younger sister of Princess Alice.[7] This was the first official visit by a member of the Royal family to the town. The stone was visible in the front wall of the hospital until alterations in 1959. It can still be discerned as part of the wall decorations of a porter's room, partly obscured by a heating radiator.

There was an unfortunate difference of opinion between the committee and the Eastbourne Provident Dispensary "which led to a rupture and the loss of £1000 which was to have been contributed towards the hospital". In the event the dispensary and the hospital went their own ways. By the end of the year the exterior was finished and the work of furnishing the interior was given a welcome stimulus by the news that the hospital was to be opened by the Prince of Wales in the summer of 1883.

The Royal family were closely involved, "Her Majesty the Queen was pleased to present several steel engravings of portraits of herself and the late Prince Consort ... and Princess Beatrice sent some embroidery of her own work". There was also liberal support by many in the neighbourhood, from £163 presented by the Dowager Lady Lilford and £100 each by G.P. Wragge Esq., G.K. Smith Esq., and H.J. Gouldsmith Esq., to ten shillings from Mrs Braybrook of the High Street.

The opening day was arranged for Saturday, 30th June 1883, when HRH Prince of Wales (later King Edward VII), accompanied by the Princess of Wales and the Princess Elizabeth of Hesse, second daughter of the late Princess Alice, would perform the ceremony.[8, 9] In the meantime, the Prince expressed a deep interest in the hospital, asked to become a patron, and gave a hundred guineas [£105] to the general fund.[10]

There was much to do for the first patient was to be admitted the next day.

Notes and References

1. Noel G. *Princess Alice.* (Constable, London 1974).

2. The Prince Philip, Duke of Edinburgh, has been helping through DNA matching to prove that the human remains recently discovered could have been those of the Russian Royal Family. His Royal Highness is, of course, a direct descendant through the female line of the unfortunate Tsarina's mother.

3. Chambers GF. *Eastbourne Memories.* (Sumfield, Eastbourne 1910).

4. The memorial window was installed in 1879 in the chancel of Christ Church, Seaside, Eastbourne. The inscription reads, *To the Glory of God and in Memory of HRH The Grand Duchess of Hesse, Princess Alice of Great Britain and Ireland, who was a worshipper in this church and took a deep interest in this parish.*

5. Princess Alice Memorial Hospital, Annual Report, 1884.

6. On 14/10/1881 Carew Davies Gilbert conveyed a "plot of land for the erection of a Cottage Hospital situate at Upperton", this was the St Leonards Road/railway bridge site. The Charity Commissioners agreed the transfer of land, 17/4/1883, but the date of the deed of exchange was not until after the hospital opened. The trustees agreed to pay Carew Davies Gilbert £250 for "one rood and two perches of land along Carew Road", and to a payment of 2/2d [11p] annually, being their proportion of the Vicarial tithe rent charge for the triangular area between Carew and Bedfordwell Roads, and 17/8d [88p] annually for the Rectorial tithe rent charge.

7. Helena Augusta Victoria, Princess Christian, was born 1846, the third daughter of Queen Victoria. She married Prince Christian of Schleswig-Holstein-Sondenburg in 1866. She died on 9th June 1923 after a life noted for its philanthropic work.

8. *Illustrated London News,* 30/6/1883: 648.

9. Princess Elizabeth of Hesse, the second child of Princess Alice, was born in 1864. She married the Grand Duke Serge Alexandrovitch in 1884. Sir Brian McGrath has drawn to my attention that after her husband's assassination in Red Square, Moscow, in 1905, she founded a religious order of nursing nuns in Russia under the name of Martha and Mary. She suffered the fate of her sister, Alix, Empress of All the Russias, being assassinated by the Bolsheviks in 1918. She has since been canonised by the Russian Orthodox Church. Her signature appears in the Princess Alice Memorial Hospital Visitors' Book. See Figure 1 the genealogical table.

10. The Prince of Wales was close to his younger sister, and she had "tenderly nursed" him through typhoid fever in 1871.

Chapter 2

A Royal Opening

The *Eastbourne Gazette* wrote, "The reception accorded Their Royal Highnesses was totally devoid of the blatant and unmeaning noise of the rabble which is held by the unthinking to be a necessary adjunct on such occasions.[1]

"The vast crowds which pressed the barriers were, it was easy to see, importations from adjoining towns, the bulk seeing their future Sovereign for the first time. These, acting with untutored judgment which did them credit, accorded the Royal party a respectful and reverential welcome, in silence unbroken until the august cortège had moved away, when one of the spectators with an irrepressible cheer, opened the floodgates of welcome borne on the breezes to the cavalcade."

Eastbourne was coming of age. The new Borough Council was to be elected in 1883, the town had doubled in size over the previous decade and civic pride was swelling in the inhabitants' breasts. The visit of the Prince and Princess of Wales to open the Bedfordwell Pumping Station, not forgetting the new hospital, set the town agog.

The only fear was that by too great a show of bunting the natural beauty of the thoroughfares, along which the Royal procession was to pass, would be marred. There was, in practice, just sufficient to demonstrate the unmistakable loyalty of the town without distracting from its arboreal profusion. The weather was, as always, the imponderable, but behaved itself impeccably - a rainstorm the previous night settled the dusty streets, and the morning was clear.

The *Eastbourne Gazette* of the day displayed a visitors' list of the worthies who had chosen Eastbourne for their holidays, along with advertisements for Scotch Whisky at 3/6d [17½p] a bottle. Mark Martin advertised from the Steam Joinery Works; Joseph Gibbs, Homoeopathic Chemist, was in Terminus Road, Nevill Strange, Ladies and Children's Outfitters, promoted the *Patent Diagonal Curative Magnetic Corset,* and A.D. Harmer, Chemist and Druggist, was already dispensing in South Street.[2]

"Those who had early taken up their positions ... were not left without entertainment. Ethiopian minstrels, recently arrived from their native village of east Whitechapel, in all the glories of burnt-cork, gave noisy if not harmonious exhibitions of their skill. Those so minded could purchase for a penny likenesses of their Royal Highnesses vended by street merchants."

After Mr Dean, the stationmaster, had announced that the train had passed Polegate, it swiftly glided into the station, met by a salute of twenty-one guns and members of the committee, whose main concern appeared to be 'What shall we wear?' and who included the Rt Hon. the Marquis of Hartington, Mrs Wallis, Carew Davies Gilbert, Dr C.N. Hayman and Mr J.G. Towner. The 1st Sussex Artillery Volunteers, under Capt. W.A. Cardwell, provided a guard of honour within the station.

The Clerk to the Local Board, Mr J.H. Campion Coles, expeditiously disposed of the address to His Royal Highness by handing the text to the Prince, who in like manner communicated his reply.

4. *The Graphic* of 7th July 1883 showing the main events of the opening day. 1. The Royal procession in Terminus Road. 2. The hospital. 3. Presentation of purses and 4. The fishermen's arch.

Miss Florence Wallis, a daughter of the mayor-to-be Mr G.A. Wallis, "a golden-haired maiden of some ten summers" and "looking for all the world like one of those pleasing creations conjured up by Hans Christian Andersen in his ever delightful fairy tales", had the privilege of presenting a bouquet to her Royal Highness. The handsome bouquet contained orchids, eucharis, white lilies, roses and maiden-hair fern.

Their Royal Highnesses had arrived from London "a little before one o'clock" and they proceeded at once to the hospital. The 4th Dragoon Guards, quartered at Brighton and commanded by Captain Darley, provided the escort. The Duke of Devonshire was not able to attend, but was represented by the Marquis of Hartington and Lord Edward Cavendish, the Lord Lieutenant of the County. The Bishop of the Diocese and Sir Thomas and Lady Brassey were among those who had accepted invitations.

The head of the procession continued past the hospital in the direction of The Avenue until a flourish of trumpets announced the advent of the Royal carriage opposite the pavilion, which had been erected outside the hospital entrance. The Royal party were then conducted into the hospital where they signed the visitors' book and were presented with a ceremonial key by the Revd Canon Whelpton.

5. Opening Day signatures of "Alexandra", the Princess of Wales, later Queen Alexandra, and "Elizabeth of Hesse", second daughter of Princess Alice, who was to be assassinated by the Bolsheviks in 1918.

The Prince of Wales, seeing that the ceremonial key was a beautiful work of art, expressed his pleasure in accepting it and his wish to take it with him.

In his address the Prince of Wales said that a more suitable monument could not have been dedicated in the light of his beloved sister's devotion, unselfishness and noble sympathy with sorrow and suffering. Their Royal Highnesses rejoiced to learn that the institution was sufficient for present wants and he hoped to be informed of its extension as the requirements of the neighbourhood increased.

The Bishop of Chichester humbly approached His Royal Highness and besought him graciously to declare the hospital open. A short pause of breathless silence prefaced the even briefer observation of His Royal Highness, 'I have now to declare the Princess Alice Memorial Hospital open'. A lofty blast from the trumpets confirmed the royal edict to the anxious multitude outside.

The Presentation of Purses ("of not less than five guineas") now took place, as the whole of the cost of the building had not been covered. The Prince of Wales received the purses "with regal benignity" and the ceremony concluded with the singing of the National Anthem.

Afterwards their Royal Highnesses drove to open the new waterworks, built at a cost of £20000 by Mr G.A. Wallis and Mr H. Currie. The procession went on to the East Parade sea wall, traversing The Avenue, Terminus Road and Seaside Road to arrive in excellent time at the Devonshire Park for lunch in the Floral Hall. After a lunch worthy of any trencherman,[3] the party went to the All Saints Convalescent Home, passing on the way the Princess Alice Tree. They left at about four o'clock.

The completed building, which cost £300 more than originally planned because of the site changes, received a long report in the *British Medical Journal*.

It was designed with the entrance hall and administration villa in the centre and the wards on a pavilion system at either side, to the right for women and the left for men, each having four medical and two surgical beds. The 22 x 20 foot wards were so planned that they could be extended to increase the number of beds. Corridors connected the wards with the central administration, although they were described as "cross ventilated to disconnect the wards from the administration block". In the left half of the central villa there was a surgery and operating room, to the right was the matron's office, and behind this administrative area were the kitchen and stores. The entrance hall and passage was shut off from the corridors by a pair of swing doors. Over the main entrance door there was an allegorical panel, 9 feet by 3 feet, with the arms of Princess Alice in the centre, modelled in terra cotta by Mr John Wilson of London.

The specifications were given in great detail. There were hollow outside walls, which had an asphalt damp-proof membrane, with the upper part half-timbered. The floors of the wards were laid with deal,[4] wax-polished, and there was no skirting so as to prevent accumulation of dust and dirt. The walls of the closets and bathrooms were intended to be lined with white glazed bricks, but this had to be omitted because of the cost. The WCs, baths and slop sinks were of white porcelain. The slop sinks were supplied with an automatic flush, and the water-closet cisterns discharged two gallons of water every time the seat was raised; "by this action the flush is not dependent on the feebleness of the patient". The drainage was described in great detail, "Every drain is taken direct into the principal drain. No drain runs under the building ... and from every water-closet a three-inch ventilating pipe is carried to the roof of the building". There was natural ventilation by window sashes with the windows placed opposite for cross ventilation, but fresh air inlets were built in the wall by every bed. In addition Sherringham's ventilators, over each bed, admitted air "at a still higher level". This approach to ventilation was a crucial part of the Victorian hospital where smells were equated with disease: it also meant that the Galton stoves, in the centre of the wards, had an essential part to play in wintertime.

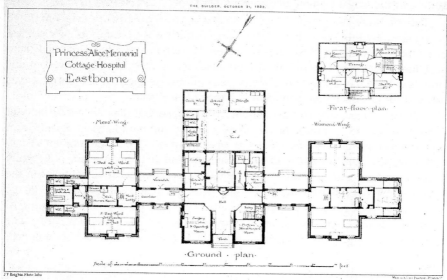

6. Plan of the Princess Alice Hospital in 1883, from *The Builder* of 21st October 1882. The cardinal points are incorrectly marked.

The wards were lit by three-light gas pendants on the Rickett principle, and the gas lights enclosed so that fumes were carried out into the flues.

Each of the nurse's rooms situated between the wards was, of course, well-ventilated, but also had a white porcelain sink with hot and cold water, and a speaking tube to the kitchen.

All the ward beds, screens, cupboards and other requisites were provided by personal gifts: "Miss Brodie contributing £240 and Miss Hall being entirely responsible for one of the smaller wards. In acknowledgement of the great bounty of these ladies,[5] two wards were called respectively by their names."

Victorian confidence abounded and the Annual Report for 1883 states: "It was originally intended to have a mortuary and laundry ... but these have been abandoned for the present". The report does, however, admit, "It is to be hoped that Eastbourne ... will not remain much longer without this hygienic necessary".

The medical staff consisted of three consulting doctors and seven assistant doctors, together with two dentists. The consulting doctors were only called in for the occasional consultation. The Colgates, Robert and Henry, were father and son, and two of the medical staff, Dr T. MacQueen and Dr A.P. Sherwood, were the fathers of doctors who subsequently succeeded them on the staff of the hospital. Dr G.D. Sherwood died as recently as 1979 at the age of 91. There was no specialisation, all the doctors saw every type of case and operated as indicated. Of the medical staff, only the two Colgates and Mr Henry Farnell were ever Fellows of the Royal College of Surgeons.

Patients were charged sixpence a day, but in cases of poverty the Committee were empowered to waive this charge. The "Admissions Committee" met weekly on a Friday morning to consider any request for non-urgent admission, and there must have been some form of "means test" for it is stated that "well-to-do" patients should pay up to two guineas [£2.10p] a day, and that the hospital was intended for those with an income of less than £300 a year.

Matron's salary was £60 per annum. It was specified that she "must be over 30 but less than 45, not to be burdened by a family and not to absent herself from the hospital for more than two hours at any one time". The total amount of pay for the nurses came to under £100 per annum, but it is not certain how many nurses there were at any one time, although five nurses' rooms (one for the matron) were provided on the first floor. Nurses, if not fully occupied in the hospital, could be hired to attend a case of illness in a private family at a fee of one guinea a week - increased to two pounds if it was an infectious case. The hospital secretary, a part-time officer, received an honorarium of £85 per annum.

Notes and References

1. *Eastbourne Gazette* 4/7/1883 (Pict. Suppl.).

2. *Eastbourne Gazette* 20/6/1883.

3. Lunch consisted of:-

Asparagus soup, salmon mayonnaise, lobster salad, pigeon pâté, lobster mayonnaise.

Roast lamb, game pâté, turkey, chicken rocket, foie gras, galantine of veal, duckling, beef, chicken with Béchamel sauce, larks in aspic, York ham, ox tongue, quails in aspic.

Swiss pudding, Charlotte russe, meringues, strawberry cream, Berlin gâteaux, orange jelly, fruit salad, apricot compôte, baskets of nougats, strawberry and pineapple ices, fresh fruit and biscuits.

4. Princess Alice Memorial Hospital, Annual Report, 1883. It was intended to use oak, but the funds did not run to it.

5. Probably Maria Brodie, eldest daughter of the ex-Vicar of Eastbourne, and her niece, Wilhelmina Brodie Hall.

Chapter 3

The morning after and early days

The winding-up meeting of the Royal Reception Committee was held in the Vestry-room on 30th July.[1] Among those present were Mr G. Gurney, Dr Gream (the Princess of Wales' physician) and Messrs Vine, Towner, Keay, and Strange.

The balance sheet which was submitted to the meeting showed that subscriptions and sale of programs brought the total donated to £748.37p, while the disbursements (including commissions, decorations, printing and advertising) totalled £734.27p.

There is no doubt that Eastbournians wanted to put on a show for the hospital and the visit by the Prince of Wales. Ever since the rash of hospital building in Britain which followed the founding of the Westminster Hospital in 1719, a local hospital had given a town a special cachet. The reasons behind support for any local hospital, however, are manifold and, despite appearances, usually self-seeking. There would be a few, with such extreme local pride, who considered that no proper town should be without a hospital, and others who saw the amount of suffering from injuries and preventable illness amongst their workmen and wished to help. Most thought that some of the glitter of associating with such a commendable cause would rub off on them; others, such as small sanitary appliance firms, thought that it might be good for business, and there is little doubt that for some a hospital presented an excellent opportunity to off-load their ill or weaker servants. It is known that some donated their gambling winnings to hospitals to ease their twinges of conscience.

Whatever the motives, there was the squaring-up of the accounts to be done. It appears that there had been a minor calamity at Sunderland earlier in 1883, when scaffolding, erected for a procession, collapsed. In the flush of enthusiasm for the great day all had agreed that provision should be made to ensure Eastbourne's great day would not be marred by a similar disaster. Now that everything had gone off so well, the Schools Committee were just a wee bit concerned in case the Reception Committee had forgotten about paying for the extra safety measures.

Superintendent Newnham was also worried about who would pay for the extra police who were on duty for the opening day. The cost came to £34.61p. The committee were quite certain in their minds, the cost would be a matter for the Local Board or the County - whatever, there would be no relief from them. It looks as though paying for policing has not come any easier over 100 years.

It emerged that the cost of the opening ceremony at the hospital amounted to £180, but the organisers were at pains to emphasise that a profit had accrued from the sale of tickets to view. So some parties were satisfied, even if the argument has a familiar ring of justification after the event.

Despite all these hiccups, the hospital was ready, after a fashion, and admitted its first patients on the day after the opening as planned.

In the first six months 37 cases were admitted, of whom eight received surgical treatment. The successful operations included excision of knee joint, amputation through the thigh, and an ovariotomy [removal of ovarian cyst] by Mr A.P. Sherwood under a Lister carbolic spray. A man "very enfeebled with diseased heart and lungs" died after a hernia [rupture] operation. Among cases cured or relieved were two each of anaemia, varicose veins, disease of hip, and in-growing toe nail, another was a man with a "lacerated arm caused by the explosion of a shell near Langney Fort". A patient with syphilis was "discharged without treatment, not a fit case".

The first patient admitted in 1884 had a cystic tumour of the breast which was cured by operation.[2] Other diagnoses included typhlitis [appendicitis], erythema nodosum [a skin affliction of the legs, still seen], psoas abscess [from spinal tuberculosis, in turn from drinking infected milk] and various injuries including a fractured jaw, fractured collar bone and a sprained ankle. Of 47 patients admitted in the first half of 1884, six died, the causes of death being: cancer (of the gullet, and the ovary), disease of the heart (two), pleurisy and peritonitis (one each). In the second six months the cases included a crushed foot, gout and hysteria.

On 28th January a patient with tuberculosis was sent home as "not a fit case" and again on 12th April a patient spitting blood from tuberculosis of the chest was recorded as "sent to Union", it being standard practice that infectious or incurable patients were not suitable for admission. The constitution of the hospital stated that "the following shall be disqualified for admission:-

-women in advanced state of pregnancy,

-lunatics and persons disordered in intellect or suffering from delirium tremens or habitual ulcers, consumption or any contagious disease".

In those days it was not really expected that any decent woman would have her baby anywhere except in a private nursing home or in her own home, attended by her family and servants - and if the hospital admitted the mad, bad and contagiously infectious (which could spread round a hospital with lethal results before antibiotics) they would lose local support and donations.

Comfort was always high on the agenda, so in 1885 "double windows" were fitted in one of the small wards following complaints of "low temperature".

The number of operations slowly increased over the first ten years, as did the admissions which reached 300 by 1893. The increase in surgical cases was primarily due to the amount of bone tuberculosis, although drainage of pus from a lung empyema [abscess] after pneumonia was another commonly required procedure. It must be borne in mind that an operation was still quite an event, having only been free of pain thanks to anaesthesia for a generation, while the risk of fatal infection had only been checked by Lord Lister's antiseptic techniques in the decade before the hospital opened.

There is the story of a lady who met a neighbour in the street only a couple of weeks after hearing that she had gone into the hospital for an operation, and thought she must be seeing a ghost because she could not believe anyone could recover from an operation so quickly, if at all.

In 1886, the year *Coca Cola* was first made and Daimler built his first car, an additional plot along Bedfordwell Road was purchased from Carew Davies Gilbert with a view to extending the building,. A year later the sum of £535.87p was handed over by the Eastbourne Golden Jubilee Committee for the proposed additions. Perhaps this enlarged scale was not accompanied by greater efficiency, or possibly it was simply an acknowledgment of the inevitable, for a mortuary was constructed in 1888, at the same time as the tender of James Peerless for £2095 was accepted to extend the ward blocks towards Carew Road. By 1889 this first extension was complete and the hospital boasted 26 beds, although "28 could be accommodated" - presumably by extra beds.

Miss Napper, the first matron, retired in 1888, the year the Leaf Homoeopathic Hospital opened. Miss Hamilton became the Princess Alice matron the next year, when the hospital was required to spend £250 on building a wall along the Carew Road frontage as a condition of the lease.

Aseptic surgical techniques [keeping germs out of the wound, using sterile instruments and covering the skin with heat-sterilised towels] had not reached the hospital by 1889. It still practised antiseptic surgery [killing germs which had gained access to the wound with carbolic] utilising the Lister spray, although this apparatus was being phased out and was hardly used after 1890, as asepsis replaced antisepsis.

In 1890 there was an outbreak of influenza and Dr Robert Colgate was able to refer to his experiences of the epidemics of 1836 and 1847. The year also witnessed a remarkable case related by Dr Thomas MacQueen.[3] "The patient, a gas fitter aged 34, was found lying in a semi-conscious state with a hammer in one hand and a nail projecting from his forehead. This was removed by pincers and, while being conveyed to a cab, other nails were observed hammered into the skull ... They were extracted at the hospital ... The man had an uninterrupted convalescence ... There was a history of drink and insanity. The man asserted that his head felt better since the 'operation'. They were 3-inch French nails."

A children's wing[4] was completed in June 1890 at a cost of £1029.09p. This had six beds and three to four cots and was named Geraldine ward after Mrs Wrangham, the wife of the principal benefactor. There was also a small ward of two or three beds, the Catherine, named after Mrs Whelpton, wife of the Chairman of the Hospital Committee. There was an informal opening of the wing, designated the Alexandra wing, by the Prince and Princess of Wales.

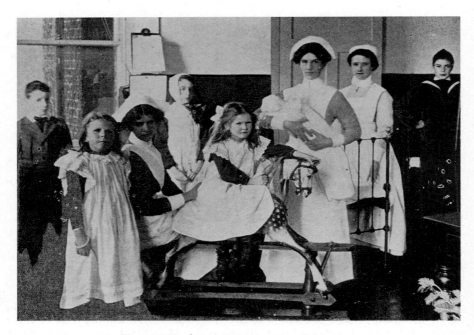

7. The children's ward at the turn of the century.

The next year 227 patients were treated, of whom 208 were admitted. Eight died and 23 were still in hospital at the end of the year. The average duration of stay was 27 days. The receipts were £1334.94p and the expenditure £1326.99p.

In 1892 Miss M. Cameron became matron, out of 40 applicants. By 1893, when 285 cases were admitted, the average cost was 1/2½d per person per day. The average payment received from patients during their stay was only 8/4d [41p] and in 80 cases the fees were remitted.

Modern therapy was being introduced. In January 1893 Dr A.E. Rook recorded treating a case of myxoedema (non-functioning thyroid gland) by feeding the patient with sheep's thyroid, a lobe every day, which proved too much as the patient developed a rapid pulse. Finally, he hit on the right dose and the patient improved on one lobe a week. Thankfully, by November 1894, it is recorded that myxoedema was being treated with tablets of thyroid extract.

Routine was otherwise the order of the day in 1894, with £440 spent on the drains, £170 on painting, and £80 on linen replenishment. The cases admitted were also fairly run of the mill (save to the patient) and included a fractured pelvis, fractured femur, fractured clavicle, dislocated shoulder, acute rheumatism, asthma, erythema nodosum, hernia, palmar ganglion, psoas abscess, glaucoma [eye trouble], mastoid [ear] abscess, eczema, and bronchial catarrh.

The Rt Hon. T.H. Huxley, who had retired to Eastbourne and was on the committee of management from 1893, died in 1895.

In April 1896 Dr Matthew Bourne described the case of a girl who came under his care "in a helpless and almost hopeless condition". He treated her at the Princess Alice by isolation, cold drenches to the spine, and interrupted current to the spine, three or four times a day. She rapidly improved and, "despite a relapse, she left the hospital completely cured of her hysteria".

It is of interest to follow the developments in the treatment of a common condition as they affected clinical practice in the Princess Alice, a typical small provincial hospital.

If we take appendicitis as an example (called typhlitis in writings of the day), the first operation for appendicitis on the world stage was in the USA in 1864; the first survival after removal of a perforated [burst] appendix was in 1886, and "McBurney's point" [the classic site of pain][5] was not described until 1889.

The first definite Eastbourne reference is in March 1887 when a nine-year-old girl was admitted with constipation and abdominal pain, worsened by an enema. She died on the fifth day and at post-mortem examination (PM) a burst appendix was found. There was a note that the surgeons discussed "the advisability of operation".

Later that year Mr Farnell thought that typhlitis might be an error of diet and 'expressed the opinion that the mischief did not originate in the appendix'. He spoke highly of the use of belladonna [an alkaloid drug].

The next year, a "healthy girl of six" who developed abdominal pain and vomiting on 10th February, recovered, ran a mild temperature for two weeks, had a recurrence of urgent symptoms and died on 19th March. At PM there was purulent peritonitis [infected abdomen] and the appendix had perforated. The surgical opinion was that operation would have been useless [because they thought the perforation had occurred after the infection].

In 1897 appendicitis was diagnosed in a woman of 68 and the appendix was removed, but she died four days later. The same year a woman of 47 recovered after appendicectomy. In 1898 Mr Treves, the London surgeon, was invited to Eastbourne to see a patient on the fifth day of illness; on this occasion he advised against operation; instead two leeches were applied and the patient recovered.

Sir Frederick Treves was to operate on King Edward VII for appendicitis on 24th June 1902 (two days before the Coronation was due) at Buckingham Palace. The king recovered sufficiently to go through a shortened Coronation ceremony on 9th August. Ironically, Treves' daughter died from a burst appendix, and he was to die of peritonitis in the 1920s.

Locally, surgical practice had so changed that by 1899 a 13-year-old girl with symptoms of perforated appendix was operated upon the next day and recovered after three weeks. Three years later, in June 1902, the shift in approach was complete. Mr Farnell, when lecturing on, "The revolution in the opinion about inflammation of the appendix" concluded, 'the prognosis [outlook] was good if the organ is removed within 24 hours'. On the international scene the figures from the Mayo clinic show similar changes - it had only 12 appendix operations in 1895, there were 186 in 1900, and over 1000 during 1905.

Finance was an unvarying problem from the earliest days, but in February 1895, the hospital was made free of debt and it was decided to abolish all fees from patients and rely on their generosity to pay what they could afford. It is worthy of notice that in the last year of fees, £110 was raised from the patients, while the following year donations from patients amounted to £160. Money was also collected by appointing Life Governors at ten guineas [£10.50], or Governors for a year (one guinea), and subscriptions were another source of funds. Despite all these efforts there was usually a deficit of about £2500, which was covered by legacies and extra subscriptions.

In 1896, Miss M. Lambert was appointed matron out of 109 applicants. The Annual Report for the year noted, "Nothing of importance to chronicle". Cases totalled 312 (17 less than in 1895) with an average stay of 23 days. There were 32 major and 16 minor operations. Florence Nightingale, writing in 1863, had said, 'It is a rule without any exceptions that no patient ought ever to stay a day longer in hospital than is absolutely necessary for medical or surgical treatment'. Nowadays in Eastbourne, there are over 12000 operations and more than 4000 medical cases admitted each year, with an average stay in an acute hospital of some seven days.

Dr Surtees recalls seeing a patient in 1972, then aged 81, who had been in the hospital about 1896 for a skin graft from his thigh to arm after burns as a child. This was one type of case which had good cause for staying in for a month, but the main reasons were the poor state of many patients and the slow healing of wound infections.

The cost per patient per week rose to 1/4½d in 1895, and there was a deficit of over £100. A further financial grumble came in 1897 when £90 had to be spent on the purchase of an apparatus for administering nitrous oxide [laughing gas] for anæsthetics, and a new set of surgical instruments was required.

In the same year a system of weekly subscriptions began. They were collected from the employers and employees of nearly every business firm in the town. This was the origin of the Penny-a-Week Fund, which allowed subscribers to have all medical treatment in hospital completely free of charge without being expected to make any additional contribution.

8. Crowden ward, 1897. Note the central stove and chimney.

The Revd C. Crowden became president in 1898, when Miss Ramsey was appointed matron, being the first to be appointed from within the Princess Alice nursing staff. Although not involving Miss Ramsey, there is the story of an appointment committee assembling to fill a vacant ward sister's post at the Princess Alice Hospital. Just before the interviewing commenced, the consultant of the ward said to the panel, 'I don't suppose there is much doubt that nurse "X" is the one for the job, is there?' 'I'm sure we all agree', replied the matron, who was determined not to have her, 'But are you all aware there is a quite unfounded rumour going round that she is the mistress of one of the doctors, and if we appointed her, good though she may be, it would be detrimental to nurse discipline at our hospital.' As there was more than a grain of truth in the stories, which involved the ward consultant, another candidate was appointed.

Another example of change in surgical practice was in the treatment of perforated gastric ulcers [burst stomach]. In 1890 a man of 38 died 28 hours after the onset of symptoms, 'an exploratory operation was thought of, but he died suddenly before anything could be done'. In June 1896 Dr Rook had six cases of gastric or duodenal perforation. None was over the age of twenty and all died, even though two had operations when, "the cavity was cleaned and flushed".

In 1901 a patient with a perforated stomach ulcer had an operation, but died of peritonitis a week later. At PM the stomach had healed.

In March 1906 Dr A. Harper had a patient with a perforated gastric ulcer. At operation there was "little extravasation of stomach contents" [that is minimal soiling of the abdominal cavity with food], the perforation was found and closed, and the patient made an excellent recovery. The same month, however, a patient of Dr A.P. Sherwood had "much extravasation" and died three weeks later. So the outlook was improving, but it still depended upon how much food had leaked outside the stomach and it wasn't until 1908 that perforated ulcer operations ceased to arouse comment.

In 1904 Dr MacQueen recommended rectal feeding for patients who bled from a stomach ulcer, followed by Epsom Salts and senna as the bleeding ceased, but most patients with a severe haematemesis [vomiting blood] just died. Blood groups were not discovered until 1900 and transfusions were not generally available until the 1920s, so it was no surprise when a 66-year-old man died from a haematemesis in 1894. At PM he had "a simple [that is, not cancerous] ulcer on the posterior wall of the duodenum [part of the bowels near the stomach] the size of a florin, which had eroded an artery".

Further hospital building was decided upon in 1897, even though the cost per head had only been reduced to one shilling [5p] per day, which was justified because extra nourishing food and drink had been required in several cases. The next year Geraldine ward was reorganised to contain four adult beds and three cots, and building commenced of a new wing of 14 beds on the north side of the hospital to bring the total number of beds and cots to 50. The cost of £3500 was financed partly by a grand fair[6] and fête, opened by the Duchess of Devonshire, partly by a contribution from the Amalgamated Friendly Societies, and also by a Diamond Jubilee appeal, helped by a visit from the Prince of Wales on 17th July 1899, who donated an up-to-date operating table. This was the year that the first specialist, Dr H.S. Gabbett a pathologist, was appointed.

Notes and References

1. *Eastbourne Gazette,* 1/8/1883.
2. Princess Alice Memorial Hospital, Annual Report, 1884.
3. Eastbourne Medical Society, minutes, 30/9/1890.
4. *Eastbourne Gazette,* 4/6/1890.
5. McBurney C. *N.Y.Med.J.*, 1889; **50**: 676-84.
6. At the Devonshire Park Fancy Fair of 20th June 1900, in aid of the Princess Alice Memorial Hospital building fund, W.L. Wyllie ARA (later RA) painted a typical sea scene which was presented to the hospital by R. Hesketh Jones.

Chapter 4

The new century and new faces

The Diamond Jubilee extension completed in 1900 increased the capacity to 44 beds and 6 cots, and the hospital was now heated by steam at a cost of £600 a year. Almost equal heat was dissipated by the disappointment expressed in the town because the "opening of the new wing was not accompanied by any official ceremony or graced by the presence of Royalty".

The average cost fell to 10d [4p] per head per day, even though there were 40 patients in the hospital on occasions, and the Annual Report for 1900 said the matron was to be congratulated on her economic management.

The next year the average cost rose to 10½d per head per day,[1] which was explained by inflation as part of the Boer War. In the course of the year Dr Charles O'Brien Harding, a local general practitioner and son-in-law of Dr Bransby Roberts, became a governor. He later became mayor of Eastbourne, was knighted, and his association with the hospital lasted for the next 28 years. Eastbourne was still a small town and many of the doctors were interrelated, for example, Dr Astley Roberts was the son of Bransby Roberts and Mr Farnell married Dr Henry Colgate's sister.

In early 1901 the governors of the hospital reviewed the regulations and adopted new rules. Most appeared sensible, such as patients must not stay in more than three weeks unless recommended by the medical staff, and no governor could vote if he hadn't paid his subscription.

The same burst of zealous activity also looked at the medical staff arrangements. By the turn of the century there had been no change in the medical staff of the Princess Alice Hospital since the opening, and there was a feeling that some system of orderly succession should be instituted. The governors, clearly aiming for an overshoot, proposed that "visiting medical staff should be subject to annual changes". The medical response was to set up a committee. In late 1901 there was another proposal that visiting medical staff should be brought from London and other centres as required. The medical reaction was to affirm "that patients at Princess Alice should be attended by staff of that hospital, urgent and exceptional cases excluded".

As part of a compromise, the privilege which had been extended to medical men, who were not members of staff, to attend their own patients in the hospital was discontinued. At the same time the position of the medical staff was brought more into line with modern trends by the introduction of rules, which can be summarized as follows:-

1. There were to be four medical officers and four assistant medical officers.

2. The medical officers were to take duty in rotation for a week at a time.

3. The assistant medical officers were to act as assistants to the medical officers and to take charge of their cases during their absence or when called upon to do so.

4. Retirement age was to be 60, or after 15 years as a medical officer, whichever came first.

5. No two medical men being partners could be medical officers at the same time. The same rule applied to assistant medical officers.

These rules remained in force for over 40 years. At this stage there was still no thought of specialists - except in pathology - and any doctor could treat any sort of medical or surgical case.

In 1902 Dr F. Marsdin did not seek re-election to the staff and, in the first new medical appointments since the foundation of the hospital, Dr A.E. Rook and Dr A. Harper were elected assistant medical officers. Frederick Marsdin was a colourful personality who had qualified in 1859, and lived in Moat Croft Road. There is a story that he performed an appendix operation on the kitchen table in the *Tiger Inn* at East Dean, riding his horse there and back, and Marsden Road [he spelt his name variously] is named after the family.[2]

In 1903, when street-lighting came to Eastbourne, the Gurney male and female convalescent rooms were completed, they later became Gurney ward. Public subscriptions covered the cost,[3] in "recognition of the services rendered" by the former Treasurer, Mr George Gurney, who had resigned in 1902.

The Princess Alice Hospital returns for the week ending 20th March 1903 were:

Number of patients	33
Admitted	9
Discharged	5
Died	0

The annual collection in the town for the funds of the hospital, in July 1903, was said to amount to £122/8/7d [£122.43p], of which £15/10/- was in gold coins, £69/19/10d in silver and £39/18/9d in copper. That year 436 patients (63 accidents) were admitted, of whom 25 died. There were 38 major and 121 minor operations performed.

One of the deaths was explained at the June meeting of the Eastbourne Medical Society, when Dr Colgate showed a specimen of atheromatous [hardened] coronary artery which had been removed from the body of a man of 46 who died suddenly at the hospital.

The next step was the construction of a new operating theatre and anæsthetic room. The town rallied round with fund-raising events of all sorts, and Mr K.S. Sargeant has brought to my attention an Amateur Performance, in February 1904, of T.W. Robertson's "Caste" at the Devonshire Park Theatre in aid of the funds. The part of "Eccles" was taken by Major H.P. Molineux [Molineux's of Lewes were the bankers for the Princess Alice, and he was Borough Treasurer 1891-1923], and the "Marquise de St Maur" was played by Miss Farnell.

9. "I paid a surprise visit to the hospital at 9.30 this morning - and found everything in admirable order - the wards being specially well ventilated. Edward R.I. July 13 1903."

The operating theatre project aroused so much interest in the town that on Monday, 13th July 1903, when King Edward VII was staying at *Compton Place*, he paid a surprise visit to see the new building and the operating table which he had donated a few years earlier. The theatre, which cost £800, was the gift of Mr C.H. Evill and family and officially opened in May 1904. The driving force in its construction was Mr Farnell, who always had the surgical interests of the hospital at heart. In his early days he went to Glasgow to see Lister operate and was so impressed by the carbolic spray that he bought one for Eastbourne.

As Mr H.G. Estcourt wrote[4] in 1976, "We, who came to surgery so much later, often damned this theatre, forgetting how old it was, but the fact that it survived without major alteration until after the 1939-45 world war suggests that it must have been a very solid and satisfactory achievement in 1904".

It appears that a Röntgen Ray Fund had been formed as early as 1904 to provide X-ray apparatus, because the Annual Report implies it was raided to help towards the new operating theatre.

That year, Mr Farnell managed to pass a rule, against considerable opposition, to give each assistant medical officer two beds for his own patients. It also saw the appointment of the first house visitors, who reported monthly to the management committee. Two years later house committees were introduced.

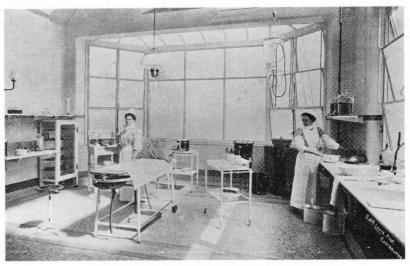

10. The new operating theatre, 1904.

Meanwhile, Miss Peile had been appointed matron in 1904. She was to be in office until the 1914-18 war, and kept a cap on the costs. The receipts for the year were £2580.38p against payments of £2539.47p, with no change in the cost at 10½d per head per day, which was to stay the same for the next two years.

The year 1905 saw something of an extravagance when a cottage for the gardener/stoker was built along Bedfordwell Road, at a cost of £377.29p. It was also the year when the Annual Report noted that Mr Farnell had pleaded for an out-patient service.

The first mention of lectures to the nurses,[5] by Dr A.A. Martin, was in 1907.

By now the hospital had a healing aura all its own, or so it would appear, for in July 1908 Mr Farnell admitted for operation a 39-year-old male patient who had been vomiting for a year, 'but he was so much relieved in hospital that the operation was postponed indefinitely'.[6]

The same year there was a demonstration of anæsthetic apparatus by which "nitrous oxide anaesthesia could be prolonged by admitting air or oxygen".[7] Nitrous oxide was a weak anæsthetic and, on its own, could only be used for short procedures, but it was safe, and in conjunction with other agents continues in use to-day. Chloroform or ether were the main anæsthetics in use. The former gave patients a pleasanter induction of unconsciousness, but inconveniently killed the occasional patient by affecting the heart, and whereas ether was safer, it was slow to work and was an irritant - patients sometimes became violent in the first few minutes, and afterwards could cough and vomit for days.

We have an idea of the anæsthetic practice of the time from a description by Dr Gabbett, the pathologist, who clearly had to turn his hand to being the anæsthetist on occasions. "Open ether is gaining favour. I use a simple mask, such as Skinner's, with two folds of gauze. The anæsthetic is commenced with a chloroform and ether mist, and when unconsciousness begins, a change is made to pure ether. At first about 15 drops are used every third respiration; about 4 oz per 30 minutes. There is less distress to the patients who find this method less smothering and there is less vomiting afterwards".[8]

The first reference to the use of ethyl chloride, as a spray to put the patient under quickly before reverting to ether, is in 1907. In the same year Dr Gabbett, wearing his pathology cap, demonstrated how to estimate bacterial opsonins, and there was also a record of a most strange surgical operation in which the patient had their coccyx ["tail"] removed for backache, with "complete relief". During this first decade of the century, in a more orthodox procedure, Mr Farnell had removed a lobe of the thyroid gland in a patient with thyroid disease.

Between 1906 and 1912 there were many changes in the medical staff as the doctors who staffed the hospital at its inauguration began to retire. In 1907 Dr Hayman resigned from the staff, followed by Dr Habgood the next year, and Mr Farnell and Dr Colgate were the next to go in 1911: all had done much to further the cause of the hospital in its early days.

Drs A.E. Rook, A. Harper, T. Turner, W.J.C. Merry, A. Deane, and D.N.B. Emerson joined the staff in their place, appointed by a selection committee of five governors and one doctor. The first mention of Mr A.H. Crook, a surgeon for 35 years, was in 1913 when he gave a lecture to the nurses.

As early as 1908 the need for further enlargement of the hospital began to make itself felt and in 1910 the Managing Committee carried a proposal, "That in the opinion of the Governors a new hospital on a new site should be built", but sufficient funds were not forthcoming. As we now know, a new hospital on a green field site was not to open until 1976.

A particular worry was the large number of children admitted for tonsil operations, one outcome of the new school medical inspections ordered by the Board of Education following the Education Act of 1907, and by 1910 the cost per bed per week had risen to £1.40p. An attempt was made, without success, to buy the nearby Clifton House School (later Roborough) until finally it was decided to abandon the idea of a new site and build instead a wing of 20 beds, at the back of the hospital towards Bedfordwell Road.

To help finance the project it was agreed to regard this extension as part of the town's memorial to King Edward VII, who had died in 1910. The first part of the wing, Cavendish ward, was opened by the Duke of Devonshire in 1912, but the top ward (Sydney Hudson) was not ready for use until the next year, the delay being chiefly due to the difficulty of obtaining a large enough lift, another factor being that the hospital did not become "all-electric" until 1913.

11. Miss Piele, the matron, and her staff, 1911 {photo M. Clack}.

The hospital now had 70 beds, hardly warranting the number of words expended by the Revd Dr C. Crowden in one of his typical orations of turgid prose, although the sentiments were well-meant.

The report of his speech at the annual meeting of the Princess Alice Memorial Hospital in 1912 extends over three pages of the Annual Report. A brief extract is provided below.

"This is a business meeting. and the report presented to you is a business document full of statistics, formulated in the terse language of the businessman. Now this is very useful but the cold figures need the magical wand of imagination to quicken them with life and to stir the imagination of the reader ... From each of these beds wan and wistful faces have looked up tearfully and hopefully to the doctors and nurses ... Night and Day their administrations go on, watching each patient, the symptoms scrupulously recorded ... Little child sufferers ... Will you make them paupers by sending them to the workhouse? Such cruelty is inhuman ... God forbid!"

The year the extension opened, the committee gave authorisation to install a Röntgen ray [X-ray] machine. A benefactor, the Revd H. Alston, gave £250 for construction of the X-ray plant and Dr F. Harwood Hardman was appointed radiologist in 1913. There had been a demonstration of Röntgen rays, in the house of one of the local doctors,[9] as early as May 1896 - within six months of the discovery - when Mr Farnell's hand was photographed "with an exposure of six minutes", but previous to 1913 the only X-ray examinations in Eastbourne had been done by Mr H.C. Browne, the leading chemist in the town and an ardent photographer. Patients had to be taken to H.R. Browne's, the family shop on the corner of South Street and Cornfield Road, for the examination.

For a short time after the plant was installed at the hospital Mr Browne performed the X-ray work until the radiologist arrived. As early as April 1914 Dr Hardman was showing X-rays taken at the Princess Alice "of several interesting conditions". By the end of 1914 there had been 197 X-ray examinations in the year, although as late as 1919 Mr F.W.A. Davis says that he was 'a nine-day wonder at school' when he had an X-ray at Princess Alice.

Among other medical advances, the first local reference to the use of the "magic bullet", namely *Salvarsen,* for the treatment of syphilis was in 1911. The doctors agreed that it had dangers, but it could also have useful results. This drug would be used for treating the long-term neurological or cardiac symptoms of syphilis; recent venereal disease infections would still not be knowingly admitted.

In 1912 it was recorded that 95% of patients tested had a positive skin reaction with tuberculin.[10] In other words 19 out of 20 of the populace had been in contact with TB, and although most, of course, would surmount their episode, there was no effective treatment for those who developed active infection.

In October 1912 Dr Turner described a chloroform anæsthetic death. The patient was a man of 25 who was having an operation on his nose. The anæsthesia was descibed as "light" and the patient died half-an-hour into the operation. Dr Turner thought the cause was "a persistent thymus" [a gland in the chest, which normally reduces in size during childhood], but almost certainly the chloroform had affected the heart rate, which is the reason why it is not used to-day.[11] Another chloroform death occurred in January 1914, when a man "struggled so violently with ether that chloroform was resorted to". No abnormality was found at post-mortem examination - only to be expected if death was due to a sudden change in heart rate. It was obvious that the doctors were becoming disenchanted with chloroform, but there were few alternatives to its use in patients with bronchitis, because ether was so irritating to the lungs.

January 1913 saw the first reference to a "Paul's Tube"[12] being tied into the bowel when a length had to be removed at operation, and in March 1913 the Eastbourne Medical Society held a clinical meeting for the first time at Princess Alice in the (as yet unopened) Sydney Hudson ward. Among the demonstrations, Drs Rook and Deane showed a case of eczema unrelieved by treatment; Mr T. MacQueen a case of spina bifida, on which he had operated "with complete success"; Dr Merry presented a man who had been struck by lightning [no doubt to thunderous applause], and Dr Willoughby showed a specimen of a bowel perforation in typhoid fever.

In this last year of peace, 695 cases were admitted, there were 197 major operations and, shades of "Edwardian" summers, a tennis court was constructed for use by the staff.

Prior to the 1914-18 war, before orthopædic surgery had become a specialty, fractures were often treated on wooden splints padded with cotton wool, although Plaster of Paris bandages had been described as long ago as 1852. Dr G.D. Sherwood tells of one patient with a fractured femur [thigh bone] who had the misfortune to acquire a nest of fleas in the woollen padding. It was difficult enough to align and immobilise a fracture with this method of treatment, so the surgeon did not dare disturb the healing fracture and, as there were no insecticides in those days to deal with the infestation, the patient just had to, in Dr Sherwood's words, ' put up with his little surgical problems'.

In 1914 the Eastbourne Eye Hospital was founded in a house in Pevensey Road, by Dr J.H. Ewart. He was an Eastbourne GP and also a doctor at the Eastbourne Convalescent Hospital [All Saints]. The new Eye Hospital took some of the strain of the demand for more specialist services away from the Princess Alice, which called upon Mr G.T. Brooksbank James as a consulting ophthalmic surgeon only as the occasion demanded, but the Eye Hospital always found it a struggle to make ends meet.

As a harbinger of future surgical practice, in May 1913 Dr Emerson described a case of ruptured [torn] liver which was found at PM after a death in a motor-car accident.

Notes and References

1. Princess Alice Memorial Hospital, Annual Report, 1901.

2. Spears HD. *Street Names of Eastbourne.* Eastbourne LHS, 1973.

3. Princess Alice Memorial Hospital, Annual Report, 1902.

4. Estcourt HG. *Eastbourne Medical Gazette,* 1976; 2: 28-33.

5. Princess Alice Memorial Hospital, Annual Report, 1907.

6. Eastbourne Medical Society, minutes, 28/7/1908.

7. Ibid., min., 25/8/1908.

8. Ibid., min., 25/1/1910.

9. Ibid., min., 26/5/1896. "Mr G.A. Skinner gave a demonstration of Röntgen rays. He used six cells, a 4" spark and a focussing tube as at King's College Hospital."

10. Ibid., min., 25/6/1912.

11. Ibid., min., 28/10/1912.

12. Paul FT. *BMJ.* 1891; ii: 118.

Chapter 5

World war and winds of change

At the commencement of the war, on 4th August 1914, the Princess Alice Hospital reserved 24 beds for the use of sick and wounded soldiers. With so many of the medical staff on active service, Mr E.H. Rainey, Mr E. Wilson Hall, Dr F.J. Nicholls and later Dr J. Gordon Wilson and Dr Margaret S. Burt were co-opted onto the staff as temporary assistant medical officers, until some of them in turn went into the armed forces - Mr Rainey being mentioned twice in dispatches. Dr C. O'Brien Harding, a local GP, was mayor of Eastbourne for five consecutive years during the war.

Although retired since 1911, Mr Farnell returned to the Princess Alice Hospital, but in 1917 he and Dr Merry were put into uniform to work at the Central Military Hospital, which had taken over the Eastbourne workhouse (later St Mary's Hospital) where most of the wounded from France were treated locally.

The nursing staff also went off to war, Sister Sherris being one of the first to join the Army. Among other changes Miss Earl succeeded Miss Peile as matron in 1915, which was the year the X-ray department had its first move to larger quarters, and when the first soldiers were admitted. The following year Miss A.C. Rastrall became the matron. Mr H.H. Coles remained as the secretary.

Throughout the war, the Princess Alice Hospital continued to care for the local populace along with many wounded troops, a service for which it was accorded recognition with an official, albeit a cardboard, certificate.

Eastbourne's main war effort was to care for the casualties, which were on a scale quite unprecedented and unexpected. The first unit to appear was the Royal Army Medical Corps, whose members were billeted around the town while they initiated the Summerdown convalescent camp. The first patients arrived at the Summerdown camp on 8th April 1915 and it went on to become one of the largest in Europe. Over 150000 soldiers had been helped back to health by the time of its closure in December 1920.

During the 1914-18 war about a dozen Red Cross Hospitals opened in the town to cope with the casualties: many were simply houses given by the owners for temporary use. They included the Fairfield Court, Hempston, Upperton, and Urmston Red Cross Hospitals. They were attended by army doctors and any of the Princess Alice medical staff left in the town. Two more substantial hospitals began about this time. They were the Esperance Nursing Home, Hartington Place, opened in 1917 by nuns to nurse the troops, and in 1919 the Ear, Nose and Throat Hospital, 47-49 Cavendish Place. The latter was founded by Dr M.V. McKechnie, a GP who had set up the *Devonshire Lodge* practice [later the Winifred Lee Health Centre] and who became an anæsthetist at the new ENT hospital as well as at the Leaf Hospital.

12. Matron Griffin with young patients invited back for Christmas presents 1922 {photo W.R. Cookson}.

For many years a children's "Throat Clinic" had been held at the Princess Alice, for example, during 1915 there were eight clinics and 65 children had operations. This service was transferred to the ENT hospital which in 1923 performed a total of 138 adenoid operations, the medical officers being Dr J.N. Donnellan, along with Drs MacQueen and McKechnie. The matron was Miss Newman and later Miss E.P. Cantlow. The ground floor of the little hospital contained the out-patients, a consulting room and a committee room. On the next floor was the operating theatre, fitted up by Mrs Macandrew, with Ewart ward (three beds for females), Aytoun ward (two male beds) and Jenkins ward containing six cots. The charges were sixpence [2½p] for an out-patient attendance, and in-patients paid three shillings [15p] a day.

In 1919 Mr Farnell finally retired from hospital practice. The same year Dr A.G. Shera was appointed pathologist on the retirement of Dr Gabbett. He was given a part-time assistant technician, and a laboratory, fashioned from the stable and carriage room of the old horse-drawn ambulance at the rear of the hospital. The new department was opened by the Marchioness of Hartington. As an aftermath of the war there was a surprising amount of malaria and dysentery in the town as well as cases of tetanus, some from the Summerdown convalescent camp, all contributing extra work for pathology.

The first resident medical officer at Princess Alice was also appointed in 1919. This allowed some degree of 24-hour care, and enabled a casualty department ["Casualty"] to be started, which that year treated 63 casualties, and 94 in 1920, the first full year. With nurses needed to tend the many desperately ill patients on the wards, a casualty service was not regarded as a priority, and at first did not even sport a pair of Spencer Wells forceps [a standard surgical instrument] on its inventory.

Out-patient treatment developed slowly because it aroused mixed feelings among the GPs, who thought they should decide who was to be referred. Up to the nineteenth century, most medicine and surgery was practised at the home of either the doctor or the patient, and this system continued for upper-class families until hospital conditions became evidently superior after the National Health Service. The introduction of anæsthetics, respectable nurses, and the control of surgical infections during the nineteenth century, meant that hospitals began to be used more and more by the middle class and as a result voluntary hospitals increased in importance. Patients began to seek help from the casualty officer, whose services were usually good, free, and easily available - except in the London teaching hospitals, where they were overwhelmed.

General practitioners, however, felt cheated of their fees and pressed for patients to consult them first and be referred only if they thought it necessary. The "Lloyd George" Insurance Act of 1911 paid doctors for looking after "the working man who was on the Panel list", and the method of payment chosen was a capitation fee for each patient on the doctor's list, although working men's families were not included in the scheme. When the Act came into full operation in 1913, general practitioners were no longer in such competition with casualty or out-patient departments; conversely, it was to the financial interest of GPs to encourage working patients to go to hospital, for the doctor had already received his fee and did not get any extra for actual treatment. In some large, poor-quality city practices the consequence was that the doctor decanted whole surgeries into the local casualty department. This did not happen in Eastbourne where, with affluent practices, general practitioners were of good quality, and kept themselves closely involved in the running of the voluntary hospital, although some expressed reservations when out-patient clinics commenced at the hospital.

The Princess Alice Hospital was recognised in 1919 as a Nurse Training School by the General Nursing Council (GNC) which had only just been formed itself, because of Florence Nightingale's antipathy to registration. Miss C.J.

Griffin, who had run the Central Military Hospital on the Union workhouse site, was appointed matron. She was known as "The Angel" by the staff.

Mrs M. Butler writes to say that in 1919 she was in Geraldine ward for an appendix operation by Mr Turner. She was in for three weeks and received the "utmost care from the nurses," although she remembers most the ward maids coming on the ward at seven o'clock and moving the beds to sweep behind.

In 1920 the first general medical staff appointments since the war were made, Mr E.H. Rainey and Mr R.C. MacQueen being elected as assistant surgeons, the new name for an assistant medical officer. For the time being, however, they performed general duties which were not confined to surgery, and Mr MacQueen kept his surgical appointment at the ENT Hospital. The Medical Act of 1858 had drawn together the university-trained physicians, the apprentice-trained surgeons and the medical apothecaries, and most GPs described themselves as "Physician and Surgeon" on their house plates, but it would not be long before increasing specialisation was to fragment the profession anew.

The new, young surgeon, Mr Ronald MacQueen, set out his principles of treatment for abdominal operation cases. 'Food and water causes peristalsis [bowel movements] when the bowel needs rest', therefore he advocated,

-primary lavage of the stomach [empty the stomach]
-Fowler's position [patient sitting up]
-feed by rectal saline and glucose drip
-no food or aperients by mouth for three days
-morphine hypodermically [by injection].

which was quite a progressive approach for June 1920.

Dr G.D. Sherwood had a temporary job at the Princess Alice in 1920 as anæsthetist to the Tonsil and Adenoid clinic. Once a week 20 breakfastless children were brought in by their parents. They walked into the operating theatre, were placed on the operating table and anæsthetised, using a drop bottle delivering an ether and chloroform mixture, whereupon the surgeon removed the tonsils with an instrument called a guillotine. After each operation Dr Sherwood carried the child in his arms to a nearby room, and laid it on a mattress on the floor, when a nurse took over: a sequence continued until the queue ended. The children were kept until they had recovered from the brief anæsthetic and all bleeding had ceased when, after a meal of soft food, they went home.

In 1920 houses in Bedfordwell Road were bought to provide the nucleus of a separate nurses' home. This had been planned in 1914, but was held up by the war. The following year Mr Sydney Hudson sold a house in Carew Road to the Princess Alice trustees for £3092. It had been built in 1889 as *Powyscourt,* but now was called *Taormina.* It was converted into office accommodation, needed now that Captain A.G. Alston RN had become the first whole-time secretary.

In another new venture that year, ladies were invited to join the committee of management. Mrs Scott and Miss Croshaw were the first to take up the offer, and

Miss Croshaw remained on the committee for many years.[1] It was also the year that Eastbourne appointed its first full-time policewoman.

With the closure of the De Walden Red Cross Hospital (another of those opened for troops during the war) the Princess Alice Hospital received the sum of £1320 in 1921, which was used to bring the X-ray equipment up-to-date, both for radiodiagnosis and radiotherapy. That year there were 345 X-ray examinations and 64 patients received radiotherapy treatment - not an unexpectedly high figure when it is borne in mind that X-rays were being tried for acne, eczema, psoriasis, tuberculosis, ringworm, excessive sweating and even pruritus ani [itchiness of the backside]. The treatment was often successful, but this was before the full dangers of ionising radiations were realised.

The first case of encephalitis lethargica [a virus sleeping sickness, of which there was an epidemic throughout Europe in the 1920s] was mentioned in February 1921. The Princess Alice returns for the third week of April that year show that 17 patients were admitted, 20 discharged, with 53 remaining.

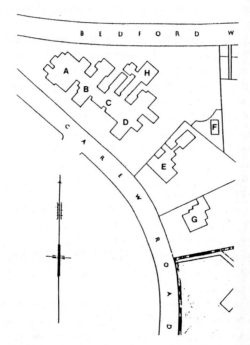

13. Plan of the hospital in the 1920s. **A** is the operating theatre and casualty area; **B** the original male ward, **C** the entrance, and **D** the female ward. **H** is the Cavendish/Sydney Hudson ward block, **E** is *Taormina*, **F** the mortuary behind a hedge, and **G** is *Harberton*.

The financial position of all the hospitals was giving anxiety, worsened by the inflation which accompanied the war. At the Princess Alice there was a deficit of £2405, despite a donation from the mayor's Sunday Hospital Fund of £430.11p, and £1000 of War Bonds had to be sold. It was pointed out that the cost of vegetables was two-and-a-half times up on the previous year, and as the local newspaper put it, possibly not without some self-interest, "The hospital must be run on a strictly business basis and as advertising is the life-blood of industry so it is an essential factor in raising funds for charitable institutions".[2]

As usual, great efforts were made not to apportion blame, understandable in the voluntary situation, where all were doing their best, and where it was important not to offend anyone who might be touched for a donation.

A special governors' meeting was held on Friday afternoon, 13th May 1921, to receive the report of a committee appointed to go into the financial affairs.[3]

The *ad hoc* committee found that "the affairs of the hospital, despite difficulties, had been managed with efficiency and economy and that changes already under consideration could be improved with advantage, in particular:-

1. The pre-war custom of competitive purchase should be reverted to as soon as prudent.

2. The matron, who also efficiently controls the housekeeping, should be relieved of the clerical work which does not properly belong to her department.

3. A weekly record of fuel used would be useful.

4. Many small jobs would be more economically done if some member of the male staff were to carry them out.

5. At present the staff consists of 28 nurses and probationers, and 15 domestics to attend upon 62 patients. The scattered position and small size of the wards render expense larger than in a more conveniently arranged building.

6. A more modern system of account keeping should be adopted.

7. The expenses of the electro-therapeutic department might well be shown under a separate heading. It was strongly the opinion of the committee that those who receive electro-therapeutic treatment should contribute towards the expense.

8. The £1298 received from legacies for the year was included in the ordinary receipts. This sum covered the cost of additions and alterations.

9. The register of collecting boxes should be kept up-to-date.

10. The committee of management should look into the question of finding ways and means to raise funds".

The committee of management agreed with all the points, but in regard to 4 doubted if the only male staff available, namely the gardener and the porter, had time to take up extra work, even if they were capable of doing it. For point 5 the committee said it was quite impossible to reduce the staff, considering that the nursing staff must be prepared for the maximum number of patients the hospital could take, viz. 76. The committee stressed that, on average, there were 72 in-patients at any one time.

Mr J.T. Helby, who had been roped in as a member of the report committee, qualified the report by proposing that registers of staff and of discharges and admissions should be kept; that coal and coke should be purchased by the truck load from the collieries; that the annual cost should not include alterations, and that legacies should not be included in the ordinary accounts. His was a proper little commercial-like approach: he made the mistake of tacking on to his submission the names - "Helby, Maitland and Plummer", whereupon Mr G.W. Plummer wrote on 12th May to the Chairman of Governors:-

> "I regret I shall be unable to be present at the special meeting to-morrow. I have received a copy of the report, including Mr Helby's qualification. May I be permitted to state that I have signed no report other than that of the full committee. Since Mr Helby has used my name without my permission and against my expressed wish, I think it only right to claim the same publicity as may be given to his remarks."

And that was Mr Helby and his qualifying remarks sunk without trace. He was a local JP who lived in Hartfield Road and took quite an active part in town affairs. In 1924 he led, with some success, the opposition to the purchase of Devonshire Park by the Council.

Goodwill was more evident by Christmas, with all the wards decorated, the ward tables laden with delicacies and, as usual, the hospital doctors acting as chefs on Christmas Day.[4] An antique pair of antler horns resided in the hospital and at Christmas the housemen strapped them to a theatre trolley and, with a Father Christmas sitting on it, the contraption was pushed round the wards.

With the doctors' agreement, the Sister of the children's ward would invite some of the in-patients over the year, to return and enjoy the Christmas celebrations. Mr W.R. Cookson, who in 1921 had been a two-year-old patient with a scald on his neck under the care of Mr Rainey, remembers being invited back for a Christmas present and says, 'Matron was exceptionally good to me'.

Miss P.K. Hall, who was later senior physiotherapist at the hospital, says 'We used to go *en famille* to visit my father's wards at Christmas-time. Dad not only carved the turkey in the centre of the ward on Christmas Day, but before the Health Service he provided the bird as well'.

The apportionment of expenditure in 1921 was £2577 for provisions (which fell to £1877 in 1923); dispensary costs were £1368; domestic costs £2413; salaries and wages £3134; printing and advertisements £154; administration £686; rent and taxes £110, and appeals for funds £48. Twelve years later there was remarkably little change except that salaries had increased to £4834; administration costs had doubled and the expense of appeals had tripled.

Over the next five years work steadily increased until, in 1925, over 1000 patients were admitted. By now the hospital was serving a population of 120000 covering an area of 180 square miles in Eastbourne and district, as against the 25000 originally catered for when it had "not less than 12 beds" in 1883.

In October 1922 the pharmacy, where Miss Bruce was the dispenser, moved to a new location below Sydney Hudson ward, where it remained until the 1970s. The best treatment for scabies in 1922 was reported to be sulphur ointment, which had been used for over a century.

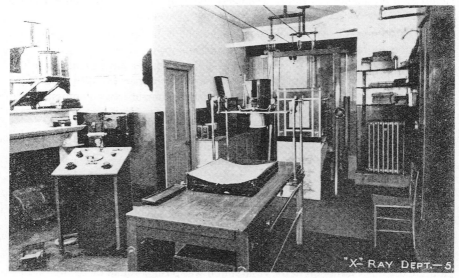

14. The X-ray department in the 1920s.

Sister Burke was on Cavendish and Sydney Hudson wards. The ward was named after Mr Sydney Hudson, a white-haired gentleman who came round the wards every weekday. Mrs L.T. Spearing (née Teague) says he always had a pocketful of sweets for the children, and in December he brought in Christmas stockings for the patients, and gave each member of the staff a Christmas present of a pair of white chamois leather gloves - every year.

Catherine and Geraldine wards were reconstructed in 1923, the cost being defrayed by Messrs W.S.D. and A.P. Marshall. Tabor ward and a second ward (both with the fashionable open-air verandas) were built near the out-patient department. The second ward was originally called after Mr Farnell, who had died that year following a stroke.

Another important addition was a new anæsthetic room for the operating theatre; itself improved by up-to-date lighting, the cost of which was borne by the honorary medical staff. The operating theatre had been built at a time when it was considered essential to have good daylight, but gradually artificial lighting came to the fore. The Princess Alice theatre light consisted of four lightbulbs suspended from the ceiling and lashed together with tape in a Heath Robinson manner. This arrangement satisfied the older staff and it was considered a gross extravagance when, in 1926, the younger surgeons eventually talked them into sharing the cost of Eastbourne's first shadowless lamp, bought for £125.

A new operating table, to replace the one donated by the Prince of Wales in 1899, was also purchased. In turn, this infamous table was not replaced for 35 years and then only when it collapsed under the weight of a tired anæsthetist's elbow. Mr H.G. Estcourt enjoyed describing the astonishment of the *Allen & Hanbury's* equipment representative when, in the late 1950s, he beheld what he described as an "archæological specimen from the Bronze Age" still in use.[5]

Other changes at the same time were new autoclaves, improvements to the secretary's offices and board room, a new boiler and boiler house to provide constant hot-water and theatre heating, and other minor sanitary alterations. The massage department was given its own massage and treatment rooms in the out-patient block because its work had increased enormously in the short time it had been open - it now kept two masseuses and a masseur occupied full-time.

By 1923, when there were 80 beds in the hospital, the massage department's patients had risen to 113, who had a total of 2596 treatments. In addition there was a massage and treatment out-patient clinic for war pensioners which went on into the 1930s, paid for by the Ministry of Pensions. The department gave 10559 treatments to war pensioners in 1925.

A successful appeal for £13000 paid for these extensions. As a separate project, but together with all this rebuilding, went the construction of the Bedfordwell Road nurses' home and other enhancements of the nurses' amenities.

Medical staff changes were few, but the death of Dr Merry following the 1922 influenza outbreak, and the retirement of Dr Emerson, resulted in Mr E. Wilson Hall and Dr G.D. Sherwood being appointed assistant surgeons. Dr Emerson, a rich man who owned land in Argentina, retired in his fifties to set up a home for retired missionaries in Switzerland.

A beneficial effect of Dr Merry's death in harness was the foundation of The Doctor Merry Memorial Fund by public subscription. It still exists to give help, in confidence, towards medical expenses where there is financial difficulty.

An out-patient clinic for Nervous Diseases, established in 1922 under the direction of Dr F.R.P. Taylor, proved of great benefit to many patients, as was an Ophthalmic clinic started the next year by Mr E.V. Oulton, who came to Eastbourne from Brighton twice weekly. The development of the eye work was not made easy by the fact that Eastbourne already had a voluntary Eye Hospital, but it was not considered that the staff were of sufficient calibre to warrant amalgamation with the Princess Alice Hospital.

Dr Taylor had been the medical superintendent since 1903 of the East Sussex Asylum, later Hellingly Psychiatric Hospital. Perhaps his services were needed by Princess Alice in-patients as well, for in May 1923 a girl kept her wound open for 16 weeks after appendicectomy by inserting keys under the dressings.

From 1923 Mr Norman Gray took on the increasing amount of dental work that was being referred to the Princess Alice Hospital. It is said that Mr Gray gave a lift to a young nurse at the hospital, who was telling him about amusing happenings there, so he asked her, 'And what do they think of that dental man, Mr Gray?' 'I've never met him', she replied, ' But I understand that when he operates he makes them put out almost every instrument they have'. The following week he telephoned the theatre sister stating that he only needed two pieces of equipment for his operations the next day. She thought he had gone mad until he explained, when they had a good laugh over the reason for his conversion.

The same year Dr G.P. Norman succeeded Dr Hardman in charge of the X-ray department. Dr Norman recorded the first opaque [barium] meal examination that year, when the X-ray department performed investigations on 525 cases, including 75 "barium meals", although bismuth was still sometimes used. There were also 663 treatments by X-ray irradiations. Three years later barium meal numbers had doubled to 154.

Dr Norman also took charge of the ultra-violet (Finsen) lamp which had been presented to the hospital. This was a popular step ever since Queen Alexandra had donated one to a London hospital. The treatment proved so popular that it put great strain on the department, and perhaps fortunately, it was a craze that did not last too long.

The first blood transfusions (two) were given in 1924, and this was also the year of the first mention of insulin in the Annual Report in an item on the treatment of sugar diabetes. This was only two years after it had first been used on a patient in Toronto by Banting, Best, Collip and Macleod.

On 27th May 1924 there was a clinical meeting of the Eastbourne Medical Society at Princesss Alice, when Dr Mathew demonstrated Folin's method of estimating blood sugar and Dr Shera showed specimens in the lab. Adjourning to the Board Room, discussion took place "...on the propaganda carried out by the local branch of the Anti-Vivisection Society against the Princess Alice on account of the certificates held by Dr Shera for the purpose of animal inoculations. The following resolution was carried unanimously:

> "That the Society desires to express its unqualified approval of the way in which the Committees of the Princess Alice Memorial Hospital have, in the face of insidious propaganda, resolutely supported the necessity of maintaining the standard of medical diagnosis, which would be lowered by the relinquishment of the Home Office Licenses in certain vital instances".

Later that year there were the first recorded local discussions on "insulin excess", or low blood sugar in treated diabetics. Dr George Graham, from St Bartholomew's Hospital, recommended, "In minor cases, if the patient is not unconscious, give a drink [presumably tea or milk] or a tomato". It is clear that doctors remained loath to administer sugar to diabetics even though they now had insulin. Dr Graham continued, "and if the patient is unconscious, give adrenalin and when the patient recovers give five or six lumps of sugar".[6]

The Medical Society donated five guineas [£5.25] to the Samaritan Fund of the Princess Alice Hospital in November 1924, for which Sir Charles O'Brien Harding, as president of the hospital, thanked them. At the same meeting "a visitor, Dr Gow of Bart's Hospital discussed a specimen of aortic aneurysm". He was, of course, the father of Ian Gow, later to be Eastbourne's MP.

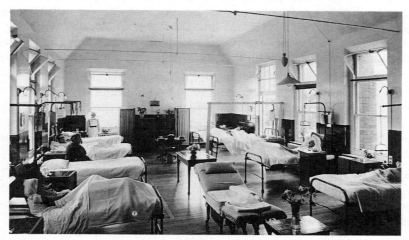

15. Gurney ward in 1925.

A Sister Tutor, Miss M. Poole, was appointed in 1925 and thereafter the state examination results were transformed. In June 1926 Miss B. MacDonald MA, from the Royal Albert Hospital, Devonport, was appointed matron. Bella MacDonald, a strict and dour Scot, herself an examiner for the GNC, greatly raised the standard of nursing in Eastbourne, by appointing sisters from the London teaching hospitals. These were the days when the best treatment for pneumonia was morphine and a Bart's nurse. Of the 603 deaths in Eastbourne in 1926, heart disease was the cause of 115, cancer 105, tuberculosis 49, and respiratory disease 67. Seventy of the deaths were in the Princess Alice Hospital.

With the recognition of the hospital as a training school for nurses a certain proportion of the beds had to be allocated for medical cases, so the other outstanding innovation in 1926 was the designation of Tabor and Geraldine, as medical wards, for male and female patients respectively. This meant that the medical staff had to be divided into physicians and surgeons. Dr Deane became a full physician and Dr D.G. Churcher the assistant physician. On the surgical side Dr Turner, Mr Crook, Mr Rainey and Mr MacQueen became full surgeons, Mr

Wilson Hall and Dr Sherwood remaining assistant surgeons. With the increasing work it was decided to appoint two house officers to the staff and have the physicians and house officers sharing the anæsthetic duties.

The work of a ward orderly is described by Mrs Elizabeth Spearing (née Teague). 'We started work at 0700h, swept the floors, cleaned the brass and got the ward ready for the nurses coming on duty. At 0730h after our breakfast, we pulled beds away from the wall, and put out the patients' flowers if the nurses were busy with operation cases. We gave drinks to the patients and put out the plates for dinner, which the patients had at noon. After washing up we had dinner ourselves at 1300h. Cutting up bread and butter for tea took up the afternoon and we were off duty at 1630h. The wooden floors were polished by swinging a heavy, blanketted bumper in an arc across the ward. While the maids applied wax to the blanket, the stoker, "Nick" Nicholson, did the actual "bumping".

'You had Sunday off at 1300h and one other half-day, all for 18 shillings [90p] a week, of course all your food was included. Most of the staff lived in. Other staff included Doris Stoner, ward maid, Hetty the cook, and Florrie the matron's maid, who later emigrated. It wasn't demanding work, and we were able to play tennis on the hospital court. I had a lovely time for eleven years, everybody was happy and contented.'

By 1926 the hospital had 94 beds, at a cost per bed of £3.24p a week. The General Fund receipts were £11371.24p and payments £12636.30p, while the overdraft at the bank stood at £1690.02p. Even so, the hospital committee decided to appoint Mr H. Jewell as consulting Ear, Nose and Throat surgeon, .

A popular benefaction was to endow a bed at the hospital. The privilege of endowment depended on the amount donated; for perpetual endowment a bed cost £1000, and an annual endowment was £50, with cots about half-price. Individuals or businesses could endow a bed and an attraction was that "persons endowing beds or cots enjoy the privilege of naming them". Thus there was an "Eastbourne Amateur Operatic and Dramatic Society Cot", a "Macandrew Bed" endowed by Mrs Macandrew in memory of her son who fell at Gallipoli, a "Miss Sarah Matilda Diplock" Bed, and even a "John Surtees Bed" endowed by John O. Surtees in 1914, whoever he might have been.

In 1927 Dr Norman introduced retrograde pyelography [looking at the kidneys outlined by X-ray opaque dye] and he described the technique of cholecystography [a similar examination of the gall bladder]. "A plain X-ray is taken, the bowels cleared and bicarb. of soda given. In the evening a fatty meal and six capsules of tetraiodophenolphthalein are administered. Films are taken and twelve hours later another fatty meal is eaten to empty the gall bladder." Sister Matthews was the X-ray Sister.

Dr Shera started a pathology specimen collection, kept in a cupboard in the mortuary. One Eastbourne patient achieved immortality of a sort when a specimen from the pathology laboratory was placed in the museum of the Royal College of Surgeons in London.

Sadly, it was also the year of Eastbourne's first incompatible blood transfusion. The patient, who had a ruptured ectopic pregnancy, died eight days afterwards with complete suppression of urine.

On 10th January 1928 the new nurses' home, to accommodate 30 nurses, a memorial to Mr Sydney Hudson, was opened by Eastbourne's first woman mayor, Cllr Miss Alice Hudson, his daughter.[7] Two houses in Bedfordwell Road, *Ruxley* and *Sunnydene,* had been converted into one large building at a cost of some £3500. The nurses themselves raised £400 towards the furnishings. Alderman Sir Charles O'Brien Harding introduced the mayor, saying that it was always the fervent wish of Mr Hudson that there should be a nurses' home attached to the hospital, and he also wanted to acknowledge the very generous gifts from Mrs Wilson and Mr Evill.

16. The Duke and Duchess of York (later King George VI and Queen Elizabeth) driving away from the front of the Princess Alice Hospital after their visit in October 1929 {photo M.E. Spearing}.

The mayor, who had white hair like her father, and always wore a blue tweedy costume, said she was sure there was no need to say how glad she was to be associated with the opening, "the services which nurses rendered could not be computed in any material way..... She wished all those who came within, that happiness and joy which was the reward of work unselfishly performed". The vote of thanks was proposed by Alderman F. Hollins and seconded by Dr Turner.

The year, 1928, which saw the discovery of penicillin, and the first *Mickey Mouse* cartoon, signalled local advances. Refrigeration plant was installed, Mr Clift Ford provided wireless earphones for each bed of the hospital, and the laboratory performed its first blood cholesterol estimation. Before penicillin and other antibiotics, however, even simple surgery remained a hazardous procedure.

Mr Frank Davis says, 'I still have vivid memories of my emergency operation performed by Mr Wilson Hall for acute peritonitis following a burst appendix. Surgical technology was vastly different then and I understand the op. took six hours. I was in for nine weeks; the first three of which I was on the "critically-ill list", to which my many wound, stitch and tube scars bear witness. Only last week my GP, during a routine check, asked "What's this b----y battlefield?" to which I replied, "A minor skirmish", which is what it was for 1929.'

Sister Tyrwhitt Drake was on Crowden and Geraldine wards. Described as a stern martinet, all are agreed she was very severe, but if she was not satisfied with anything, she worked on the principle that you did it yourself, and it was not unknown for her to get down on her knees and scrub the floor. Perhaps it was because of such commitment that in 1929 a patient recovered after tetanus.

In March 1930 a patient of Dr Deane with pernicious anaemia was the first in the hospital treated with raw hog's stomach [which supplied the deficiency in this otherwise fatal condition] and "showed improvement" - in the anaemia if not the appetite. That year Dr Shera introduced the Ascheim-Zondek test for pregnancy. It involved injecting a mouse with the patient's urine and the result was obtained four days later. Such tests were mainly used when there was an abdominal tumour and the surgeon wanted to know whether a pregnancy was present as well. The next year Dr Deane recorded using tannic acid therapy for scalds.

While the cost per bed had fallen to £2.58p a week, the next few years saw the hospital bursting at the seams, owing to the steadily increasing work. The tiny casualty department, which still consisted of little more than a nurse with a pair of scissors, was overwhelmed. The 63 patients of 1919 became over 400 in 1928, of whom a considerable number were motor-car casualties. Motor accidents also added to the bed problem by supplying nearly 100 in-patients during the year at a cost well in excess of £1000.

When it was found to be quite impossible to finance any further building from income, it was eventually decided to launch an appeal for £25000 to carry out the many necessary upgradings. This was placed in the capable hands of Mr Clift Ford, a wealthy man who owned property in London and who was to manage the hospital finances over the next decade. Its inauguration was helped by a visit from the Duke and Duchess of York (later King George VI and Queen Elizabeth) on 29th October 1929. Their visit was commemorated by placing seats on Beachy Head, which are still there, although not in the original spot.

Just as the Princess Alice was preparing for another leap forward, the Eye Hospital, at 49 Pevensey Road, and "Royal" from 1925, was at its peak. It had six beds for males and eight for females, who were looked after by the matron, one nurse and two probationer nurses. About 1930 the staff consisted of Miss Jessie Weston, matron, who had come from the Leaf Hospital, Nurses Grace Billings, Nelly Spice, Betty Meas, Dorothy Weston (niece of the matron), all of whom lived in, and Nurses Nelly White and Doris Thorne, who were part-time, and mostly worked in the out-patient clinic. There were also three domestics - Hilda Weller, May Guy and Esme, and a boiler man, Mr Banks, who came daily.

The staff changed little, Miss Weston was matron up to the 1939-45 war, with Nurses White and Dorothy Weston, with the addition of Nurses Russell and Barker, and juniors Betty Bradley and Kathleen Hyder (later Mrs McGuinness). At the outbreak of war the cook was yet another member of the Weston family.

17. The building which housed the Royal Eye Hospital, at the junction of Pevensey Road and Cavendish Place, Eastbourne. It is a hotel in 1993. The flight of steps on the Cavendish Place frontage led to the Out-patients.

Dr D.V. Giri was the only doctor. He called daily and all his operations were done under local anæsthetic, so no anæsthetists were on the staff. He had an honorary appointment, but was allowed a single-bedded ward for any private patients. He did an out-patient clinic twice a week starting at 1400h, which often went on to 1900h and later. On occasions he used leeches into the late 1930s. He was popular with the staff, always giving them a present at Christmas, and in turn they always tried to ensure that he had his favourite snack - asparagus - after an operating session. As Mrs McGuinness remarks, 'I had never seen asparagus

51

before I started at the hospital'. She goes on to say, 'In those days patients kept eye pads on for ages after operations, so I used to sing to them'.

Mrs Grace Harriott (née Billings) first assisted at an operation for a squint in a little boy when she was there to hold his hand. She didn't intend to look at the operation, but once Dr Giri started she couldn't take her eyes away. From that moment began her general and midwifery training which led to 36 years of nursing. If Dr Giri removed an eye, the youngest nurse was deputed to take it to Harmer's the Chemists in South Street, who arranged its dispatch for histological examination. On these occasions Mrs Harriott recalls that a certain Nurse Billings was full of apprehension at the thought that she might drop the jar and, horror of horrors, the eye would roll out over the pavement.

The Royal Eye Hospital was dependent on voluntary subscriptions, with boxes in the waiting and treatment rooms and there were two shutes in the wall outside, one for coins and notes and one for silver paper. Once a year the hospital had a Pound Day when well-wishers would donate a pound of sugar, tea or other groceries, and the hospital also had a float on Carnival Day.

The Ear, Nose and Throat (ENT) Hospital had the address 47/49 Cavendish Place, although on the opposite corner of Pevensey Road. Its main claim to fame is that it was a part of the same building (49/51 Pevensey Road) as the Eastbourne Provident Dispensary, founded in 1863. In 1932 it had four beds for males, five for females, eight for children and three pay beds, while the staff consisted of one aural surgeon, one general surgeon, two anæsthetists, Miss Rimmer, the matron, (succeeded by Miss K. Magrath), three Staff Nurses and two probationary nurses.

Mr E.F. Bartholomew, who was a patient there in the 1920s having his tonsils out, remembers the box on the railings outside for donations of silver paper. In 1993, the building was derelict and had been used over the years as an old persons' home and as holiday flatlets, but it was still just possible to make out the notice "⇐ Out-patients" on the gate post - when over 50 years had elapsed since it was last used as a hospital.

Notes and References

1. Princess Alice Hospital, Annual Report, 1920.
2. *Eastbourne Gazette*, 2/3/1921.
3. *Eastbourne Gazette*, 18/5/1921.
4. *Eastbourne Herald*, 31/12/1921.
5. Estcourt HG. *Eastbourne Medical Gazette*, 1976; **2**: 28-33.
6. Eastbourne Medical Society, minutes, 30/9/1924.
7. *Eastbourne Gazette*, 11/1/28.

Chapter 6

Developments of the 1930s

On 30th June 1931 the foundation stone for the new building at the Princess Alice was laid by the Prince of Wales, the future King Edward VIII and Duke of Windsor. Long-time local resident, Mr John Cant, then aged 13, was one of the Boy Scouts who lined the route. Mr Cant's main recollection was of his shock on discovering he was the same height as the "little prince". Mrs Eileen Goldsmith (née Gillam) was one of six invited from the Day Continuation School, and Mr W.R. Cookson, who represented Christ Church Junior School, had already sampled the Princess Alice when admitted at the age of two in 1921. The Royal Visitor may have been diminutive, but he was an innovator because he travelled to Eastbourne by aeroplane, landing "in a field off Kings Drive", in the days when people would rush out of the house to view an aeroplane as it flew over. He also called at Princes Park, the Soldiers' and Sailors' Convalescent Home in Upperton Road, and Eastbourne College.[1]

While this extension appeal was in progress, Mr and Mrs Norman Holland donated and equipped two children's wards of 12 beds each, together with a small isolation ward. They were named Anne Elizabeth and Michael Francis after Mr and Mrs Holland's children. The first patient in the new wards was a son of Robinson's, the builders, with appendicitis, and the second was E.F. Bartholomew, who had an infected eye injury. Mr Bartholomew says, 'They were very strict in those days. We all had to have an afternoon nap, and any presents from visitors - eggs or sweets - had to be shared, however, I loved the daily spoonful of "Cod Liver Oil and Malt". Before long we were having visits from well-known locals; I remember the Revd Canon F.A. Corbett, vicar of St Philip's, and Mr Gilbert Soddy of *Gilbert's the Bakers,* who had been the mayor.'

As a matter of interest, the half-brother of Gilbert Soddy's father was Frederick Soddy FRS, professor of chemistry at Oxford and a Nobel Laureate in 1921. He coined the term "isotope" to describe forms of the same element.

The new wards meant that the Princess Alice Hospital had 26 children's beds, in place of the old ward of 12 beds. With an open veranda at the Carew Road end of Anne Elizabeth they typified the importance ascribed to open-air therapy over the early part of the century. Mrs E.M. Fuller (née Walder) says that when she was a patient in 1938 suffering from rheumatic chorea [involuntary movements], 'I was pushed out on to the balcony most days'.

The children's wards came into full use in 1931. when Mr D.E. O'Connor Cuffey was appointed Ear, Nose and Throat surgeon, on the death of Mr Jewell. Mr Cuffey, also on the staff of the Leaf Hospital and the Bexhill Hospital, continued to do the routine work at the Pevensey Road ENT Hospital, with Dr R.M. Barron as anæsthetist; in effect during the 1930s he was only called for emergency work at the Princess Alice Hospital. It wasn't unknown in those days for Mr Cuffey to say to Dr Barron, 'Let's change ends and I'll give the gas'.

18. Souvenir programme of 1931.

Mr D. Holding describes how he was visiting his mother one Sunday in 1931, 'and as children will do I sat on the bed, but not for long. The booming voice of Sister Drake from the other side of the ward ordered, "Get that child off my bed". However, I was assured she was a good nurse'. Mr Henry Wilson describes her as, 'a good nurse, but tall and dragon-like'.

In 1932 Mr W. Russell Rudall was appointed hospital secretary on the death of Captain E.G. Fenning, who had held the post for the previous five years.

The new buildings were opened that year by the Marchioness of Hartington. They comprised Arno ward (thanks to a handsome donation of £10000 from Mr T. Arno),[2] the X-ray department, the domestic block, and better accommodation for the resident doctors, pathology department, and pharmacy.

The original laboratory, a converted coach house, was so short of space that the surgical specimens were initially delivered to Dr Shera's house - or at least until a large ovarian cyst burst, to deliver its contents over the kitchen table, when Mrs Shera cried halt. In 1931 Dr Shera had anticipated his good fortune of additional laboratory rooms by isolating a new bacillus, known to this day as *Salmonella eastbourne*.

These were really big advances which, with the increase in children's beds and an extra six male beds, brought the total number to 116. This was made up of 44 male beds, 44 female beds, two beds in cubicles which could be used for either sex, and 26 children's beds. The other changes also meant that portable X-rays were available on the wards for the first time.

The staff were now two resident doctors, 12 visiting medical attendants, two visiting dental surgeons, six consultants, the matron, one Sister Tutor (who doubled as the Nurses' Home Sister), seven ward Sisters, seven Staff Nurses, 30 probationer nurses, 14 daily maids and 12 living-in maids. The only shadow on the horizon was that the hospital's accumulated deficit had risen to over £7000.

19. Casualty department entrance Princess Alice Hospital, 1932.

During 1932 there were 1460 in-patients, with an average stay of over 22 days, and the 12985 out-patient attendances were nine-times greater than at any other hospital between Hastings and Brighton. The year also recorded the first use of a liver injection *Hepatex* for treatment of pernicious anaemia (instead of having to chomp through pounds of raw liver or hog's stomach every day) and gastric milk drips for stomach ulcers are mentioned. There is a comment that half of all biochemistry tests were blood sugars [for diabetes], the next most frequent request was for blood urea [a kidney test], and there were only occasional requests for calcium, diastase and basal metabolic rate tests.

Mrs Miriam Pratt, in Sydney Hudson ward in 1932 for a minor operation, surely had an increased metabolic rate when she learnt that her 3½-year-old son had been telling his friends that, 'Mummie has gone to sleep with the doctors'.

Although only 4½ that year, Mrs Ivy Jean Breach (née Miller) remembers being taken by her GP to the Princess Alice with 'pyaemia' [generalised infection]. She was 'critically ill' for several weeks and had 'trips to the theatre for incision of abcesses and I was given injections of anti-bacterial vaccines, which my mother was told cost ten shillings [50p] each ... the infection cleared up, leaving me with a stiff hip and elbow, so after six months in the hospital I was taken to Chailey Heritage for a further twelve months.' It didn't stop her doing her nurse training at the Princess Alice in 1945-49, and 'apart from having an arthrodesis of my hip [joint fusion] in 1969, I otherwise kept pretty good'.

Vaccine injections were one of Dr Shera's specialties. Mr F. Battye describes Dr Shera treating him with vaccines, 'and as he gave me the injection he said, "If you were a private patient this would cost you ten shillings", so I said if I were I would do without'. It has to be admitted that although Dr Shera was doing his best before antibiotics, it is doubtful if his vaccines had much effect.

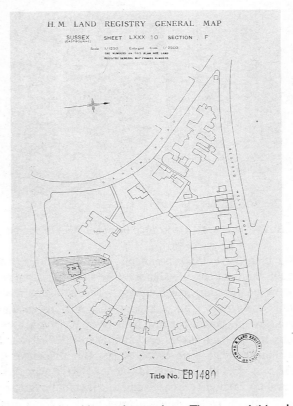

20. Princess Alice Hospital site plan. The new children's ward block is shown. The "island" site of the hospital is clearly seen. The large square building is Roborough school, with the playing field in the centre. No 3 Upper Avenue is highlighted. By the 1960s the hospital owned most of the former houses round the island.

In 1933 the hospital celebrated 50 years of steady progress and achievement. The 116 beds represented nearly ten-times the modest, original number.

Among the year's special events was a Princess Alice Hospital garden party, providing all the fun of the fair, with flags on sale from the nurses, hoop-la stalls, and patronage from the oldest visitor, Mr R. Chatfield (aged 79) to the youngest, Thomas Preston, aged six months.[3]

The year also saw the conveyance of the lease to the Town Council and in the April Mr Clift Ford (chairman of the hospital finance committee) and Alderman Gilbert Soddy (chairman of the governors) launched an ambitious campaign to mobilise an army of householders to fight the annual deficit. Mr Clift Ford said, 'Income from subscriptions and donations has shown a decrease due to economic depression, but on account of the advances in treatment there is an ever-increasing call for the services of the hospital. The aim is to place a hospital collecting box in every home in the area served so ably by the Princess Alice Hospital. We are asking for two pence a week, although naturally we should not object to a larger weekly sum from those homes where it can be spared. For this nominal weekly payment the hospital offers treatment for adults, and children in the family, without any request for further contribution. In view of the great work the hospital does, the committee commend this scheme to everyone, and especially when, at any moment, any of us might require hospital treatment for ourselves or our families'.

Mr Ford added, 'This is no haphazard experiment, the Household Box Scheme has been tested and found practical, notably in Canterbury where the committee have placed boxes with no fewer than 14000 families'.

The next year, 1934, Mr H.M. Pimm was appointed dental surgeon, with Mr A. de Mierre continuing as consulting dental surgeon. Changes also occurred in the medical specialties about this time, mainly involving anæsthetic practice.

The status of anæsthetists was low, and they were the butt of all the surgeons' jokes, such as, 'I don't know what the patient's like your end, but he appears to have had an anæsthetic death from where I'm operating'. As late as 1930 anæsthesia had hardly moved out of the "open ether" age, when it was customary to have a strong porter nearby who could restrain any patient who became violent. By the mid 1930s, premedication [giving the patient a sedative beforehand] and a choice of inhalational agents were being introduced, and it was slowly realised that the anæsthetic played as important a part towards the patient's survival as the surgery. Instead of deputing the "gassing" to the most junior doctor, a common practice into the 1940s, the trend was for doctors to specialise in anæsthesia, and in 1935 Robert Macintosh, the first Professor of Anæsthetics, was appointed at Oxford University. Designated anæsthetists, in Dr J.B. Adams and Dr F.H. Gillett, were first appointed at the Princess Alice Hospital in 1934, although at the time neither had specialist qualifications.

Dr Gillett says, 'At first the hospital could not provide an anæsthetic table so I had to carry my own ... until a patient donated one'. The celebrated Dr Bodkin Adams, who usually "gassed" for Mr Crook, was notorious as the anæsthetist "who snored over the body", although he introduced intubation to the hospital and never had an anæsthetic death in his career. Mrs Ruth Tucker (née Saunders) can recall Mr Snowball saying at the end of an operation, 'Wake up Bodkin, we have finished', and Mrs Doris Kingsford (née West) says that in the 1940s a special pillow was kept in the theatre for him to rest his head. Dr Adams was also renowned for munching a chocolate snack in the middle of an operation.

In November 1934 the Eastbourne Medical Society made the Princess Alice Hospital Board Room their regular venue for meetings. At one meeting the routine use of intravenous *Evipan* anæsthetic to induce the patient was discussed, Dr P.W. Mathew saying that he gave "1cc. every 15 seconds" until the patient was asleep, when he carried on with ether. Mr MacQueen also recorded his use of Rammstedt's operation[4] to treat two infants, suffering from pyloric stenosis [vomiting in the new born].

That same year Dr Deane retired, being replaced by Dr Churcher, and in turn Dr J.W. Joule became an assistant physician.

Dr Archibald Deane, described by staff as "very severe", retired to Abingdon where he died in 1948. Dr Duncan Churcher, on the other hand, was said to be

21. Dr D.G. Churcher.

"much more happy-go-lucky", possibly in contrast. He had come to Eastbourne after active service in the Royal Navy, followed by the post of medical inspector in the Sudan Medical Service. Apart from being a hospital physician, he was a general practitioner, and a doctor to the lifeboat, police, fire brigade, post office, Eastbourne and Chelsea colleges, *Compton Place* and *Chaseley*, as well as an Admiralty surgeon and agent, and it was he who looked after the Royal Household when King George V and Queen Mary came to Eastbourne for the King's convalescence in March 1935.

He made a daily visit to the Princess Alice and the houseman knew that he had to meet him at the front door. If the front door glass window was dirty he would notify the telephonist 'so that she could instruct the porter before matron's inspection'. He had a heavy workload, a remarkable diagnostic acumen, and he was renowned for his financial commitment and expertise. After a diabetic patient in coma had been admitted into his care, the family - going on the theory that you only get the best by paying - insisted on obtaining the opinion of a leading London specialist. The great man arrived at the Princess Alice to be greeted with a handshake by the patient at the ward door. The Harley Street specialist felt so embarrassed that he said to Dr Churcher, 'I won't charge'. 'Of course you must charge', he was firmly told. 'You must charge your usual fee in view of all the trouble you have taken.'

Dr Churcher was well-known for driving round Eastbourne in an open-top *Morris Minor* well into his eighties, and he kept up his police work until 1975. Such was his fearless nature that even when past 70 he was saddened if he had to miss a helicopter rescue at Beachy Head.

Before the National Health Service, outside doctors were brought in for consultation on rare occasions only. They were usually well-heeled physicians or surgeons from Harley Street, or from the teaching hospital of the local specialist; for example, Mr Wilson Hall would call in Sir Gordon Gordon-Taylor who had been his chief at the Middlesex.

In 1935 Mr Turner was retired on the time limit, and with Mr Crook soon to become the surgeon-in-charge of the fracture clinic, Mr Wilson Hall and Dr Sherwood became full surgeons in their place. Mr Wilson Hall was a neat operator who could well have held a teaching hospital appointment, although somewhat unforgiving if anyone fainted in the theatre, for he would not have them back again.

Mr H.G. Estcourt and Mr T. Henry Wilson were elected assistant surgeons on the same day and, having polled equal votes, a further vote was taken which gave Mr Estcourt the seniority: an arrangement which Mr Henry Wilson thought 'very fair'. He had joined the Churcher, Turner practice in March 1935 and, after a six-month assessment, was on a one-fifth share, which was then a fortune of £1651, guaranteed for three years. Dr Benjamin Reid, the Medical Superintendent at Hellingly Mental Hospital on Dr F.R.P. Taylor's retirement, also joined the Princess Alice staff to take charge of the Clinic for Nervous Diseases. Finally that year, Mr Clift Ford succeeded Mr G.B. Soddy as chairman, and Mr Arthur Beckett of Beckett Newspapers became the deputy chairman.

Just before his retirement Dr Turner reported on his 54 operations for stomach ulcers at Princess Alice with 5 deaths, over the ten years 1926-1935. Tommy Turner was a great character who lived into his nineties, dying in November 1974. He was also famed for bringing into the hospital the mimosa plants which his wife cultivated in their conservatory.

Mr B.J. Pumfrey started as deputy hospital secretary in 1935. Educated at Eastbourne Grammar School, he had worked in the local education department after leaving school. He was to give long and loyal service to the hospital.

Dr A.G. Shera was an active member of the Association of Clinical Pathologists who held their Annual Provincial Meeting at the hospital in the June. Apart from the pathologist, the staff of the pathology department was now one senior assistant, one junior assistant and a part-time worker. Investigations had increased from less than 200 a year in 1919 to nearly 4000 in 1935: the year that rapid frozen-sections were first available in the Eastbourne laboratories.

It was also the year Dr Bodkin Adams went to the USA, partly to visit the Mayo Clinic, but also to obtain specially ground *Bausch and Lomb* glasses for his clay pigeon shooting at which he was a champion shot. The next year, a patient, Mrs Matilda Whitton left him £3000 in her will, a bequest which was contested by the family and he decided to fight the case. Although he won the court judgment, the episode did his standing no good within the medical fraternity.

Mr Crook set up the fracture clinic in April 1936, primarily because the numbers of fractures and accidents were increasing and needed more expert care, but also he was due to retire from his general surgeon appointment on the time limit and by taking up a new appointment he was able to continue in hospital practice. Even so, it was not until 1947 that an orthopædic department was officially established.

A mild disadvantage for the rest of the hospital was that plasters of the time were often left untouched for months, so more plastering meant that a distinctive aroma clung about in the air. It was standard practice to rest arthritic joints in children for six weeks, and if not better to assume they were tuberculous and treat by fixation for two years. Considering that TB-infected milk was the usual source of bone and joint infections, it is not surprising that at a meeting in "the New Clinic" at Princess Alice in 1935 the local doctors voted 38 to 3 for the pasteurisation of all milk. On the same occasion, however, Lord Horder speaking on dental infections said that "all doubtful teeth should be sacrificed" - a sacrilegious statement to any dentist of the present day, but a pillar of the "focal sepsis" theories of the time.

Arthur H. Crook, known affectionately as "Daddy Crook", was a great character, a good surgeon, and pleasant to patients and staff alike. He was an outstanding athlete, captain of rugby at Guy's Hospital, an England trialist, and he came from a family with a great tradition of medical service, with brother Frank, two of his sons (Anthony and David) and a nephew, James, in the medical profession. One of the last of the true general surgeons, he would turn his hand to abdominal surgery, broken bones or midwifery, although his orthopædic successor used to say that all he knew about "Orthopædics" was that it started with the letter "O", and he hoped he knew more about "Obstetrics", a comment which probably says more of his successor than Arthur Crook. He had studied with Böhler in Vienna, a leading orthopædic surgeon of the day, and Dr Paula Gosling says that Mr Crook rejected the Judet artificial hip long before some of the London surgeons, proving that he kept up to date.[5] It needs to be said that by the date of his retirement in 1951, the war had taken its toll of "Daddy Crook", and that when he was in training, in the early 1900s, elective orthopædic surgery was still severely limited by the risks of infection. Whilst not at the pre-antisepsis levels of 75% of compound fractures going on to amputation, all too often a compound fracture [when the sharp edge of the bone has torn the skin] was compromised by osteomyelitis [bone infection] which could finish in a fore- or hind-quarter amputation.

Of the many amazing stories about Arthur Crook, none is so redolent of his times as that recounted by Dr Basil Kent, who was acting as his anæsthetist for the occasion. They were about to operate at the Leaf Hospital on a young man for a bleeding stomach ulcer, when it became clear that the patient was so exsanguinated he would not survive unless he was given blood. 'Too late for pathology, you must take some from me', ordered AHC. Dr Kent bled from him the best part of two pints into a wax-coated flask with a spot of citrate. Matching of the bloods was by rolling donor and recipient specimens on a slide. Best of all, both patient and surgeon did well and were soon restored to full health.

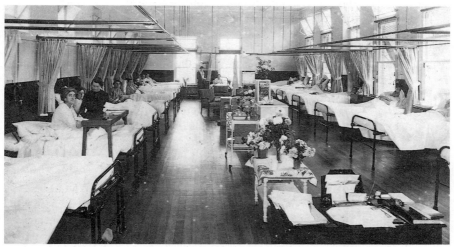

22. Geraldine ward, c. 1935, with curtain rails round each bed.

Miss MacDonald remained matron. Her staff, as in 1932, consisted of 45 nurses and 26 ward-maids to cope with the hospital's 116 beds into which 1561 patients were admitted over the year with an average stay of 23 days. There were now 900 major operations and the average cost per patient per week was £2.80p.

Throughout its existence the management committee spent an inordinate amount of time revising the hospital rules, but despite these regular rehashes, in 1936, it was reiterated that, "Matron should be a single woman or widow not more than 45 years of age ... and shall reside in the hospital and not be absent without leaving the assistant matron in charge"; hardly any change since 1883.

The completion, in 1935, of an extension to the nurses' home in Bedfordwell Road was a major benefit. It included the Silver Jubilee lounge presented by Mr

Clift Ford. The following year, four small wards Brodie, Geraldine, Catherine and Marshall, in the original part of the hospital, which were unsatisfactory and wasteful of staff time, were largely rebuilt as one surgical ward, and named Geraldine ward. This brought the total number of beds to 120.

In 1936, the year Miss L.M.T. Drake retired after 17 years as a Sister at the hospital, there was the first local reference to gold therapy in rheumatoid arthritis, and in a lecture at Princess Alice there was mention of per-urethral [without incision] removal of prostatic tissue with diathermy for small adenoma [tumours], although this more simple operation was not generally adopted for some years. All the time the hospital dealt with the routine work of any general hospital, for example, John Stevens was in Arno ward in 1936 for Mr Wilson Hall to operate on a cartilage of his right knee.

Between 1934 and 1937, starting with Geraldine, most of the adult wards of the hospital had cubicled curtains installed around each bed.

Inevitably, with the increased number of beds and increased use of the out-patient clinics and departments, the costs soared. By 1937 the Household Box Scheme had overtaken the Mayor's Penny-a-Week Fund and, run energetically by Mr Russell Rudall and Miss Eileen Peyton, the almoner, it became the most important source of regular income. The Household Box Scheme really did consist of cardboard boxes about 4 x 3 x 2 inches deep, which were kept in many households. They had a slot for coins and were sealed by an orange label. Mr R.A. Pavey, who has lived in Eastbourne all his life, remembers one in the family home, with a build-up of partly torn-off labels. Miss Peyton travelled round to the houses by bus, emptied the boxes, marked the amounts on a green card and resealed with a new orange label. In a commercial variant of the scheme employers stamped a card for their staff who contributed 2/2d [11p] a quarter.

Even with subscriptions and donations, and despite the Household Box Scheme bringing in over £6000 a year during 1937, the income never reached the £17500 which it cost to run the hospital that year, and there was a yearly deficit of some £3000. Legacies had to be used to balance the accounts and later there were inroads into the capital account and more borrowing from the bank.

Already in 1936 the fracture clinic - only opened on 1st April - was short of space, but all that could be provided was a new plaster room. Something had to be done and plans were laid to amalgamate with the Eye and ENT hospitals, to scrap the old operating theatre and build twin theatres, one of which would be used by the fracture clinic, and in addition build a private patients' unit of 26 beds, to bring in extra money.

An appeal was launched to fund these improvements and on 4th May 1938 Princess Alice, Countess of Athlone, a niece of *the* Princess Alice, opened a Fête at the Winter Garden which raised a clear £2007.

Sufficient money had been raised by the end of 1938, but the approaching war caused the scheme to be shelved and it was never implemented.

The Diplock bequest fiasco did not help. Caleb Diplock, son of the founder of the brewery, left money to "Charitable or Benevolent Institutes", believing that he had no issue. According to Mrs Doreen Peyton (née McFadden) because the will specified "or" instead of "and" it was contested by distant relatives in Australia, and the case went to the House of Lords. The Princess Alice Hospital, along with other charities, had to give back money disbursed, some of which had been earmarked for the new private wing. As late as 1946, Plummer Parsons, the Honorary Auditors, were qualifying the balance sheet with a note that, "A claim by the trustees of Caleb Diplock deceased for the return of the sum of £7500 with interest at 4% from the date of payment (28/11/1936) has been received".

Local fundraisers rallied round to replace the Diplock money, and perhaps the most magnificent effort was by the Lady Foley who organised a Golden Ball at the Grand Hotel. The theme of gold was carried through the occasion - all dresses had to be gold in colour, the hotel was decorated in golden bunting, and all the tombola prizes were of gold. It was just slightly unfortunate that a gold cigarette case was won by Miss MacDonald, who not only did not smoke, but strongly disapproved of the addiction.

As part of the attempts to off-set the financial deficit, the almoner, Miss E.C. Peyton, whose office was in the conservatory beyond the board room, interviewed patients and relatives who were asked to pay what they could towards the cost, now nudging £4 a week. Eileen Peyton, worked very hard and 'was never known to leave the hospital before six o'clock'.

Various methods of payment were used. Many people paid a regular amount to a Friendly Society, such as "The Ancient Order of Foresters", to cover hospital costs plus one shilling [5p] for the use of a St John Ambulance. Farmers would be asked to bring in eggs, vegetables and fruit. Like the Eye Hospital, the Princess Alice also had Pound Days when people would be asked to bring in a pound of cheese, rice, sugar - almost anything. Weighty, but never enough.

In 1937 Mr Rainey resigned for family reasons and moved to Norfolk. He was considered by Mr Henry Wilson 'a good surgeon'. Mr Geoffrey Estcourt became a full surgeon and Mr L.A.H. Snowball was elected an assistant surgeon. Mr Estcourt, who incidentally was left-handed, specialised in abdominal and thyroid surgery and had a charming manner, which made him a popular figure. Dr Joule also resigned, his place taken by Dr A.G. Emslie, with Dr A.M. Lester coming onto the staff, and Dr R. West Phillips was appointed an anæsthetist.

There was a publication in the *British Medical Journal* in 1937 by A.G. Shera and E.H. Rainey, entitled "Triple pregnancy with extra-uterine twins", relating to a patient in the Princess Alice, which is of special interest because, of course, maternity cases were not normally admitted.[6] Perhaps the title is strangely apposite because staff always describe Mr Rainey as "having a tribe of children".

In the departmental reports for this year there appears a paragraph about the introduction of sulphonamide therapy, and also the first comment on the treatment of fractured hips by "pinning".

Smith-Petersen's stainless steel pin (more like a thick knitting needle than a pin) had been introduced between 1925 and 1931, and in 1937 Mr Crook performed the first hip-pinning in Eastbourne. It was a great success, with the patient soon back to riding a bicycle. This treatment added further to the work and cost of the orthopædic and accident department, which altogether treated 400 patients in the year; before pinning, however, most elderly patients with a fractured hip would not walk again and many died within six months of their fall. Mr D.J. Richards, the orthopædic surgeon, in a childhood memory of pre-war days, recalls seeing bath chairs on the Eastbourne sea-front and being particularly impressed by the red blankets used to tuck-in the passengers. He is pleased to think that his specialty, by pinning fractures and replacing arthritic hips, has helped to sweep away the need for bath chairs.

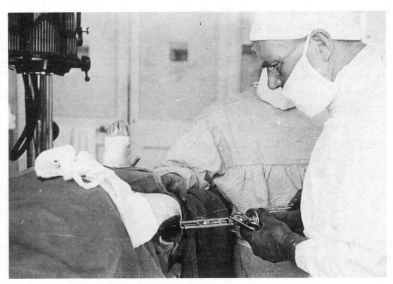

23. Mr A.H. Crook pinning his first hip in 1937.

Of sulphonamide chemotherapy the Annual Report stated: "This remarkable drug has been found of great value in combating streptococcal, coliform and Neisserian infections[7] and is also said to be invaluable in cerebrospinal fever."

While the foundations of chemotherapy had been laid in 1906 when Ehrlich synthesised the anti-syphilitic drug, *Salvarsan,* the real step forward was in 1935 when Domagk introduced *Prontosil.* No longer was nursing care the sole treatment for pneumonia, nor did a diagnosis of bacterial meningitis [cerebrospinal fever] mean almost certain death. The world had to wait for penicillin to become available before syphilis was easily curable, but these discoveries meant that early diagnosis was now essential if treatment was to start before the patient became moribund. In turn, as more specific therapy became available, more precise diagnosis by investigations (blood tests or X-rays) was mandatory. For 1937 pathology tests totalled 5251, with 21 blood transfusions.

If the surgeons were specialising, there remained some generalists in the hospital, in particular Mr Nicholson, the stoker, who not only swung the floor-polishing bumpers, but also assisted in the mortuary, took the hospital money to the bank, brought the staff wages back, and did a bit of stoking. He lived with his wife in the little cottage along Bedfordwell Road - and had a reputation for sneaking to matron if he saw nurses creeping into the home after hours.

Mrs Doreen Peyton (née McFadden) started in November 1936 as an assistant to Miss Peyton in the Almoner's office, and when Ben Pumfrey was called up took over his work, until she left to have a baby in June 1942. When her son was born in July 1942 one of the doctors is said to have exclaimed, 'Bless my soul, had a son! I was only giving her letters a week or so ago and didn't even realise she was pregnant.' Assisted by the office boy, Henry Fairburn, her duties consisted in completing numerous registers, dealing with incoming bills and balancing the books. One day a man came into Miss McFadden's office and said to Miss Clark, the secretary, 'Would you take this letter down?', and started dictating. When he stopped and picked up a pen, as he said, to clear out the drains, she took fright and called in Mr Pumfrey. The dictator turned out to be one of Dr Ben Reid's psychology clinic patients.

Among Miss McFadden's duties was to collect radium needles required for cancer treatment, from the Royal East Sussex Hospital at Hastings. She travelled there on the bus and, as a shield from the radioactivity, she was provided with a lead box covered in leather.

Notifiable diseases were normally admitted to the fever hospital [Downside] but the Princess Alice had an "iron lung" before the war. This was obtained for a Pevensey Bay man, with poliomyelitis [infantile paralysis], who had difficulty in breathing. Miss McFadden tried out what it was like to be put inside and found it 'quite scary until you got into the rhythm of it, when you could let yourself relax, and allow the machine to do the breathing for you'. Whilst an iron lung could take over the breathing for a patient, they were inflexible and in the long term tended to underbreathe or overbreathe the patient.

Any patient in the hospital for over eight weeks had their name entered in the "Eight-week book" and their case had to be brought before the House Committee for review. The purpose was to stop long-stay convalescent patients blocking the beds, but many poorly-nourished patients with festering wounds were in need of prolonged treatment. One little girl, Dorothy Whittington, whose burns were painfully dressed every Monday, was in for many months, but before antibiotics every hospital had its fill of "septic cases", carbuncles, abscesses, septic joints, bone infections, any of which could mean weeks in hospital on the "dangerously-ill list" and all could have a fatal outcome. Mrs Grace Taylor says, 'I was in the PA for kidney trouble before the war and even with a simple matter like that at times I wondered if I would ever get better. The treatment was not like to-day, but the wards were tidier'.

There was also a "Waiting List book", again examined regularly by the House Committee, presumably to weed out any "Two-Year-Waits" of the day. Among the house visitors in the 1930s was Mrs Edith Morrell, the patient Dr Bodkin Adams was accused of murdering in 1957.

In 1938 Dr E. Owen Fox was appointed assistant radiologist, Mr A.L. Young assistant ophthalmic surgeon, and Dr A.M. Lester became an anæsthetist, mainly for Mr Estcourt, his partner. Dr Owen Fox's secretary, who also helped at the Esperance Hospital, was Brenda Aylward. Mr Young was renowned for talking in an "indecipherable babble", so nurses made sure he wrote down every word of his treatment instructions.

Dr Basil Kent, who came to Eastbourne in 1938 to join the Astley Roberts, Crook, McSwiney practice, and who was later to be an anæsthetist at the Princess Alice, says that professional practice was very "formal and proper". All GPs wore gloves and hats - 'I wore a black Homberg in the winter and a grey one in the summer in an endeavour to look older. Professional houses sported a silver salver in the hall for the ritual of visiting cards, and each partner ran surgeries from his house, assisted by his wife and a uniformed maid - our maid, living-in, was paid ten shillings [50p] a week. The average fee was about six shillings [30p], but varied from a guinea [£1.05] at the Grand Hotel to nil in Seaside.

'All the GPs did some surgery and midwifery and a great deal of school practice. I well remember a patient in Upperton Road with a cancer of the breast who flatly refused to be admitted to either the Princess Alice Hospital or the Esperance Nursing Home. Arthur Crook carried out a radical mastectomy (and his were radical) with her lying on her hammock-like bed, whilst I developed temporary weakness of my arms leaning over the head of her brass bedstead giving the anæsthetic. She died 17 years later of a stroke.'

Miss Nancy Poulter ("Polly") started training as a nurse in 1930, but in 1935 joined the X-ray department, where she worked until 1967. Just before the war she was joined by Miss Phyllis M. Newman, who stayed for 18 years as radiographer-in-charge. Miss E. Millen, who came in 1944, was one of the radiographers trained by *Ilford* the photographic firm; she later went to St Mary's Hospital. Miss Newman lived in and messed with the Sisters, later sharing a flat with Sister Acfield. She says there was no automatic developing of the X-ray films so she had a porter who manned the darkroom and transported patients to and from the X-ray room as well.

Before the 1939-45 war, Sister Andrews was in charge of Sydney Hudson and Cavendish wards, Sister Gee was on Arno and Casualty, Sister York was the operating theatre sister, and Sister Masters was tutor, later assistant matron. Sister Swallow had succeeded Sister Rainham on the children's wards.

Nurses comment that "tall and commanding" Sister Masters was very "uppity", bringing in a mention of her Guy's Hospital ("Gaise", as she would say) at any opportunity. They envied her navy-blue belt with its marvellous silver buckle, depicting a hunting scene. She wore this on all occasions, except for the children's wards where these prized buckles were not worn in case they became caught up in a baby's shawl. Her teaching was of plasters and stupes and she was still demonstrating leeching in 1941. Mrs Ruth Tucker (née Saunders) hasn't forgotten her concern the day a leech slipped down behind a radiator and could not be enticed out.

Sister Harrison was on Gurney and Tabor wards plus the fracture clinic, and according to Mrs Esther Field (née Saunders) she was 'strict, serious and efficient'.

Sister K. Lancaster on Geraldine ward was strictly teetotal. One day, while she had a short break in the afternoon, the busy nurses gave one of the patients a bedpan. Every so often they would ask at the other side of the curtains 'Are you finished Mrs ..... ?' And consistently they had the reply 'Not quite yet, nurse, thank you'. When Sister Lancaster came back two hours later, she asked, 'What are the curtains doing round Mrs ..... ?' and pulled them back to find the lady lying comatose on her bed with an almost empty half-bottle of gin beside her.

In those days junior nurses never spoke to a Staff Nurse or a Sister unless they were spoken to first. "You spoke to the next senior nurse and hoped that your comment would be transmitted." Needless to say, it was unheard of for a probationer to address a Sister by her forename.

The hospital provided the material for the new nurse's uniform, 'but your mother made it up. The skirt had to reach to one inch below the patella [kneecap] or nine inches from the ground with three tucks in the hem.' The correct length for a uniform was that it reached the floor when the nurse knelt down. The green shaded light in the centre of the wards at night was on a pulley system so that it could be brought close to the nurse's notes without lighting up the ward, and in the male wards it was a regular occurrence for the patients to push the shade up to the ceiling so that the diminutive nurse had to clamber on the table to pull the light down, 'Not that there was any danger of them catching a glimpse of our knickers with the voluminous dresses we wore'. Caps with "tails" hanging down were for first year nurses, after prelim. "tails" were pinned up, and after finals nurses wore a large broad cap. First year nurses wore a white belt, afterwards a blue belt, with a buckle for a staff nurse.

Other less distinguishable but substantial differences were that first year nurses were paid £20 a year plus board, second year nurses £25, and a third year nurse £30.

Probationer nurses always shared a bedroom with another who had just started, and sometimes there were three or four in a large bedroom. The nursing hierarchy was of crucial importance. The probationers had one dining room, the staff nurses another and the Sisters yet another. The precise date a nurse commenced mattered because the probationers sat at one long table with a staff nurse at one end and, as the months and years went by, a nurse moved up until she found herself sitting in that exalted place as head-in-charge of that long table. The most junior at the bottom of the table was served last and had to break off to open the door for matron and senior staff. Mrs Esther K. Field (née Saunders) comments, 'You soon learnt to eat quickly', but as Mrs Pamela E.J. Milne (née Fillery) says, '... the feeling of gradually ascending the table was magic'.

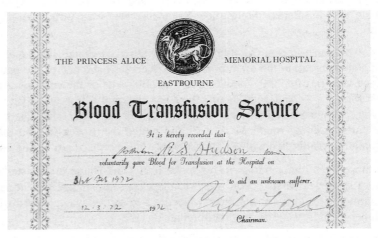

THE PRINCESS ALICE   MEMORIAL HOSPITAL

EASTBOURNE

Blood Transfusion Service

It is hereby recorded that

R S Hudson

voluntarily gave Blood for Transfusion at the Hospital on

3rd Feb 1972 ... to aid an unknown sufferer.

12.3.72 ...19⁷²

Chairman.

24. A Princess Alice blood donation certificate.

In other ways life was much the same as it would be for years to come. The pharmacy was called the dispensary, George Bradley was a porter and did the telephone, and Sidney Pilbeam had just started as a porter. He exasperated some of the staff, but they agreed "he was thoroughly capable of doing his job and wonderfully kind to the patients". The nurses thought he was just "a mother's boy", for when it suited he had a good memory and could recite every person's commencement date to collect their NUPE subscriptions. Arthur Brearley and Vic Reynolds were also on the staff. Mr Reynolds, porter, Scout Master, and general factotum, was another who showed great empathy with the patients, easing their ignorance and fears.

The custom of ringing a bell to signal the end of visiting lasted until after the war as did the strictly applied rule about only two visitors at a time, which meant members of a family had to swop turns at the bedside.

There were to be some changes over the years, for example, in pay. In 1938 Miss Durrant, the main cook, was paid £2.50 a week and Mr Farmer, the potato peeler - and so titchy that he stood on a duckboard - a mere £1.50 a week, both living out. The time would also come when there would no longer be the need for Mr Thomsett, a technician in the path lab., to give lead injections to a nurse who was pregnant by him, or for special "trusted" nurses to nurse "miscarriages".

Those days patients were never told they had cancer. Mrs Field (née Saunders) remembers 'the time a Mrs R----- in the top centre bed in Geraldine ward found out, with the result that there was a great inquisition by Sister Lancaster as to who had let the cat out of the bag'.

In 1938, the last full year of peace, the fracture clinic attended to 113 in-patients and attracted 259 out-patients, the commonest fracture being a Colles [a broken wrist from falling on the outstretched hand] with 87 cases. Radiography had 617 in-patients, 2088 out-patients, and performed 405 opaque meals; the massage department gave 6358 treatments; while the psychological clinic saw 66 new patients and 274 in total.[8]

Aga ovens were installed in the kitchens, each surgeon did a week on-call at a time, the nurses held their annual swimming sports at the Devonshire Park Baths, the ENT specialist was called in seven times over the year, and among the paediatric admissions there were two cases of malnutrition and one of rickets.

The first mention of medical photography was in 1938, when pathology did 5667 tests including 36 blood transfusions, the first year that blood transfusions passed the 30 mark. The donors were nearly all St John Ambulance volunteers, along with a few relatives. To show the thanks of the hospital a transfusion certificate was introduced. The Annual Report stated, "The generous and ready response of volunteers is to be acknowledged by a special certificate issued by the hospital authorities to all who give blood other than relatives and friends." The arrangements were in the hands of Dr Shera, for the National Blood Transfusion Service did not start until the war. Even into the 1960s, for urgent or exceptional transfusions, it was necessary for the pathologist to call upon local people to donate blood at the laboratory.

In other peaceful activities, the secretary's offices and the Sisters' sitting room were refurbished in tribute to the memory of Rupert Gwynne, MP for Eastbourne from 1910 to his death in 1924, and the sun-dial by the door of the main nurses' home was presented to the hospital on 12th March 1940 in memory of Lily Bush.[9]

War clouds, however, obscured the sun. At the Munich crisis in 1938, plans had been made to provide accommodation for 164 casualties in huts in the grounds, but preparations for war really started in April, 1939, when a scheme was presented to increase the accommodation by 44 beds, with an extra 100 in hutments in the grounds. Fortunately, the casualties were never on that scale.

Notes and References

1. *The Owl.* Magazine of Southdown College, Eastbourne. 1931; **1**: 3.

2. On 25th June 1931 Thomas Arno endowed ten beds in a ward. The endowment consisted of £2500 in 5% Conversion Loan, £5000 in 3½% Conversion Loan and £2500 cash. In the endowment deed he specified that for six of the ten beds certain "Selected Classes" should be given preference. They were defined as: blind men; Automobile Association patrolmen; postmen; police constables; chauffeurs; lifeboatmen; bakers' men; solicitors' clerks; ex-servicemen; firemen and railwaymen.

3. *Eastbourne Gazette* 5/7/33.

4. Rammstedt WC. *Med. Klin.,* 1912; **8**: 1702-05.

5. The Judet arthrodesis was a plastic hip replacement introduced in the late 1940s. It had a number of disadvantages in that it squeaked, which could be embarrassing for certain movements, and more important it tended to collapse.

6. Shera AG, Rainey EH. *BMJ.* 1937; i: 610.

7. Respectively, skin, bladder and bowel infections, and venereal diseases.

8. The Princess Alice Memorial Hospital, Annual Report, 1938.

9. Horn H, Stanley AJ. *A History of the Princess Alice Hospital,* Nursing Project 1967; (Pamphlet 491).

Chapter 7

War comes to the Princess Alice

Between 1st and 4th September 1939 thousands of London evacuees descended on the town, including 4657 unaccompanied children, although many returned home over the next few months. The many pregnant evacuees were nicknamed the "Barrage Balloons", after the gas-filled anti-aircraft devices.

A feature of Eastbourne's war was how rapidly the town swung from being a safe-haven to the most bombed town on the south coast. In 1939 it was considered a safe area and therefore designated a Reception Centre. The evacuees poured in, and the Princess Alice Hospital received 78 patients directly from London hospitals under the Emergency Hospital Scheme (EHS). Most were elderly and had no idea where they were until they had a cup of tea, when they read the crockery marked with the name of the hospital and town. On the other hand, by late 1940, when Eastbourne was in the front line itself, most of the town's children were evacuated, only residents were allowed to enter, the population fell from 60000 to less than 20000, and grass grew in the streets.

At the outbreak of war, as part of the Emergency Medical Scheme, organised by the Ministry of Health, the hospital was ordered to increase its bed complement from 120 to a potential maximum of 164, of which 96 were to be at the Minister's disposal. The Ministry undertook to re-imburse the hospital with the cost of the emergency services provided. With the almost complete cessation of fund-raising, this income allowed the hospital to survive financially.

Luckily, the house *Harberton, 2* Carew Road, had been purchased[1] in July 1938 as part of the scheme for a private patients' unit and this accommodation was used to provide the extra bedrooms for the increase in staff. In the early days of the war a matter of considerable pride was the efficient manner in which, at short notice, the discharge of over 50 local patients and the reception of over 70 patients from London hospitals was carried out within a few hours.

For most of the war about one-third of patients came under the aegis of the EHS, although by September 1940, when Eastbourne ceased to be a reception area, the numbers fell, both for the emergency scheme patients and the local sick.

The most topsy-turvy year was 1940. The hospital worked at high pressure for eight months of the year, the average number of patients being 121 and the maximum 146, until the Regional Commissioner ordered "voluntary evacuation", after which the Ministry of Health restricted the beds in use to 25% of the total, and for several weeks there were less than 40 in-patients and only 32 for one week. As some consolation this meant there was only one child in for Christmas 1940. In 1941, because of the war situation the Ministry of Health allowed half of the 164 beds to be used.

Rationing of foodstuffs started on 8th January 1940 with butter, bacon, sugar, and at first, some confusion. Emily, the matron's maid and easily flummoxed, couldn't understand what was so precious about a teaspoonful of sugar and doled out a couple of helpings to anyone who asked - until it was realised that she was giving away the matron's ration. By March eggs and meat were also rationed.

Dr Francis (Frank) Gillett took Dr Alfred Emslie's place as physician when he joined the forces, and the surgeons who were left struggled on, with Mr Estcourt in the forces and Mr Henry Wilson and Mr Cuffey prisoners-of-war. Dr Lester, Mr Oulton and Mr Pimm were also in the forces, along with many of the hospital staff, including Mr Pumfrey.

Otherwise the Princess Alice Hospital faced the war with Miss MacDonald's strong personality firmly in charge. Staff included Sister York (originally from St Thomas's Hospital) who was shortly to become Home Sister and hand over her operating theatre post to Sister Dodds. The out-patients and Arno, the casualty ward, still had Sister Muriel Gee, assisted by Sister Stammers, soon to go on night duty, and be replaced by a Sister from St George's known by the housemen as "Tweetie" Bilson.

The ward apportionments were: Gurney ward which had male orthopædic patients; Tabor, female orthopaedic, with Sister Harrison; Cavendish ward was male medical (mainly hacking coughs) and urological, where as Mrs Field says, 'The prostate operations were grisly, two-stage procedures over three weeks, with an Irving's box for drainage'. Sister Coggan, one of many good nurses, and daughter of a local market gardener, was in charge of both Cavendish and Sydney Hudson wards; the latter being male medical and prostate convalescent, in other words, patients who could be moved in an air-raid. Towards the end of the war, Sydney Hudson had troops awaiting boards, mixed in with the civilians. It also received the attempted suicides, when Dr Churcher would supervise a stomach washout, if indicated, following up with the words, 'Tomorrow you come up before the magistrates'; because suicide attempts remained a felony until 1961. Geraldine ward was female medical and surgical, along with some eye and gynæcology patients; and Crowden was male medical and surgical, with Sister Lancaster in charge of both. Surgical techniques demanded that hernias were kept in bed for three weeks, and the state of anæsthetic art was such that surgeons seldom operated on people over 60 years of age. On the children's wards Sister Swallow, who had done her children's training at the Westminster Children's Hospital, did a good job. She married in 1942, and Sister Maureen Potter filled-in when she became pregnant. Perhaps appropriately for a children's nurse, she had twins, and Sister Potter stayed as ward sister.

The senior physiotherapist at the beginning of the war was Miss Annette Tonks, assisted by Dorothy Watkins.

The night nurses slept in *Harberton,* the day nurses in the main home. In 1940 a nurse's salary, actually received, was 25/- [£1.25p] a month. When Mrs Peyton (née McFadden) left in 1942 she was on £2.50 a week for 5½ days' work, having been responsible for every penny that went in and out of the hospital.

The first wartime activity involving the Princess Alice was a drama of the sea. At 2230h on Wednesday, 20th March 1940, the ss *Barnhill,* a merchant ship of 5000 tons was attacked off Beachy Head by enemy aircraft and set on fire. The blazing ship drifted ashore at Langney Point and later broke up. Four of the crew were killed in the attack and nine injured were admitted to Princess Alice, which was so full at the time that they had to be placed on mattresses along the central corridor. One died, shortly after admission, but the others recovered.

The captain's tale is a saga of wartime bravery. Captain Michael O'Neill had been blown from the bridge and there was no trace of him when the surviving members of his crew were rescued. Later, watchers on the shore heard the sound of a bell ringing on the burning ship, and the *Jane Holland,* the Eastbourne lifeboat, under Coxswain Mike Hardy, set out again with Dr D.G. Churcher to provide immediate aid to anyone left on board. Braving red-hot deck plates, Alec Huggett and Tom Allchorn reboarded and found that the captain had been blown on to the deck and, despite fractures of his arms, collar bone and ribs, had managed to seize hold of the bell rope with his teeth to ring the bell which alerted his rescuers. Captain O'Neill recovered sufficiently to return to the town a year later and publicly thank the lifeboat crew for their efforts.

Eastbourne's population had already benefited from the attack, for tins of food and typewriters were among the ship's cargo. For some months afterwards many a family did not know what they were about to receive until the tin was opened, as the label had been washed off.

In May 1940 the Princess Alice admitted Lieutenant Tommy Brooke, the son of Field-Marshal Alan Brooke (later Viscount Alanbrooke and CIGS). Many staff can recall the entourage of top brass sweeping in to visit him. The lad was a subaltern with the British Expeditionary Force and, on the first day of the German attack on France and the Low Countries, developed severe abdominal pain and despite struggling to keep going, finally succumbed to emergency surgery for the appendicitis which, of all things at such a time, was the cause. With stitches in and with difficulty, he was evacuated to England and landed up at the Princess Alice for convalescence after peritonitis, where he stayed until the middle of August. Even so, at discharge he was so frail that he needed a stick for support.

Miss P.K. Hall, whose father was on the staff and who was herself a physiotherapist in the summer of 1940, says that in a quiet moment the gunfire of the retreat to Dunkirk could be heard.

Mr Crook was in the RNVR, having seen service in the 1914-18 war, and as Commodore of the Eastbourne Sailing Club, and with his son Anthony in the BEF, it is no surprise to learn that he set off in his own craft to the Dunkirk evacuation beaches in late May 1940. It is perhaps also not unexpected that in more peaceful times, a becalmed "Cmdr Crook" was equally renowned for finding himself stuck in the Channel and having to miss a clinic.

On 17th June, town names were removed from signposts, hoardings and vans, so that any German trippers might think they had come to the wrong place, and on 3rd July a curfew was introduced along the sea front to really put them off. In turn, the Princess Alice patients were issued with red, green or yellow cards for priority classification in case evacuation was necessary.

With the death of Dr Norman in July 1940, Dr Owen Fox assumed charge of the X-ray (radiological) department. Dr Fox did attempt to join the forces, like other staff, but he was told that his place was to provide a service for any bomb casualties and the troops who were based in Eastbourne.

Dr H. Colgate also died in 1940. One of the original medical staff and a trustee, he had donated a copy of a newspaper every day since 1883 for the use of patients. He was outlived by Dr A.E. Rook, his assistant in GP for 30 years from 1883. In 1913, when Dr Rook asked for a partnership, Dr Colgate dismissed him - to-day a young GP might jib at being kept as an assistant for three months.

Princess Alice carried on virtually unchanged, caring for the locals, except that Gurney ward was reserved as a resuscitation ward to which all air-raid casualties were initially admitted for assessment and treatment of shock. An added job for Miss McFadden was to note the names and addresses of bomb victims who had been admitted, not always so easy if they were shocked and could hardly answer. As the war went on, ill and wounded troops were admitted more often, including those injured in air-raids on the town; for example, Canadian soldiers training for the Dieppe landing, and after the bombing of the Cavendish Hotel, where the RAF were billeted, but military personnel were routinely dealt with by their own MO or were shared with St Mary's Hospital.

Servicemen who had no local unit and required treatment before transfer were admitted direct. They included airmen who had force-landed at the emergency landing ground at Gayles Farm, near Friston,[2] and a few Germans who had baled out at insufficient height and sustained broken legs. Mr Snowball remembers, 'One truculent pilot who demanded to be transferred to a German hospital. He firmly believed his pre-flight briefing that the Germans already controlled a large area of northern Britain. We managed to convince him otherwise with the help of our Resident Medical Officer who, strange as it may seem, was a young German doctor. Dr A. Katz was an anti-Nazi, who escaped from Germany a few days before the declaration of war. After a short spell in an internment camp, he came to the Princess Alice and worked hard as the only junior doctor through part of the war ... although on the occasion of the truculent airman his fluent German was a greater asset than his medical knowledge'. There was only one minor problem with Dr Katz (who went on to be a successful paediatrician in the USA) and that was his indecipherable writing, so bad that the coroner wouldn't accept his signature because, it was said, it looked as if a length of dirty string had crawled across the page.

Another German, shot down in 1940, was in Cavendish ward. He, too, was said to be very arrogant and unpleasant. Miss McFadden was worried to find that bullets, which had been surgically removed from him, had been placed along with the petty cash inside the hospital safe in her office.

A number of German pilots, admitted to Gurney ward with horrific face burns, were transferred to the Burns Unit at East Grinstead and nurses sometimes visited the unit to follow their progress. Later in the war, Mr Percy H. Jayes, the plastic surgeon, came from the facial unit and restored the face of a patient at the Princess Alice Hospital.

Bombs were dropped on Eastbourne on 98 occasions during the war and only the evacuation of a large proportion of the population kept down the casualties. Even so, there were 174 deaths and over 1000 injuries among the civilians.[3] Hospital staff would rush into the cellar shelter if there were bombs, some with more alacrity than others. Miss Clack, who worked in an office above the cellar, would 'shoot into it at the speed of knots if she heard anyone going down there for whatever reason'.

Eastbourne's first air-raid was on July 3rd 1940, although the first casualties were not to occur until four days later when bombs dropped on Whitley Road, near St Philip's Avenue. Two persons died, one from a heart attack, and 22 were injured, of whom nine were admitted to the Princess Alice, including Mr Ronald Turner and his parents, driven in by Mr Burnage of the St John Ambulance Brigade. Mr Turner's father, who had multiple fractures, died the next week.

These early raids generated some indignation, for it was felt that as Eastbourne had no industry it could not be a legitimate target. Very soon all this changed, as troops were stationed in the town, tank battles were practised on the Downs around, fighting vehicles were tested for amphibious use, and the Canadians and other forces used it as a staging post for raids into France.

Mrs Doreen Peyton (née McFadden) observed members of the Home Guard, which consisted mainly of 1914-18 World War veterans, staggering across the hospital garden, as they relived the shell-shock and horrors of that war, when they first heard the guns and the bombs of the air-raids. When the raids commenced no shelters had been built at Princess Alice; so those who could, repaired to the laundry and hid under the tables. Miss Phyllis Hall says that she was sitting under a table with an elderly out-patient when they were surrounded by a group of shell-shocked troops, just admitted from France, who kept yelling, 'Down! Dive bombers, down'. Miss Hall says that she found the most daunting sound was machine-gun fire and, 50 years later, she still doesn't like some fireworks which make a similar noise.

One surface air-raid shelter which was built is still just visible, in 1993, surrounded by shrubs at the corner of Carew Road and Enys Road.

For the duration of the war the Eastbourne Medical Society and the local division of the British Medical Association joined activities and held combined meetings in either the board room or the children's ward of the Princess Alice. One concession to the air-raids was that during an alert the meeting split in two, half remained in the children's ward and the rest adjourned to the out-patients department to await any casualties. This arrangement also ensured that one bomb would not wipe out all the doctors. At an October 1941 meeting, amid discussions on the use of plasma and the cleaning-up of air-raid casualties [who were often thickly covered with dust and dirt], it was suggested that keeping the reception beds warm helped to reduce shock.

Among the doctors who worked at Princess Alice throughout the war were Dr Sherwood, always charming to patients and staff; Mr Wilson Hall, fussy, but appreciative; Dr Bodkin Adams, Mr Crook, Mr Young, Mr Snowball, Mr MacQueen, Dr Gillett who was called upon to give most of the nurses' lectures, and Dr Churcher who, having been assistant TB officer for years, became deputy Medical Officer of Health in 1943. Dr Shera was another ever present and although the Emergency Blood Transfusion Service was organised nationally during the war, the Princess Alice laboratory carried out the cross-match testing, and for one 18-month period Dr Shera carried on single-handed in pathology. Just after penicillin was introduced it was in such short supply that he was also appointed custodian of the stocks in Eastbourne.

Others there at this time were Sister E. York, Home Sister, Miss P. Boulter, the admissions officer, Nancy Laird who did secretarial work for the surgeons, Miss I. Wilkins, out-patient receptionist, and Mrs M. Morris. Mrs Ruth Tucker (née Saunders) who had already done her children's nursing, was student nurse 1941-43, deputy Sister Sydney Hudson ward 1944, and Night Sister 1945-46.

This was the day when generalist surgeons, such as Crook, MacQueen, Snowball and Wilson Hall came into their own. Not only did they help to keep a general practice service going in Eastbourne during the war, but with the multi-system injuries sustained in the bombing, the old-style surgeon was often of more use than a specialised orthopædic surgeon who would find difficulty coping with abdominal as well as bony damage. Mr Crook, in particular, treated many air-raid victims with much success, and amassed a tremendous amount of extra work, for example during the war he took on the ante- and post-natal clinics at the Maternity Home and the school orthopædic clinics. Mr Snowball was also highly suited for such work, being one of the few doctors to hold a surgical fellowship (FRCS) and the higher medical qualification (MRCP).

One of Mr Wilson Hall's tasks was to perform leucotomies [a personality-changing operation] on violent patients in mental hospitals. In the early days of the conflict, with no tranquillisers and total war expected at any minute, with fear of widespread disruption and threats of gas and biological means of destruction, there was genuine concern that thousands of uncontrollable lunatics on the loose would affect morale.

A grim week-end began on Friday, 13th September 1940, with a series of air-raids. Two casualties, one a girl of 16, died shortly after admission and further attacks on the Saturday and Sunday ended in seven deaths, one lady dying in the hospital three weeks later.

Scheduled for that Friday afternoon was a Committee of Management meeting, including the big four, Arthur Beckett, Clift Ford, as Chairman, Dr Churcher and Geoffrey Bowes. It was held around a table in Anne Elizabeth ward, because the hospital maids now slept in the board room and staff went under these beds during daytime air-raids.. As the bombs dropped uncomfortably close, Beckett, Ford and Bowes threw themselves onto the floor under the table. When they extricated themselves they found Dr Churcher waiting for them to get on, but they decided they'd had enough and the meeting was abandoned, almost before it began. When Mrs Peyton says that a full account of the meeting, in particular mentioning that all the proposed motions had been passed, was circulated the next day, before the admin. realised the meeting had been aborted, doctors and nurses will recognise that "admin." hasn't changed much.

During these raids the Ophthalmic surgeon, Mr Arthur Young, assisted by Nurse Doreen Acfield, continued a delicate eye operation despite bombs dropping nearby. The hospital story was that, most appropriately, Mr Young didn't bat an eyelid.

On Saturday, 28th September, high-explosive bombs demolished four shops in Cavendish Place and several persons were trapped in the cellars. Three were dead when reached, but five were recovered by the rescue services who had to tunnel through concrete, while keeping a check on water from a burst main by constant pumping. One victim remained trapped by a steel girder. Mr L.A.H. Snowball recounts[4] that he crawled to her with Dr Barron, the anæsthetist, in order to amputate her legs, the only way she could be released. 'She was a young girl of 17 - I still recall her name, Peggy Harland from Stone Cross ... she was anuric [unable to pass urine] for two days before she died the following Monday in the Princess Alice Hospital. Her death was probably due to a "crush syndrome" ... it was a feature in several other deaths'.[5]

Another especially poignant victim of the raids was the lady who died in the hospital from coal-gas poisoning, after a gas main, which ran under her house, had been fractured in the bombing.[6]

Princess Alice remained the locals' hospital, but admissions increased of bomb victims, and of soldiers injured in training around the town. On 26th October 1940, a soldier from a Bomb Disposal Squad was admitted after a delayed-action bomb exploded, killing his colleague and a policeman. One Belgian commando, wounded during exercises with live ammunition, contrived to sustain four wounds from one bullet as it passed through and out of his buttocks. There is a story that his unit, No. 10 Commando, were hardened to the sight of blood by observing operations at Princess Alice, although unless the surgeons were particularly heroic, it was surely easier to demonstrate blood letting by spilling a bottle of transfusion blood which had run out-of-date.

If numerous air-raid or army casualties were admitted over a day or two, they were sent to hutted hospitals inland or, if they had burns, to McIndoe's unit at East Grinstead. Sometimes, as Mrs Ruth Tucker (née Saunders) recalls, a nurse had to accompany them in a St John or Red Cross ambulance and 'if you were late back and missed supper, you went without'.

In the midst of the war, life went on and Mrs D.E. Griffiths was admitted for a Caesarean section in June 1941. She was in for six weeks and had to pay £1.05p a week as she had a private room and her husband was in the Army. 'There were no other mothers and while I was there most of the wards were taken over for patients from the armed services. I never saw any of them, but they would send in chocolates when my son cried'. Mr Roy Kibble came in under Mr Crook after falling off his bicycle and he recalls the soldiers having a ward sing-song in the evenings, but his abiding memory is of the man in the next bed who smoked pipe after pipe of *St Bruno,* a particularly pungent tobacco and, as he says, 'Now it would be considered quite anti-social to pollute a hospital in such a manner'. Mrs Eileen Goldsmith (née Gillam), another local patient, was admitted "for tonsils" under the care of "young" Mr Snowball, 'I remember it well. On the day I went in, 23rd May 1942, a German plane had crash-landed in a field near the barn between Black Robin Farm and Halfway Cottages, where I lived, and everyone in the hospital was so excited because I could tell them all about it. I saw the pilot being led away: he could only have been about 18'.

In 1942 the hospital admitted 1140 local sick (1027 in 1943), 68 air-raid casualties (87), and 389 of the "fighting services" (604).

Food rationing was strictly enforced, but Mrs Muriel Sutton (née Terry) remembers discontent only when the nurses' potato portions were cut. Bath-water was also restricted to save fuel and most of the nurses kept punctiliously to the regulation six inches depth.

There were, however, a number of nurses from Eire and Jersey who resented the shortages. One from a very good family, her father being a top racehorse owner, was openly heard to say she did not care who won the war and, as this was on Sydney Hudson ward and crowded with soldiers from the front, she found herself dumped in a bath which, for this occasion, was brim-full of cold water.

The menus included Burma Road Rice Pudding and Golf Ball Porridge - one hardly wants to imagine the taste. Dried egg squares were like leather when fried, but commonly found on the breakfast menu, and sometimes for supper the fare was fried potato peelings with an egg. All the nurses agree with Mrs Esther Field (née Saunders) that the "most ghastly" wartime food was dried egg, oven-cooked in a dish and solid enough to hack into squares.

It does seem that, apart from tropical fruit, the commodity in extremely short supply during the war was a fresh egg - dried egg will always remain in the memory bank of the stomach of anyone who lived through those times. In the laboratory the use of Loeffler's[7] diphtheria culture medium (made with egg white) and the use of egg white to remove phosphate in culture media increased considerably. These eggs could only be acquired on a special indent, but no-one bothered about the cholesterol content so omelettes were an easy way of disposing of the surplus yolks, that is, until some clever person wrote a scientific paper proposing that horse serum was an effective substitute for egg white. In Mr R.A. Elliston's words, 'Never was an advance in medicine so unpopular'. By 1943 hens were kept in the hospital grounds to provide eggs for the patients.

A fantastic gift from the Canadian soldiers, billeted in Roborough School (which had been evacuated), was a consignment of tins of delicious, unheard-of, maple syrup. This was a one-off delicacy, but it brightened the lives of patients and staff alike.

Nurse Eileen Cook (was Richardson, later Cook) remembers that when *Roborough* was occupied by the Canadian Medical Corps, the nurses were often invited to square dances, when the food "was super after our rations".

Sweets were now rationed, but Nurse Pantook, who was there through the war, was the daughter of the owner of *Panto's,* a local chocolate and confectionery firm, and she was able to obtain a steady supply of "misshapen" sweets from her father. Harvest thanksgiving services provided a change but not variety, for as Mrs Tucker says, 'if there had been a spate of marrows that year, the nurses suffered weeks of marrows with everything'. Miss D. Eyre recalls that before the war nurses had to finish off the harvest festival loaves even if they were quite stale.

Clothes rationing meant that shoes and stockings were always a problem for the nurses, being on their feet all day. The big decision, of course, being whether to ape the latest film fashion or to buy sensible shoes.

The hospital kept the ration books of the nurses, but gave each a jar of sugar to last the month for drinks and porridge, and a small pat of butter every week. 'If you ran out you had to wait until the next supply'. Once a month nurses queued up for a one pound [450g] jar of jam, which had been "on the ration" since 1941. The senior nurses had a choice, but a probationer always landed up with either "Mixed Fruit" or, occasionally, nothing at all.

Nurses were under a tight rein in many ways. Mrs Pamela Milne (née Fillery) recalls that once a week you could have a late-pass till 2300h, but this was frowned on unless you had a good reason. The name of any nurse two minutes late went into the "Late Book", and next morning she had to report to the matron and explain the reason why. Mrs Milne remembers putting her name down on a list for an Officers' Mess Dance and 'to my utter amazement ... I was called to the matron's office to be told that she had telephoned my mother and it had been decided I was not to go and that was the end of it.'

A month or two later the nurses clubbed together and, with the permission of the matron, 'we were allowed to invite the Canadian soldiers to a dance at the nurses' home, but none of the nurses was allowed to leave the dance, while matron, home sister and other sisters stood guard at every possible exit. The dance ended at eleven o'clock on the dot and it was never repeated'.

The restrictions also had some untoward results. When a nurse was on night duty she had to be in bed by 1100h and she was called at 1900h: only on Saturdays was a nurse allowed to get up before 1600h. One nurse, who was going out with a houseman, had borrowed the hair drier and forgot to return it before she went to bed. The Home Sister knew she had the drier and decided to retrieve it to save the nurse having her sleep disturbed. The Sister crept into the nurse's bedroom at 1500h only to find her dressed and preparing to meet the doctor for tea at *Bobbys,* a local store. The Sister said that if the nurse went back to bed she would go to *Bobbys* and explain the situation. The doctor was grateful to the Sister for her efforts, but they were seen talking together in the store. The consequence was great scandalmongering which, as the Sister dare not tell the truth, she was unable to scotch.

Holidays for the nurses were two weeks a year, and no Bank Holidays. Any time off for any reason was taken into account, so if a nurse requested leave she could be greeted with '... But nurse you had a week off with chickenpox'. The Sisters were allowed a long week-end around Easter as an extra treat.

All the staff had to work hard during the war. At a time when "flab" was non-existent, no-one needed to exercise to remove it, but the doctors tended to bicycle to and fro to save petrol.

The last Annual General Meeting of the Eastbourne Royal Eye Hospital was held on 19th February 1942. It reported the closure on 4th October 1940 because of its vulnerable position, *vis à vis* air-raids, and because in 1939 it lost £385 and "in 1940 this loss went up to £481, which made it more serious still". At the height of the war, in 1940, the Princess Alice and the ENT hospitals were amalgamated and the Pevensey Road hospital closed. About the same time the work of the Eye Hospital was transferred to the Princess Alice Hospital, and another Eastbourne hospital was demolished. This was the small army hospital attached to the Drill Hall in Seaside, which had been there since the early part of the 19th century: local lore says that it was built by French prisoners-of-war, possibly because of its balconies. It does not seem to have been much used after the 1914-18 war.

The second phase of Eastbourne's bombing, the so-called "Hit and Run", attacks started on 4th May 1942. Two local fishermen, Micky Andrews and Alec Huggett, were brought into Cavendish ward, having been sprayed with machine gun fire. Both were badly injured and one had a bullet lodged in an eye. That evening "Lord Haw-Haw" on his Hamburg radio station announced that German fighters had attacked an armed trawler off Eastbourne.

One fisherman, hit at sea, developed tetanus. The hospital had been short of anti-tetanus serum and it was not administered to him because it was thought there was little risk. Amazingly, he recovered and was given a bonus of a new set of false teeth, of which he was really proud and which he would not have been able to afford otherwise. Another patient, injured in the lower back during a raid on the railway station, died of tetanus a few weeks afterwards. The distressing death was the first witnessed by Mrs Field (née Saunders). In January 1943 a man died in the hospital shortly after being hit by machine-gun bullets while walking in the street.

A patient in the orthopædic ward in 1942 was the first to have penicillin at the Princess Alice Hospital. His leg was going gangrenous and the precious penicillin was brought from East Grinstead, in the middle of the night, escorted by police, and the leg was saved.

This second phase of bombing was severe on the town. Through 1942 and 1943 the hospitals were kept busy, seeing up to 50 casualties at a time. Over the two years 155 were severe enough to be admitted. Fortunately, the hospital sustained no direct hit. It was machine-gunned, and incendiary bombs fell in the grounds, but the worst damage was during a night attack on 11th August 1942, when most of the windows were blown in, many slates were dislodged from the roof, and the electricity was cut off, but without injuries to patients or staff. The theatre windows were shuttered and work went on, often operating with two tables in the theatre and using the fracture clinic as an operating theatre as well. Mr Snowball said, 'I opened quite a few abdomens in the old fracture clinic'.

As usual with air-raids, there were some extraordinary stories. The hospital came closest to disaster when a bomb landed on a stack of coke just at the Bedfordwell Road entrance. Mercifully, it failed to explode, although pieces of "black diamonds" were scattered all over the hospital. On another occasion, one of the domestic staff was walking down East Dean Road towards the town when, in front of her, German planes swept over Old Town from the Polegate direction and she realised that they were flying lower than where she was standing. Another day, Phyllis Newman, the head radiographer, was walking on the Eastbourne Downs golf course with Dorothy Watkins, a physiotherapist, when a German plane swooped down; as they dived into a sand bunker for cover, she saw the pilot smile and wave before flying out over the Channel.

Two bright spots were the honouring of Dr D.G. Sherwood on 22nd October 1942, when he was elected president of the Eastbourne branch of the British Legion, and the publication, in December 1942, of Sir William Beveridge's Report which was to put health care on a proper basis after the war.

By 1943 the war was having another effect. The use of radium needles was no longer allowed, because it was said that they might affect the radar monitors assembled on Beachy Head, so patients requiring radiotherapy had to go to the Kent and Sussex Hospital, Tunbridge Wells. Around this time Sarah Churchill was stationed with the ATS [women's services] at Beachy Head, but kept herself fit enough not to require any administrations from the hospital.

On Sunday evenings a local vicar, accompanied by one of his parishioners, trundled a harmonium round the wards to give a service in each by turn. He became most upset if he found the men playing cards on the Sabbath, and as he pointed out, card-playing was forbidden by the hospital rules, but as Mrs Tucker says, 'What could you do with the troops? It was even impossible to stop them nipping up The Avenue for fish and chips at night'.

Standards did not drop for the nurses. Nurse Muriel Terry (later Sutton) mentions that applicants to be a student nurse in 1944 had to be recommended, reach an educational standard, and "come from a good home". Junior nurses still shared a bedroom and the Home Sister inspected it at least once a week. Nurses were only allowed to display six items on their dressing tables, any more were confiscated and only returned after a request to the Home Sister.

Mrs Sutton vividly remembers 'the awakening bang on the bedroom door from the runner, "Six-thirty, nurses!"; the day I dropped a tray of crockery while a committee meeting was in progress; crying after hurting a patient for the first time; having to wash the ward walls for Christmas, "You wash the walls and Nurse O'Donagh will follow behind you polishing them, and do the bed wheels with *Vim*" - the patients thought this a great joke; and running along The Avenue to get in by 2200 hours before the doors were locked, although a friend on the ground floor could usually be found to leave a window open'.

Mrs Tucker found the "ten o'clock time" very irksome because her bus got her to the hospital at 2205h and to get an earlier one meant leaving home an hour earlier. As she says she used to risk it, for while she was a devoted nurse she thought that at the age of 21 she was capable of managing her own life.

Nurses organised concerts at Christmas and had a Nurses' Dance for which the custom was to invite the doctors, but not their wives. Mr Cornell, one of the porters, would sit on the entrance stairs to the nurses' quarters to dissuade any unauthorised entry. It would appear that the most fun and excitement to be had was when one of the nurses read her colleagues' tea leaves.

Sister Emily Coggan was the Sister of Cavendish and Sydney Hudson, the male surgical wards, where in Mrs Milne's words, 'As probationer I seemed to spend most of my time cleaning the sluice, lavatories, bathroom and lockers and making beds twice a day, at 0730 and 1630, usually with the patients in them, and tidying the beds after every meal. We topped and tailed the patients three times a day; two nurses turned every patient and rubbed their bottoms with methylated spirit and powder. I also had to do the urinal and bedpan rounds. Once a month we had to lift the end of the bed and scrape and polish the bed castor, so they would move freely.

25. War time nurse prizewinners, from left Nancy O'Donnell, Esther Saunders, and Esther Ford, with Miss MacDonald, 1943.

'Matron MacDonald always examined the sluice and checked that the refuse buckets had been properly cleaned. Flowers had to be removed from the wards at night as it was considered they used up oxygen. They were brought back again in the morning, spruced up with fresh water. Woe betide the nurse who gave the wrong flowers to a patient, understandably for after all they were the only link with their loved ones for most of the time'.

Dusting was with a damp cloth soaked in 1:20 carbolic, which made the nurses' hands red and rough. The floors were usually cleaned by the ward maids, but the probationer nurse did not always escape. The routines were unchanged in that beds were pulled out into the centre of the ward, and saved tea leaves (to lay the dust) were sprinkled on the floor, which was then swept with large brooms. The beds were pushed back for the centre of the ward to be treated in turn. Mrs Milne (née Fillery) remembers one morning, rather more hectic than usual, with air-raid sirens wailing and bombs dropping, 'Yet when Miss MacDonald came to the ward she routinely wiped her finger along a ledge to check it had been dusted'. Nevertheless, the nurses agree, "She was such a nice woman".

The ward maids "helped the nurses no end", by this the nurses meant they warned them of the approach of the Sister, or gave the thirsty probationer a strictly forbidden cup of tea off the patients' trolley.

It was usually the probationer nurse who placed the ward laundry into two wheeled skips, one for clean and one for dirty. The "dirty" had to have any faeces cleaned off before being sent to the laundry. Each ward had a laundry book, and every item had to be counted and signed for, with a repeat on its return. If anything was missing it had to be hunted out and accounted for before the nurse could go off duty. The linen cupboards were kept in perfect order, with all the items neatly folded in precise stacks.

Mr Eric W. Wooller, of Polegate, experienced the nursing care in 1943, as a 15-year-old in Sydney Hudson and Cavendish wards. 'The matron, or her assistant, came round every day. Because I was anaemic I was put on iron-medicine, or "nuts and bolts" as we called it, and transfused two pints of blood. I was not allowed any roughage in my diet, so I was fed on sieved vegetables and charcoal; if I had egg and toast, the crust was trimmed off. Another condition of my treatment was that I wasn't allowed out of bed - with the inevitable struggles with bottles and bedpans. Not easy at any time, but most inappropriate in the middle of a "Tip and Run" air-raid, which happened while I was there.

'There were quite a few servicemen in the ward, one had a hernia, another an appendix, and one with burns was transferred to East Grinstead.'

After Nurse Fillery's first year the continuous cleaning became more intermittent, she learnt to give blanket baths, take temperatures, how to do dressings, poultices and administer medicines. 'If a nurse broke a thermometer, she had to go to the matron, explain how it happened, and pay one shilling [5p], towards its replacement, this out of her meagre ten shillings [50p] a week salary.'

To obtain their monthly pay envelope nurses queued outside matron's office while the Home Sister sat by the door, expecting all to buy 2/6d [12½p] National Savings Stamps. Purchase was in effect compulsory, but the nurses rushed off to a post office on their first off-duty to redeem them into hard-earned cash.

The duty rota was made out by matron or one of the assistant matrons. Each nurse did three months' day-duty and three months' night-duty alternately throughout her training, moving wards at the same time and fitting in three months in the operating theatre and the orthopædic clinic. Each move involved changing bedrooms so, as Mrs Milne says, '...we were kept on the go pretty well'.

The first night duty was spent as "runner", a thankless task which meant running round, from 2000h to 0800h, relieving other nurses for their breaks and waking up the cook at 0530h and (with some trepidation) the matron at 0630h.

If the nurses knew a patient was not expected to live they would call in the priest to give the last rites and "strangely they often got better". If a patient died during the day the nurse would lay out the body. 'Usually they were put in their best nightie or pyjamas, but sometimes they had to be dressed in their best clothes or in their wedding dress. The nurses always placed a posy in their clasped hands. Night deaths were more awkward, nurses on some of the wards pushed the body to the mortuary on a trolley, for during the war there were no porters on night duty. In the event of fire or flood Mr Nicholson, the stoker and ex-Navy, was called from his cottage, but otherwise a body was placed on a trolley in the lift for the porter to remove in the morning. If two deaths occurred it became very difficult, especially as the lift was antiquated and was opened by a key which was attached to the gate and a common prank was to hide the key.'

Adjacent to the mortuary was the animal house where the licensed use of laboratory animals continued for many tests, including tuberculosis tests (guinea pigs) and Friedman[8] pregnancy tests (on rabbits, with the result two days later). As Mr R.A. Elliston says, from his experience of labs during the war, pregnancy tests were popular among the lab. staff, because to obtain the result the rabbit had to be humanely killed and this left an eight-week-old fresh rabbit carcass to be disposed of - with a meat ration of 1/3d [6½p] a week, this was no problem.

When the sirens sounded at night the nurses had to lift the children out of their cots and crawl with them into the ward shelter. It was distressing for everyone, with the children crying and some in a lot of pain. There was one little girl, about four years old, brought in with severe burns caused by boiling fat from her parents' fish and chip shop. The treatment was Bunyan's Bags, which covered each limb and allowed irrigation with a weak *Milton* solution three times a day - all very painful. Mrs Milne remembers calling her "Darling" and "My little girl" while replacing her dressings when, in spite of all her discomfort, she suddenly piped up with, 'My name ain't Darling, its Heather'.

Nurses who trained there during or just after the 1939-45 war include Barbara Bailey, Mary Easther, Esther "Bibby" Ford, Rosemary Harflet, Zila Hayward, Joan Hutt, Joe Hutton, Nancy O'Donnell, Mary Roach, Joan Sharp, and Phyllis Thackeray, who became a well-respected district nurse in the local downland village of East Dean.

Sister Lancaster became a legend in her lifetime. She worked fantastically hard, and the nurses and patients adored her. In charge of Geraldine (female medical and surgical) and Crowden (male medical and surgical) wards, she was the most dedicated, devoted and highly efficient sister you could imagine. From Cheltenham College, she obtained a degree at London, where she rowed for her college. She joined an Anglican order as a nun, took up nursing and the only possession she kept was the gold medal she won in her nursing finals, otherwise she gave her worldly goods to the Salvation Army and any gifts were passed on to others, except for wool which she made up into blankets for the poor in Africa. Her only relaxation was a bicycle ride and, in latter years, the television. She was a strict disciplinarian and loved every one of her patients with intense devotion.

Each morning she would lead the ward on bended knee in prayers, with all the nurses kneeling round the table. She made up every bed, everyday; if she wasn't available at that moment the nurse covered the patient and waited for her. She was "a great one for kaolin poultices", and she would never leave the dressing on a wound for the regulation five days, but had a peep everyday to see how it was healing (or not). After long hours on duty, before she retired herself, she would stay until she had tucked up and comforted every patient for the night. As Mrs Esther Field puts it, 'she said a personal "good night" to each and every patient'. Miss Betty P. Drury says, 'On Geraldine ward night-duty you were working as soon as you put your foot in the door; other wards at least gave you a moment to wake up while the report was given'. Mrs Mavis Constable adds, 'With Sister Lancaster there was no cut-off time, she would tell you to go and have a bite to eat and when you returned to the ward there would be a list of jobs to do as long as your arm. Even if you were ill in the nurses' sick bay [Wealden side ward, mainly surgical] you were landed with odd jobs, such as checking linen stocks'. Mrs Ruth Tucker confirms that Sister Lancaster tested every patient's bath water with her hand to check it was not too hot - 'and the nurses always checked again because her hands were so tough she could stand almost boiling water'.

Mr Ronald MacQueen was the senior surgeon by the time of the war and was another most conscientious, dedicated and exceedingly hard working individual. As Dr Vincent Harris expressed it, 'He got through a lot of work'. In the 1914-18 war he had been invalided home from Salonika and spent a year in a sanatorium, making a full recovery. He held the FRCS and tackled almost every field of surgery although, like the other hospital doctors, with the exception of the pathologist, radiologist, and the Eye and ENT surgeons, he was also a general practitioner. His hobby was fishing in Norway. He was beloved by patients and staff alike, as was his partner, Dr Frank Gillett, who anæsthetised for him. There may be no truth in the story, but it was said one reason for the affection was that he always warmed his hands on the radiator before examining a patient.

The nurses' name for him was "Codface", this was partly because there was some resentment that they were given no option but to have him as their doctor whenever they fell ill.

Mr MacQueen did not drive and employed a chauffeur, who had been his batman in the 1914-18 war. Even when not driving, the chauffeur processed ahead of his master, carrying a case of special instruments, which Mrs Ruth Tucker says included a large brass ear syringe. The nurses called him "the disciple", although some said that as he prepared the way he was more of a "John the Baptist". He punctiliously saluted staff as they passed if he was waiting by the doctor's car - presumably only if he wasn't carrying the instrument case at the time. The chauffeur did not like driving at night, so if Mr MacQueen was called out after dark he rode to the hospital on his sit-up-and-beg bicycle.

He was an excellent surgeon, with a well-deserved reputation as an obstetrician; sadly, his one big surgical mistake had to be one of the Princess Alice Sisters. During a gall bladder operation on Sister Elliot just before the 1939-45 war he tied the common bile duct instead of the biliary duct - a known hazard, but possible if it is situated aberrantly. As a result the patient, who was only 42, died shortly afterwards. A similar error was probably the cause of the protracted illness of the Earl of Avon (Sir Anthony Eden).

Mrs Milne (née Fillery) also calls to mind Dr Bodkin Adams, 'a stout man with fair, curly hair and a florid complexion'. As he was anæsthetising one patient she recalls him whispering in his soft lilting voice, 'Just imagine you are in your little white cot by the sea and all will be well'.

Mrs Tucker (née Saunders) recalls that it was still possible in 1943 for an old farm worker to be admitted wearing a rabbit skin round his chest. 'It had been sewn in place to last for the winter. At first he resisted attempts at removal until it became apparent that it was ridden wth lice.'

Another of Mrs Tucker's memories was when the Fire Station, Public Library and shops were bombed on 4th June 1943. She went out that morning, being on night duty, to find, 'Scattered about all along The Avenue, there were books from the Public Library and fish from the MacFisheries. People were picking up food for both body and mind.'

At a June 1943 meeting in Princess Alice the doctors heard talks on air-raid casualties and the effects of blast, with a personal description by Mr Karl Wilkinson, a local engineer, who had been buried for 12 hours after a raid.

There were still two housemen [junior doctors] at the hospital, each there for six months, but the appointments were staggered every three months. In the early days of the war one was appointed who turned out not to be a doctor, but a smooth-talking Canadian jewel thief who was dodging the police. Until he was unmasked he was noted for encouraging the staff to play dice games, which he always won. As he was led away, he admitted using loaded dice.

The housemen were not up at night as often as to-day's junior doctors, but they had long, indeterminate hours of work, they had to follow each patient throughout their hospital stay, be ready to see a casualty, give an occasional gas (anæsthetic) and be on-call through the night, even if not often out-of-bed. In other words, training for the general practice to which most of them aspired. It meant that they had little relaxation, and some of the housemen were so tired that they gave the night duty nurses a pain in the neck.

"You called them, they slept on, you went up and shook them, and eventually you were forced to strip their bed before they would get up to see the patient. When they did leave the hospital, they would go out on a pub crawl leaving a list of telephone numbers which you rang in order up to closing time and afterwards you started again from the bottom of the list. They came in demanding milk drinks, pinched the "runner's" bottom and did handstands on the operating theatre table. They were never to be found when a 20-stone [130 kg] patient needed lifting, they left doors open, and they raided the kitchen for midnight feasts, frequently making inroads into the special diets prepared for the next day. One helped himself to a drink from the children's ward refrigerator, which was only discovered when it was found that all the expressed breast milk for the babies had disappeared from the fridge, and the night sister had to obtain more from a nursing mother." All in all, it sounds like a typical late night performance at your friendly, neighbourhood hospital.

Mrs Ruth Tucker, as Night Sister, saved the housemen's bacon one night in 1945. 'They had the use of the room to the left of the front hall and often kept a barrel of beer there. One night they left the tap on and I had to rouse the maids to clean up the sticky mess before Sister York made her entrance on the scene.'

One night, as searchlights were ranging across the sky, a load of incendiary bombs landed. The mobile patients were put under their beds and those who could not be moved were covered with blankets and pillows. By this time the nurses were well trained to keep calm, no running or shouting or show of fear was allowed, and at the All-Clear it seemed that the bombs had fallen behind the hospital. The houseman of the moment had a motor-bike which was his pride and joy. He was afeared it would be stolen so he refused to leave it in the car park, but stowed it away in a most safe spot, behind the hedge just by the detached mortuary at the back of the hospital. It was rough justice when an incendiary landed right on his bike and burnt it out, the only casualty of the night.

Odd fire bombs fell among the hospital grounds in a number of raids, but the greatest fire danger was the night on Gurney ward when a nurse, who had a phobia about cockroaches, sprinkled "ether meth." all around the base of the kichen walls. A houseman (needless to say) came in, turned up the flame of the *Ascot*-type gas geyser to make tea, and fire also shot up all around, but it was extinguished without the patients being aware of the danger.

As the war continued the concentration of troops preparing for the invasion of Europe built up along the coast. Miss N. Poulter, of the X-ray department, says, 'The town was filling up with soldiers, sailors and airmen, the cinemas were full of them and crowds of them went dancing at the Floral Hall'. Mr B.H. Wright, whose family lived at Langney Farm, discovered a part of Eastbourne's hospital history when he was among the troops guarding the Crumbles, for his guard-post was the old Smallpox Hospital, just east of the present marina. Put up in 1895, it was used on a few occasions to receive smallpox cases, although the severe epidemics were over before its time. It had not been in clinical use for some years before the war and has since been demolished.

Early on D-Day, 6th June 1944, the Princess Alice received the first casualties from the Normandy landings. An aircraft carrying paratroopers over France was peppered when an anti-aircraft burst exploded underneath the plane. They were ordered to return and the aircraft just managed to bellyflop at Friston.

As Mr Snowball said, 'The staff of the hospital spent the rest of the night and part of the next day digging out pieces of shrapnel, in two cases from the abdomen, while all they did was to bemoan their disappointment at missing the invasion'.

Shortly afterwards the V1 bombardment started, the engine flame of the first pilotless aircraft being seen from Beachy Head. Fifteen flying bombs, or "doodle-bugs" as they were called, landed on Eastbourne and many injured were admitted to the Princess Alice, but there were no deaths among the civilians.

In the midst of the V1 attacks, Nurse Fillery (later Milne) came on night duty to be told that her mother had been admitted with spinal injuries. Matron said she would be allowed to see her mother for a few minutes, but she would then be moved to another ward, and she was reminded that she was expected to keep to the visiting times, 'as allowances cannot be made and work has to go on'. Nearly all the wards had extra beds down the middle of the ward full of her neighbours from Astaire Avenue, where six houses had been damaged. She remembers removing shrapnel from one neighbour's bottom, who was so embarrassed that he could not bring himself to look at her for years afterwards.

Mrs Doreen Newman (née Acfield) remembers that earlier in the war, Miss Poulter had been admitted with her mother after a bomb fell in front of their house. Miss Poulter says that her mother was trapped on the landing and she was on the stairs unable to get up or down. 'I shouted for help and air-raid wardens lifted me over the mess, laid my mother on a blown-off door and took her to the hospital. I was just filthy, covered with dust, but my mother had a broken femur and knee and she stayed in hospital for three months until the September.'

Visiting remained twice a week, Wednesday and Sunday afternoons from 1400-1600h. No other visiting was allowed except in a dire emergency. Visitors often brought in eggs for their relatives and, as was the custom, these had to be labelled and it was the probationer's job to cook them for the patient's breakfast.

Towards the end of the war a probationer nurse was on a mid-point salary of £45 a year, a staff nurse £60 and a newly appointed sister was on £90 a year.

During 1944 Sister Ruth Saunders instructed the Polish soldiers convalescing on Sydney Hudson ward in occupational therapy, mainly rugs and wicker work. The Education Corps provided the materials. Their Brigadier-in-charge, who would call in occasionally, dropped dead from a ruptured aortic aneurysm while climbing the stairs to the ward. Some of the convalescent troops on Sydney Hudson discharged themselves almost equally abruptly, not even waiting for Dr Churcher to say, 'Get your boots on', his usual gruff discharge note.

Mrs Sutton recalls night duty on 8th May 1945, VE night, with all the patients playing cards, and also VJ night, in the August, which she spent on the beach with the Royal Navy, sharing their rum ration.

At a meeting on 30th October 1945 in the Princess Alice, Mr Russell Rudall opened a discussion on "A New Hospital Policy for Eastbourne". He suggested a hospital of 800 beds in 12 acres on the Princess Alice site would satisfy the accessibility and capacity requirements. Others present thought that the Princess Alice site was not big enough and that 20 acres at Willingdon would be best. All agreed that the out-patient services would be important and that one single hospital was needed. Quite a prescient discussion in view of what was to come.

In the course of the war the hospital had maintained the high prestige it enjoyed even if the area covered was small, for apart from troops almost all the patients were Eastbournians; Seaford, for example, looked to Brighton for hospital care. The wards were spotless, and the standard of nursing was good, even if somewhat limited in paediatric and long-stay care. The entire atmosphere at the Princess Alice was that of an extended family, but at the end of the war the hospital was at the brink of change. Change from almoners who saw to the monetary affairs of the patients, from generalist doctors working voluntarily, from the doctors' wives visiting their husbands' patients, and from the time when a nurse had to obtain special permission from both the matron and the hospital committee before she could marry. One aspect hasn't changed much - the nurses and the housemen were paid a pittance, and they had long hours on duty.

Notes and References

1. *Harberton* was built about 1889, when it was called *Rippingale*. It was bought by the Princess Alice trustees for £3000, having been sold to its previous owner 12 years before for £3100.

2. Friston Emergency Landing Ground (TV 534982). *Action Stations. The Airfields,* 1992; **9**: 115.

3. Humphrey G. *Wartime Eastbourne* (Beckett Features, Eastbourne 1989).

4. *Eastbourne Medical Gazette.* 1978; **2**: 95.

5. "Crush syndrome", a term used to describe a condition affecting certain patients trapped for hours under bombed buildings. They often appeared well on release, only to stop passing urine and die in kidney failure a few days or weeks later. This was long before kidney machines, but it was soon realised that if only the patients could be tided over (by various regimes) for about three weeks the kidneys usually recovered naturally. This condition, acute tubular necrosis, is occasionally seen after any severe crushing of muscle, but it was the concentration of such victims in the raids which alerted the medical profession and led to its recognition and cure. In Mr Snowball's words, 'Perhaps it may be said that they did not die in vain'.

6. *Eastbourne Herald,* 23/11/1940.

7. Loeffler F. *Mitt. k. GesundhAmte,* 1884; **42**: 145-47.

8. Friedman MH, Lapham ME. *Amer. J. Obstet. Gynae.,* 1931; **21**: 405-10.

Chapter 8

Post-War Recovery

The end of the war saw the retirement of Miss MacDonald, who had done so much to maintain the nursing standards, and of Mr W. Russell Rudall, who was succeeded as hospital secretary by Mr R.F.P. Glegg in 1946. Mr Clift Ford, numbed by the bombing of his London properties, resigned as hospital chairman in February 1942, so Mr Geoffrey Bowes, appointed the next month, had the major task of bringing the hospital into the National Health Service (NHS).

Despite a deficit of £4000, he negotiated the purchase of next-door Roborough School[1] for physiotherapy premises, as well as the London Homoeopathic Home, 36 Enys Road, at the corner of Carew and Enys Roads, for additional night nurse accommodation. The Home, which opened in 1888, had been closed for some time. It is still named *Bowes House*. The purchase price was £4565, the cost of refitting was "tedious and expensive", but it was finally occupied by 22 night staff on 1st February 1947.

The gravity of the deficit can only be assessed by realising what a substantial sum £4000 represented in the mid-forties. The average expenditure on each in-patient amounted to £12.77p for the whole of their stay. The annual salary bill for all the nursing staff came to a mere £6400, domestic wages were £3321, the laboratory £522, porters and stokers £311 and the dispensary £240. The bill for drugs was £639, for dressings £382, and instruments cost only £378 for the year.

At least, owning most of the buildings on the Princess Alice "island" (including the ground behind *Roborough*) meant that the central field could be used for staff sports activities, and it was the site of a magnificent bonfire every Guy Fawkes' night.

When Miss MacDonald retired in May 1945, worn out by the strain of the war, Miss A.M. Boxall became the matron. She was a tall, handsome woman, and though she was not quite so distant a figure, there were few changes. Mrs Doris Kingsford (née West), who started training in July 1946, says the custom persisted that nurses had to press themselves against the wall if matron came along a corridor. 'One day Miss Boxall slipped and fell, but the nurses were so petrified that instead of assisting her, we all continued to press ourselves against the wall'. Miss Diana Eyre recalls that when she was doing her children's nursing at the Princess Alice in 1934-35, she ran up the stairs and, seeing Sister Drake at the top, stood aside to allow her to pass, but that august personage waved her back, announcing, 'Nurse, descend, and allow me to proceed down the stairs'.

In 1946 the nurses worked six days a week, from 0730h to 2000h. They either had a break from 1000-1300h (which included lunch) or from 1330-1700h, which included lunch and tea. Night duty was from 2000h to 0730h with an hour's break. Late-passes were only granted one night a week, and nurses were still charged for any broken equipment, such as glass syringes. As Mrs Kingsford says, 'I well recall an incident when, as I was about to go out, I realised that I had inadvertently taken the lotion cupboard key with me, so I attempted to return it, *en route* to the town. Such behaviour was not acceptable, and the Sister made me go back to my room and redress in uniform before returning the key'.

Student nurses were not allowed to live-out, but this encouraged much friendship and comradeship. As they had only pocket money, most entertainment was of necessity home-spun, such as table tennis and dancing to gramophone records. 'The housemen joined us and male students from the newly-established teacher's training college in Meads were also invited.'

Conversely, Mrs Pavey (née Elliman) says that when, around 1950, student nurses were allowed to live-out she jumped at the opportunity to be rid of the restrictions and "shop talk" of hospital life. 'This was despite the Sister Tutor being only too right when she warned us that we would find many flats without bathrooms and unlimited supplies of hot water'.

Sister Acfield took over Gurney, Tabor and the fracture clinic from Sister Harrison, with Staff Nurse E. Saunders. In 1946 Mr D.J. Hoad and Miss M. Harding were appointed as the first chiropodists, the same year Miss Durrant died: she had been the cook for 23 years.

By 1947 Sister L. McIlwraith, ex-WAAF, was the Theatre Sister, but some staff continued unchanged, such as Miss Netta Tonks in physiotherapy, and Lily Wortley of the domestic staff.

Whilst all the hospital doctors who went into the armed forces returned, most suffered a hard war. Mr Desmond O'Connor Cuffey and Mr Thomas Henry Wilson spent five years in POW camps, Drs Alfred Emslie and Vincent Harris served in India, Dr Mark Lester was in North Africa and Italy, and Mr Geoffrey Estcourt took part in the Castellammare, Anzio and Salerno landings, where he operated under such appalling conditions that he never talked about the experience.

Dr Doris Rose, a charming person and a clever surgeon who lived at the Hydro Hotel, was elected assistant ophthalmologist in 1945, and on returning from the army Mr Henry Wilson became a full surgeon, along with Mr Snowball. Dr Alfred Emslie, an innovative and respected physician, started an ECG [heart beat tracings] service in 1946 and was to establish Eastbourne's diabetic clinic in 1950 (although Dr Gillett had held a clinic during the war). In June 1947 Dr R.V. Harris inaugurated a skin clinic.[2]

Although the Charity Commissioners declined to sanction the amalgamation of Princess Alice, the Royal Eye and ENT hospitals, "owing to the imminence of State control", on the incorporation of the ENT Hospital, Drs R.M. Barron and H.J.A. Pollard were appointed anæsthetists to the ENT department, where Mr Cuffey recommenced after his release from captivity. Mr C.E. Dobell recalls being under his care just after the war when he broke his nose playing football.

Through all these upheavals the routine work of the hospital went smoothly on. In December 1945, 13-year-old Diana Wratten (later Miller) was admitted into Sydney Hudson ward under the care of Mr Henry Wilson with osteomyelitis of her left tibia [infection of a leg bone]. As she says, 'In those days it was a serious matter and my parents were warned that I was in danger of losing my leg ... I was fortunate to be treated by the wonder drug, penicillin, because it was still not easily available, being earmarked for the treatment of service personnel. The staff were preparing the ward for Christmas and I helped with the making of paper flowers, but I recall the kindness of the nurses who rigged up a set of earphones for me to hear the next instalment of *The Count of Monte Cristo,* which I had been following on the radio at home. There was a piano in the ward and one of the patients played carols, which both patients and staff would sing. Although appreciative of my care, I pined for my family and was pleased that I had progressed enough to return home on 23rd December. The staff had been so kind that I felt ungrateful to want to go home.'

Jeanne Levett (later Fry) was in the children's ward in 1947 after being knocked off her bicycle. 'The visiting was one hour on Wednesday, Saturday and Sunday and what a long time it seemed between visits and how I tried not to cry when my mother went. I also remember how awful the food was, we had fish pie quite a lot and the nurses would get very cross with me because I didn't eat it'.

April 1947 saw the appointment of the Revd E.Lloyd Sporne as full-time chaplain to the hospital. Before he was appointed, the job was done voluntarily by the Rural Dean of Eastbourne.

At the onset of the NHS the following year, Mr Sporne became chaplain to the Eastbourne Hospitals Group, combining the ministry for all the hospitals. At Princess Alice a small chapel was provided by converting the library, which was transferred to the reception room. It was dedicated by the Bishop of Chichester, the Rt Revd George Bell, on 29th November 1947. Arrangements were made so that services could be relayed to patients in the wards.

Sisters Coggan and Lancaster were always there for 0630h Friday Holy Communion, and Miss Muriel Baker, one of the domestics, cleaned and looked after the chapel for many years.

In the last full year before the NHS the hospital admitted 2183 patients into 120 beds. There were 1346 operations in the main theatre and another 152 in the out-patient department. The Casualty department saw 2621 new patients, the X-ray department had 4122 attendances for diagnostic tests (and 174 for treatments), "Electrical and rehabilitation" had 862 new patients, and there were 8511 pathology investigations.

The VD clinic (punctiliously referred to as the "Special Clinic") had been at *Avenue House* from 1939 to 1947, went to Downside Hospital with the onset of the NHS, and after 1953 was held in Roborough for many years. The pathology work had been done by Dr Shera and his staff at the Princess Alice laboratory since 1923. In 1947 they did 418 WR tests and 416 Kahn tests [for syphilis], 527 examinations for gonorrhoea, and 19 CSF [brain fluid] tests.[3]

The pathology laboratory consisted of just two rooms. Histology and biochemistry were in one (separated by the secretary's desk in the middle) and in the other there was bacteriology with haematology/blood transfusion. All the TB work, of which there was quite a lot, was done on the open bench, with a fine disregard for the Health and Safety at Work Act - still 30 years away. Miss Dorothy Head, one of the technical staff, acted as secretary until 1947, when Miss Eileen Martin was engaged as a full-time secretary for Dr Shera. Albert, "a little man on a bike", one of the former workhouse inmates, brought any specimens from St Mary's Hospital.

Dr Raperport, one of the housemen, gave an account in May 1947 of 14 cases of neonatal diarrhoea, with two fatalities, which had been admitted to the Princess Alice Hospital.

Miss E. York, although nearing retirement, still kept her "beady eyes" open to catch any nurse creeping in late, 'She caught me once' says Eileen Cook. She also had a quiet sense of humour, exemplified by the morning when Nurse (later Sister) Betty P. Drury, then in training, was alone on the ward and a patient gave her a sweet. She had just popped it into her mouth when she saw Miss York approaching the other side of the glass door, 'I swallowed my toffee whole. We did the usual ward round, name, diagnosis and progress of each patient, and I opened the door for Miss York to depart. She thanked me - and in a soft voice added, "Nurse, next time you'll choke". To obtain the full flavour of the episode you need to understand that, in those days, it was unthinkable to have a sweet in your mouth at any time on duty, let alone on the ward round'.

In June 1947, the matron, Miss Boxall, resigned. She undoubtedly dropped out suddenly and surfaced in Jersey, but there were various interpretations of these actions. The official one was that she had been called to nurse a sick friend, the others were much more exciting and the nurses' favourite was of an affair with a handsome naval officer, whose ship was berthed in the Channel Isles. Whatever, Miss York, as assistant matron, filled the gap until the appointment of Miss Hilda J. de Pinto, who came from Chichester, in October 1947.

Everyone agrees that Miss de Pinto was an outstanding matron, from Mr Henry Wilson's, 'A good, sound matron', to Nurse Flora Clark's comment, 'A marvellous matron. She always seemed to know when there was work to do, and she would go down to Casualty, put on a white coat and buckle to'.

Miss de Pinto was undoubtedly able, but she was also a kindly person, who ameliorated the nurses' lot to some extent. As Mrs Kingsford says, 'The rules were relaxed about late-passes and breakages, so that it was no longer necessary to gain access to the nurses' home at night by clambering through windows'. Miss de Pinto also took on the tough job of amalgamating the nursing staffs of all the Eastbourne hospitals when the NHS started.

Mrs Hilda Wells (née de Pinto) sets out what she found when she joined the hospital, just before the start of the NHS:-

"Beginning at the north-east corner, near the junction of Carew and Bedfordwell Roads, there was an entrance for casualties. To the left was the physiotherapy department, and to the right the main Casualty and Arno ward under the care of Sister Gee. X-ray was near the corner of the main long corridor.

"On the opposite side of this central corridor was the operating theatre suite. Sister McIlwraith was an excellent theatre sister, but a fearsome sight to any nurse who did not match up to her standards. Below the theatre were the sterilising room and porters' room; above was accommodation for the housemen.

"To the south-west side of the theatre there was a steep staircase which led down to the cramped ophthalmic and ENT out-patients. This is where the little chapel which had just been opened was situated.

"Moving further down the main corridor towards the direction of the town, the orthopædic wards were next, Gurney on the right and Tabor, with the plaster room, on the left, all in charge of Sister Acfield.

"This brings us to the centre of the old hospital. Coming up the entrance steps there was the doctors' office to the left, and matron's room to the right - next to a staircase leading up to the staff dining room, and a two-bed sick bay for the nurses. If I was interviewing in matron's office, the thunder of feet rushing down after meals and always jumping the last two treads was more than annoying. On the corridor wall facing the entrance was an oil painting of Princess Alice, just by a telephone room.

"Here, at right angles to the main corridor, a short corridor led back in the direction of Bedfordwell Road. There were kitchens on the left, and the library on the right. This was a most dignified room with good quality bookcases, used as a waiting room during the day and as an office for the night Sisters.

"At the end of this short corridor was Cavendish ward, male medical, and above, reached by stair or lift, was Sydney Hudson ward, now female medical; both wards were under Sister Coggan. Above Sydney Hudson there were a few rooms for resident domestic staff.

"Continuing south-west down the main corridor the next wards were Geraldine (female medical) on the left and Crowden (male medical) opposite, with Sister Lancaster.

"At the end of the main corridor were the children's wards, Anne Elizabeth and Michael Francis. Sister Potter was a superb person to gain the confidence of her young patients.

"A short, partly-open corridor joined the main hospital to two separate houses. The first, *Taormina,* held the board room to the right, which was also Mr Glegg's office. Mr Pumfrey worked in the adjoining conservatory which, as you can imagine, was always either too hot or too cold.

26. The pre-NHS Nurses' Prizegiving of 1948. From left, Miss Sykes, Mr Pumfrey, Dame Barrie Lambert, Mr MacQueen, Miss de Pinto (speaking), and Mr Glegg.

"On the opposite side (towards Bedfordwell Road) was a large room used by Miss Eileen Peyton, still the almoner, and her assistant, Miss Claire Lace. Miss Peyton was a worker of wonders and able to sort out anyone's troubles. Miss Lace was on the secretarial staff, and also acted as a clerical locum for the consultant letters. It was said that in her time she had acted as secretary for everybody, and that when a Work Study of the clerical department was carried out the investigators got fed up with recording her non-stop movements.

"On the first floor was the matron's flat with its own front door. It comprised a large bedroom (over the board room), a spare room, a delightful sitting room over the almoner's office and, towards the back, a dining room, kitchen and bathroom. Truly a home from home for any matron, away from the hospital bustle and yet on the spot. A room on the half-landing was for matron's maid and rooms on the top floor were available for resident domestic staff.

"The next house along was *Harberton* which contained the school of nursing. The senior tutor, Miss Sykes, lived on the top floor, where there was also a room for three nurses."

Mrs Wells doesn't mention that it must have been restrictive for three young nurses to live in such close proximity to a senior sister. It is said they would wait for her to go out before any high jinks, but it wasn't unknown for Miss Sykes to return unexpectedly and exclaim, 'I knew I'd catch you'. When she retired, her flat was also used for night nurses.

The nurse training school was fortunate, just after the war, in always being able to recruit a full school. In line with modern trends, the first arrangements for training male nursing students were mentioned in the Annual Report for 1947, and girls from the Commonwealth were recruited in the 1950s, leading to some raising of eyebrows, because as Mrs Wells says, 'Eastbourne changed its ideas slowly, but gradually they came round to these "strange ideas of matron" and accepted them enthusiastically'.

Despite Nurse Connie Stewart's 1949 PA Christmas concert - music by Peter Knight - having a chorus line which pleaded for, "An increase in the male staff and of the single state", the first male nurse, who was ex-navy, was not overtly welcomed by the nurses. As Nurse Doris West, now Mrs Kingsford, comments, 'When we had our rest hour, instead of relaxing by throwing off our caps and sprawling over the furniture, we made a point of keeping our caps on and sitting demurely'. Nurse West, who trained from 1946 to 1949 (and whose sisters Margaret and Audrey also joined the staff), spent 15 happy months as Staff Nurse on the children's ward with Sister Potter until 1951, when she married Dr Bryan Hunt, one of the housemen. At the time, if nurses asked for a reference to take up a midwifery post, it was the common practice for them to be told that they owed it to the hospital to give at least one year's service as a staff nurse. As Mrs Kingsford says, 'What a different climate to-day when sometimes nurses have difficulty being kept on after qualification'.

According to Mrs Kingsford, several children spent recurrent periods in the children's ward: there was Malcolm who had severe eczema [a skin condition], and who came in during the worst episodes; a young diabetic, Bernard, who even kept his bicycle at the hospital; and a little girl with ear infections, who preferred hospital to home, and on numerous occasions a nurse had to take her home and put her to bed to persuade her to stay there.

Mr D. Holding, a student nurse in the early 1950s, says that even with an ex-serviceman's allowance, his pay was only £15 per month. 'Mr Pumfrey had said that with a wife and baby son to support he didn't think I could manage on the salary, and he was right.' Mr Holding remembers the cold classrooms at *Harberton* and asserts, 'The girls were allowed to wear cardigans, whereas the three male nurses were not, but had to shiver in their uniform of ill-fitting gowns, which had blue collars for students and green collars for orderlies'.

Not unexpectedly, the first changing room for the male nurses was at the utmost corner of the hospital in the old wartime security post, and converted for £226. Mr R. Spicer says that it was often visited by the patrolling beat constable, for a warm-up and a cup of tea as well as the usual social chit-chat with any of the nursing staff who happened to be there.

Payment for the doctors commenced in July 1947. The Ministry had made some payments during the war, but beforehand hospital doctors held honorary appointments and relied on the kudos of the hospital post to attract private patients. The first payments were made quarterly in the form of a block honorarium for division among the doctors; at this stage it was not considered a full payment for services rendered and, as Mr Henry Wilson adds, 'Not all the doctors were included'. The management committee stressed that the payments did not alter the status of the doctors or their rights of committee membership. Another change was that the medical staff, especially the younger ones, considered that the "assistant surgeon or physician" system should be ended and the governors agreed that all the specialists should have full status.

In other ways the shape of things to come became more evident. With the financial deficit rising from £707 in 1944, and £4278 in 1945, to £31834 in 1947 it was obvious that the voluntary hospital system, which had served this country up to the 1939-45 war, was no longer a viable proposition. This was despite contributions from the government Emergency Hospital Scheme of £12108 in 1944, £6551 in 1945, and £3518 in 1946. In the words of the 1946 Annual Report, "the hospital is now running on the basis of an annual deficit of at least £20000, which clearly cannot be met by voluntary contributions".

Among items bought by the committee of management in 1947 were electric ward-sterilisers, electrically-heated food trolleys and a *Dennis* motor lawn mower. With the need for additional accommodation for nursing staff in mind, they also bought Nos 28, 29 and 31 Bedfordwell Road over 1947 and 1948. "Admin." found that their needs were greater and moved into "29" on 20th September 1948: in time, it became the main offices of the finance department.

The National Health Service Act became law in 1946 and on 5th July 1948 the Ministry of Health took over the country's hospitals. As from the appointed day the Princess Alice, along with other hospitals in the Eastbourne Group, was administered by the South East Metropolitan Regional Hospital Board through the Eastbourne Hospital Management Committee (HMC). It was a pleasing gesture that the Regional Board appointed Mr Bowes, the Princess Alice chairman, as chairman of the new HMC, together with eight members of the Princess Alice Hospital Committee, including four of its doctors - R.C. MacQueen, D.G. Churcher, T. Henry Wilson and E. Owen Fox.

Mr Robert Glegg records that the Regional Board was in Upper Regent Street in an office shored up by beams, presumably following war-time damage. The chairman, Ivor Julian (later knighted) was fairly tall, but the deputy Sir Frank

Lessor was so short that even when he stood up to address a meeting he was smaller than Sir Ivor sitting down.

In the 1939-45 war the country had been united and people had accepted many national establishments; the troops had come to accept that medical care was available for all; and doctors found the war-time Emergency Medical Service surprisingly congenial and were impressed with the efficient provision of national services, such as blood transfusion, compared with the *ad hoc,* fragmented, pre-war service. The Lloyd George Act of 1911 had only catered for the breadwinner, and the country now wanted medical care for the family. The nation, many politicians and most of the medical profession supported the 1946 Act, and opposition from the British Medical Association, which is often quoted, was not against the principle of a service for all, but on the extent of local authority involvement and the practicalities of how it would be funded. Still cogent questions if there is not to be overt rationing.

At the commencement of the NHS Robert Glegg became the Eastbourne Group Secretary and Ben Pumfrey the Princess Alice Hospital Secretary. The HMC was now busy administering St Mary's Hospital, Church Street (299 beds); Princess Alice Memorial Hospital, Carew Road (120); The Leaf Hospital, St Anne's Road (31); The Isolation Hospital, later Downside, East Dean Road (64); Gildredge Sanatorium, Longland Road (24); the Maternity Home, 9 Upperton Road (25); two convalescent hospitals - *Seaside,* Seaford (122) and *Merlynn,* 5/7 Devonshire Place (48), along with two clinics - the VD Clinic, and a TB Clinic at *Avenue House,* Eastbourne. Although the work of the Royal Eye Hospital at 49 Pevensey Road transferred to the Princess Alice in 1940, apart from an occasional out-patient clinic, it was not formally closed until 4th October 1949.

At this time general medical and surgical cases were shared between St Mary's and Princess Alice. All the Orthopædic and ENT work was at Princess Alice, with the ENT out-patients in the "dungeon". The Eye out-patients and most of the surgery was also at Princess Alice, but some in-patient beds were on Glynde ward at St Mary's Hospital. The Leaf Hospital was still a general hospital, although taking most of the gynæcology patients.

Mr Keith Walker started as a porter in 1947 and remembers being taught his job by Sidney Pilbeam. 'My first task was to polish the floor with a heavy "bumper", ... and Sid emphasised that I must not bump the beds. Of course in the presence of Sister Lancaster I had to bump a bed. She said, "I'm known as Tiger, because when I see anyone doing anything wrong I pounce", this did not improve my self-confidence'. He also remembers scrubbing the floor in Casualty, struggling to get it finished before Sister Gee arrived, while the nurses kept walking over it and kicking the soap out of his reach. Relations between the porters and nurses were good, and Miss York delighted in telephoning the porter's room when one was needed to demand, 'I want a man, right now'.

During the summer of 1948 Eastbourne had activity of a different nature, with one of its worst food-poisoning outbreaks. Dorothy Head recalls the laboratory working flat out over the August Bank holiday weekend, before Dr Jamieson and a team from the Brighton Public Health laboratory took up residence to cope with the number of tests involved, as each case needed to be checked and followed-up. The first case was a child admitted to St Mary's Hospital on 16th July 1948, but the first specimen was not submitted to the laboratory until the 25th, yet by the 27th the lab. indicated that the town was dealing with an outbreak of *Salmonella* paratyphoid B, Vi-phage type *taunton*. The child was transferred to the Isolation Hospital (later Downside) and during the next six weeks over 120 cases were tested, of which 30 females and 14 males were confirmed infections, and 42 of them were admitted to Downside. The lab. also confirmed that six persons from other parts of the country had contracted their infection while holidaying in the town. All recovered. Circumstantial evidence, from the early cases, pointed to the *Scotch Bakery (Eastbourne) Ltd,* a high-class confectioners near the station, as the source of the infection. Valerie Feint, one of the laboratory staff, was married in the middle of the outbreak and Dr Shera declined to eat the cream trifle at the wedding reception.

In the late 1940s, Miss Brenda Maxted (who went on to became a senior nurse) was a staff nurse on Sydney Hudson ward, with Sister Coggan and assistant nurse Best, while Mrs Joan M. Hales (née Bellhouse) was on Geraldine and Crowden with Sister Lancaster who was, as she says, 'quite original, but a wonderful nurse'. Miss Kemp was the Home Sister.

Mrs Wells (née de Pinto) says, 'Both Sister Coggan and Sister Lancaster were outstanding in their devotion to their patients and it was difficult to get either of them to go off duty. They belonged to the "old school" and it was not easy for me to make changes to fit in with the new ideas of the medical staff. I was prepared to develop a good relationship with them, to ensure that they knew their devoted work in the care of the patients and their thorough training of the nurses was appreciated by everyone'.

Mr D. Holding mentions that when he was on Cavendish ward, 'No matter how fast you worked, Sister Coggan always made you look as if you were standing still'.

There was another example of nursing at its best when a man was admitted with gastric trouble and had to have a tube passed into his stomach. He was not at all keen and was about to discharge himself when Staff Nurse Aggie Kent said, 'You only have to swallow it. Now you watch me'. She passed the tube down into her stomach without flinching. 'Now,' she said, 'I'll leave you with another tube while I see to a very ill patient'. Of course it worked.

In 1948 the Patients' Association (later the Friends of the Eastbourne Hospitals) started a weekly record request program at Princess Alice, which grew into Radio District General Hospital as from July 1976.

As Mr E.J. Porter says, 'When I started in 1950 it was a very friendly hospital, more like a home'. And the hospital had retained much of its self-sufficiency. In September 1949 Mr Pumfrey was reporting to the catering committee that he had bought nine turkeys, at £2.25p each, for fattening up for Christmas. The same year he reported that the Princess Alice fowls had laid 340 eggs during August, making a total of 5596 over the year. Mr Pumfrey was still mentioning the purchase of Christmas turkeys in 1952, even though in 1951, following complaints by the resident staff, it was decided to spend an extra sixpence per head, on staff meals only, and to serve the patients from ward trolleys to reduce waste.[4] The Princess Alice catering officer was Miss A. Greaves, with Miss Hingley as head cook. The rest of the staff consisted of three assistant cooks (two resident), five kitchen maids, one kitchen porter, three pantry maids (two part-time) and four dining-room maids, numbers which the HMC catering committee agreed were insufficient, accepting that extra assistant cooks and a diets' cook were needed. Miss Bridget Greeney, who worked in the catering department from 1948 to 1951, returned to work after marriage as Mrs Salter, and was to become the catering manager.

One of the dispensary staff developed an ovarian cyst, which was removed, but unfortunately she died of post-operative pneumonia. Her replacement was Miss K.G. Foxall, who gave 22 years of service as pharmacist until her retirement in April 1970. Miss Philips was another member of the staff at the time. Dr Harris records that at first Miss Foxall was quite nonplussed if there were more than four or five components in a prescription - not uncommon for dermatology in those times. Miss D. Martin, who joined the pharmacy later, says that gentian solution had to be mixed very carefully into creams, otherwise there were dire results, and it was not unknown on Monday and Wednesday clinic days for the pharmacy to "have all hands on deck".

The children's ophthalmic clinic, which had been run by the local authority, transferred to the Princess Alice in April 1949 and the orthopædic clinic followed at the end of the year[5]. By 1949 Dr Ian Brown was building-up a Staff Health Service, and he took over as the doctor for the resident nurses when Mr MacQueen retired in 1951.

The Princess Alice bed-state in November 1948 was 120 beds available, of which 94 were occupied, with a waiting list of 277. It is always necessary to keep some beds empty, otherwise emergency patients would have to be sent all over the county chasing an empty bed, and if a patient had just been discharged that bed would be counted as empty at the time of the tally.

An early effect of the NHS was that fully-qualified consultants began to move out of the main centres, such as London and Edinburgh, now that there was a national salary scale. Until 1949 all Eastbourne's senior hospital doctors had other work, such as general practice, which was essential in the days when hospital posts were unpaid, but after the NHS no GP was allowed to do more than four hospital sessions a week. Some of the hospital specialists, such as Dr West Phillips and Dr Sherwood, were "not classified" and had their posts terminated by the Regional Board at the onset of the NHS: others, such as Dr Bodkin Adams, not fully qualified to be graded a consultant, were offered the sub-consultant position of Senior Hospital Medical Officer (SHMO). The pay for a full-time SHMO was £1300 rising to £1750. Mr Gray and Mr Pimm were given the status of Senior Hospital Dental Officers.

On 14th June 1948 the group medical committee expressed, "grave disapproval of the proposed gradings" and went on to "strongly protest against the unfair way these gradings have been made". It is understandable that some of the borderline decisions, especially concerning established specialists, created some dissension, but it has to be said that Douglas Sherwood did not possess an FRCS, the surgical qualification, and everyone agreed that Robert West Phillips could not find a vein even if his job (or the patient's life) depended on it. Venkata Giri, from the Royal Eye Hospital, was initially graded "consultant", but this rapidly changed to "unclassified" and he retired at the age of 65 in May 1950. He had maintained prickly relations with the Princess Alice staff - it was said that he was a competent enough surgeon, but there were persistent rumours that he compounded unethical treatments, such as putting patients on a course of sterile water injections at £3 a shot. Mr Sydney Freedman says that Dr Giri did not stay in the town, but emigrated to Australia.

On analysis of their timetables, it is amazing how little time the specialists were expected to spend in the Princess Alice Hospital, possibly suited to a time when an opinion was all that was required, but becoming less appropriate with active intervention, interpretations and investigations. In 1948 the two physicians, Drs Churcher and Emslie put in only 24 hours a week between them; of course, this was besides their general practice, private practice, and other duties - Dr Churcher, for example, did eight hours a week at the infectious diseases hospital and was also on the staff of the Gildredge TB hospital. The dentists were contracted for a mere six hours a week at Princess Alice altogether, Dr Fox spent 17 hours a week there, Dr Bodkin Adams seven hours, and the two specialists in psychological medicine, Drs Reid and Fitzpatrick, were only supposed to do two hours a week at Princess Alice in total.

Two types of part-time consultant contract finally emerged. A "Maximum part-time" contract paid 9/11 of a whole-time salary, where the doctor contracted to devote substantially the whole of his time to hospital work. It was introduced to discourage Regional Boards (who employed the consultants) from advertising only full-time posts. For a "Part-time" contract the doctor worked the number of sessions for which he was contracted, up to a maximum of nine.

Senior doctors received £200 a year, per half-day session, and were paid quarterly. Nurses received much less, monthly, and as Mrs Audrey Swann (née

West) says, 'We had to stand outside the office and sign for a brown envelope which contained your pay in cash, at first £6.50p per month, board deducted'.

Nurse Audrey West started in 1949, when the Preliminary Training School (PTS) was run by Miss Sykes and Miss Horsley, and from her description little had changed since before the war. 'The first duty of the day was cleaning the school including the lavatory, and lessons did not start until the cleaning was complete. By now the uniform allowance provided a clean apron every day, but as the nurses had only three dresses, three belts and three collars, these were changed weekly. First year nurses still had white belts, second year grey and third year blue. No nurse was allowed to wear any jewellery, except a wedding ring, and no nail varnish. Nurses were not allowed to wear uniform outside, except when going from the hospital to the Nurses' Home; so I remember showing off that I was a nurse by walking along Bedfordwell Road to my room. Sisters were held in great awe and all nurses were addressed by their surnames.'

27. The old Roborough School, later a nurses' home, physiotherapy and OT departments, VD clinic and psychogeriatric day hospital.

'Dressing trolleys were still set up by swabbing a rubber-covered trolley with the antiseptic *Eusol*, and bowls were taken from the boiling-water steriliser in the ward. Often we ran out of dressing towels and had to use triangular bandages instead. Preparing a trolley after "lights-out" was not only hazardous for the nurse, but noisy for the patients.

'During bed-pan rounds a screen would be placed across the ward door and only if a patient was about to have a bowel movement were they individually screened; some wards still had wooden-framed mobile screens, which had to be carried to the bedside.' Tabor ward did not have cubicle curtains until 1950.

'When I arrived in 1949 *Harberton* in Carew Road was the school and a nurses' home', writes Mrs Dorothy Pavey (née Elliman). 'The tutors were Miss Sykes and Miss Taylor, who had just commenced, but what I remember most was that the rooms were bitterly cold. There was no central heating and a small gas fire in the lecture room had little effect. *Roborough* was in a terrible state when taken over, having been occupied by various Army units throughout the war. The plan was to have physiotherapy and the Special Clinic on the ground floor, and have the upper floors filled with nurses' residencies.'

From Mr Holding's comments it wouldn't seem that the heating had improved by 1951, when Margaret Prempeh, daughter of Sir Osei Prempeh Chief King of the Ashanti, started her training in the nursing school.

Training was strict. At the end of a nurse's probationary time, there was a hospital examination by Miss Sykes and Mr Henry Wilson. 'If you didn't pass you were called to the office and you didn't stay if you were too bad'. By the 1950s the GNC were saying that only nurse tutors should be involved in such tests, so Mr Wilson and Mr Snowball, who also helped, were eased out.

Dr D.C.Taylor was appointed as an extra consultant pathologist in 1950, and a laboratory extension built. His office was at the Princess Alice, and he visited St Mary's and Hellingly Hospitals. Shortly before he arrived the first lab. porter, Mr Carpenter, was appointed, to cope with washing up specimen containers (for all specimen bottles, reagents and antibiotic discs were prepared in the lab.) as well as to assist with the mortuary work. Before the appointment, one of the technical staff would have left his bench work to act as assistant.

Dr John L. Linacre, Dr Leslie G. Scott and Dr Robert D. Moyle also joined the staff as consultants in 1950. Dr Linacre was the first fully-qualified anæsthetist at the Princess Alice, and Dr Scott the first paediatrician. He was greeted at the children's ward by Sister Maureen Potter, who had been at the Kent and Sussex Hospital, Tunbridge Wells, when he was a House Surgeon there during the Battle of Britain in 1940. Dr Moyle was a part-time visiting dermatologist, whose main claim to fame was that he was well over 65 before the Regional Board discovered they had his wrong birthdate. Officially, consultants could retire between 55 and 65, depending on preference and specialty.

Dr A.M. Stewart-Wallace was appointed consultant neurologist as from 13th February 1950. He started at Princess Alice on Monday mornings, where he was "accommodated in the Audiometrician's Room", but he rapidly moved to St Mary's out-patient clinic.

Lord Moran (known to the doctors as "Corkscrew Charlie") spoke at Tunbridge Wells, on 23rd August 1950, about Merit Awards; Mr Crook, Dr Owen Fox, Mr McSwiney, Dr Moyle, Dr Scott, Dr Sherwood and Mr Henry Wilson attended.

The houses, 17 and 21 Upper Avenue, and a further part of Roborough were opened as additional nurses' homes with the ground floor of Roborough continuing as the physiotherapy unit under Miss Tonks, who was a great friend of Sister Lancaster. An occupational therapy service was started in July 1950, but lapsed when the one occupational therapist resigned. The final cost of all the Roborough alterations was £11960.

The 1950 HMC Annual Report stated that 369 nurses were employed in the Eastbourne hospitals, with student nurses from Ireland, Jamaica, Lithuania and Poland, and of 25 who entered the state examination (SRN) 24 passed.

Sister Levack was a Night Sister and Sister Peppercorn one of the Home Sisters. Mrs Patricia Hassell (née Dow) says, 'The Home Sisters were very strict. It was known for nurses, coming off duty at 2000h, to find their bed stripped by the Home Sister because it had not been made up properly. About the only perk for the nurses was breakfast in bed on your day off, if you wanted it you put your name in a book the night beforehand.' Mrs Hassell points out that 'even in 1950 the hospital was remarkably self-sufficient, growing vegetables and keeping poultry; including turkeys; everything was freshly cooked, no frozen foods then'.

Just before the war, Mrs E.M. Fuller (née Walder) had been a young patient in Geraldine ward cared for by "lovely" Sister Lancaster. In 1950 she started her nurse training with the same Sister on the same ward, 'Sister Lancaster was a marvellous teacher and taught me so much. For Matron de Pinto's daily ward rounds, when she was sometimes with her pet dachshund, you had to know the name of every patient, their age, diagnosis and prognosis. Well beforehand the nurses had made the beds, done a bed pan round, dusted the lockers and "high dusted" the walls, put out flowers and drinking water on the lockers, and then cleaned the baths and lavatories. There was no question but that beds had to be lined up, wheels pointing inwards and no creases on the covers. When the round started you had to wear your hard cuffs. If we answered a telephone enquiry we were only allowed to say, "No change, please ring sister at [a given time]".

'On night duty, apart from filling autoclave drums with gauze and cotton wool balls at any spare moment, we had to clean all the instruments, empty and clean the sterilisers, which had big heavy lids, and replace the gallipots and receivers ready for the next day. Needless to say, you never wore your cardigan for rounds by the Night Sister. On nights I was so tired at first that I slept right round the clock and didn't wake up until nearly midnight, when I should have been on duty at eight o'clock. My Goodness, was there trouble. I was told in no uncertain terms to get an alarm clock'.

Nurse Mavis Taylor (later Sister Constable) adds that in the operating theatre the nurses did all the cleaning, instruments and walls.

Until effective anti-tuberculous drug regimes were generally available around the early 1950s, TB remained a killer. Joan James, a young Welsh nurse who shared a room with Nurse Walder, contracted and died of the disease, and many nurses had to have a year off with "fluid on the lung". Teenagers were especially at risk, the onset was often insidious and some families were known to be more vulnerable than others (witness the Brontës), but every town and hamlet suffered its ravages: "where youth grows pale, and spectre-thin, and dies".[6]

Staff Nurse E. Hill (later Mobey) who was on Geraldine and Crowden wards 1949-51 is unstinting in her praise of Sister Lancaster. In those days her wards were a mixture of medical and surgical patients, with a two-bed private ward. She recalls asking Sister Lancaster whether she could have Christmas Day off to see her family in London, to be told, 'No, you cannot, nurses work on Christmas Day'. At noon on Christmas Day, Sister Lancaster said to her, 'Do you really want to go off, because if so we are not too busy and you can be spared'. When Nurse Hill was married, Sister Lancaster gave her as wedding presents a bottle of perfume and a tea-towel - with the words, 'A little luxury and a little domesticity'.

Mrs Doreen Stringell (née Hardy) started as matron's secretary on 3rd September 1951, when Miss Aylward moved to the Esperance Hospital, but her first job each morning was to type the X-ray reports and deal with Dr Fox's correspondence. 'I also took dictation from Mr Geoffrey Estcourt after his Monday clinic, and I have taken three consecutive phone calls as matron's secretary, X-ray secretary and Mr Estcourt's secretary. When appointed my desk was in matron's office, just to the right of the entrance, which meant that I could not go in if she was engaged, so matron pounced on a space just past the children's wards. It was long and slim as befits a linen cupboard, but when the carpenter made a desk top with a set of drawers, I was in heaven, except for one day when there was much giggling as staff passed the door. I looked out and found that the sign-writer had gone off duty leaving my door labelled "MATRON'S SECRET". I was relieved when he eventually added the final - ARY' - and no doubt matron too. Sign-written notices, instead of stick-on letters or labels were used in the hospitals until the late 1960s.

In 1951 Mr Arthur Crook retired. 'A splendid chap', in Mr Henry Wilson's words. He was succeeded on 1st November by Mr S.A. Jenkins, who had been mentioned in dispatches during the war, was said to be one of the youngest candidates for the FRCS qualification, and who had shown great promise at the Hammersmith Hospital. Mr J.A. Cholmeley remained an occasional visiting orthopædic surgeon, dealing mainly with childhood bone conditions. Appointed on the same day as Mr Jenkins, Mr Peter Smith replaced surgeons Mr MacQueen and Mr Wilson Hall on their retirement. Mr Smith worked nine sessions, that is the most a part-timer could do apart from any private work. but he was almost entirely at St Mary's Hospital; of the other general surgeons, Mr Henry Wilson's time was split between St Mary's and Princess Alice, and Mr Estcourt had all his beds at Princess Alice. Mr E.V. Oulton, the part-time ophthalmic surgeon since 1923, also retired and Mrs Rose succeeded him, working along with Mr S.S. Freedman, who had commenced in 1951.

When Sister M. Gee moved from Princess Alice to take charge of the out-patients and casualty department at St Mary's Hospital, Sister J.F. Simmonds took over at Princess Alice. Among her staff over the years were nursing orderlies M. Astridge, D. Breach (who later went to X-ray), P. Drury, G. Flinders (sadly, imprisoned for assaulting a patient), D. Patterson (whose duties included washing Mr Jenkins' car), E.J. Porter, and B. Urrey.

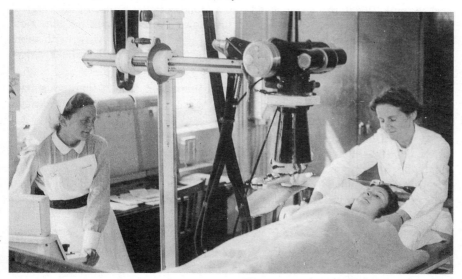

28. The X-ray department in 1950. Nancy Poulter on the left and Phyllis Newman right.

As a response to the cold war situation a civil defence National Health Service Reserve had been formed. Locally, the meetings were usually at St Mary's Hospital or the civil defence headquarters, but members of the Princess Alice staff, for example Dr Churcher, were on the committee.

About this time a more heartening measure was an extension to the kitchen. Princess Alice also prepared itself for a foot-warming visitation. Mrs Barbara P. Nicholls recalls the evening that Ted Heath, the famous big-band conductor, was due to visit a patient. The publicity hadn't bargained for a foggy night and, when the celebrity failed to turn up, the gentlemen of the press sloped off. Around midnight, the delayed Ted Heath arrived to be met by just one nurse.

In 1952, when Mr Pumfrey was growing potatoes in the garden of *Roborough* and carrots at 21 Upper Avenue, you could easily believe that there was no "bleep" system at the Princess Alice, that metrication in the hospital was minimal, and that the Salmon Report on "Nursing as a Career" had not even been trawled - never mind thrown back, but can you believe that the Minister of Health was a Mr Harry Comfort? At least the Princess Alice was using sliced bread in the recently extended kitchen.

In the March Dr W.R. Watson was appointed a part-time consultant anæsthetist to the Eastbourne hospitals' group. At the Princess Alice Hospital he anæsthetised Mr Jenkins' patients for his Thursday and Saturday morning operating sessions. Mr Jenkins' routine Saturday morning session (which he worked until 1966, when he switched it to a Monday in the course of the surgical reorganisation that year) is worth a mention now, if only to point out that most hospitals worked quite routinely on Saturdays until the 1950s when, with more married nurses and overtime costs, it became impossible to continue. Most surgeons' families welcomed the change too.

In other changes, Mr A.M. Macarthur commenced as part-time consultant thoracic surgeon in September 1952, while Miss York retired in the December after 30 years at the hospital.

It was also the year Mrs Hassell (née Dow) remembers a Sydney Hudson patient, of Drs Dunlop and Emslie, who had developed a type of pneumonia which did not respond to treatment. Investigations revealed psittacosis, the parrot's disease, and the patient confessed to Sister Coggan that she had been caring for an ill budgerigar. Staff Nurse Brenda Maxted wrote up the case for one of the journals.

By now, most of the staff from the 1920s, having given good service, had retired. Well-qualified and experienced consultants were being appointed and with a capable matron in charge, the hospital was ready to play its full part in the NHS if given the resources.

The "austerity" shadow of the 1940s still fell on the HMC Annual Report for 1951-52 which stated that war damage repairs had not yet been completed. The final reference to war damage was as late as 1952, when repairs to the nurses' home cost all of £23.

The next year perhaps marked the start of a bright new post-war age.

Notes and References

1. *Roborough* was Clifton House School in 1888. It became Roborough School for boys about 1914. The site was bought from Barclays Bank in July 1947.

2. Princess Alice Memorial Hospital, 64th Annual Report, 1947.

3. Medical Officer of Health for Eastbourne, Annual Report, 1948.

4. Eastbourne HMC, catering sub-committee, 10/1/51, min. 320.

5. Medical Officer of Health for Eastbourne, Annual Report, 1949.

6. Keats, J. *Ode to a Nightingale,* 1819. John Keats (1795-1821) who qualified as a doctor, died of tuberculosis.

Chapter 9

A Slice of the National Health Cake

By 1953 most rationing had been abolished and there was the Coronation to celebrate in the June. For the occasion the hospital was decorated with flags and bunting, there were gifts for the patients, entertainment for the staff, and teak garden seats were provided for all the Eastbourne hospitals.

The "Eastbourne Hospitals Patients' Association", formed in 1948 by enthusiasts of the Princess Alice Household Box Scheme (which raised £95000 between 1933 and 1948) and the Ladies Guild, was re-established in 1953 as "The Friends of the Eastbourne Hospitals" by Mr Cecil Ward and Mr G.F. Bowes, to provide extras for patients and staff outside the scope of the NHS. Miss Eileen Peyton took on the work of Secretary with Miss C. Francis as her assistant.

On 15th October 1953 when Princess Alice, Countess of Athlone, once again came to Eastbourne it was to the Nurses' Prizegiving, but with her wrist in plaster having recently sustained a Colles fracture. It had been decided to make this, the 70th birthday of the hospital, a special occasion, but not in quite such a fashion. As it happened, Princess Alice presented the prizes with ease. Incredible as it may seem to-day, every nurse who came onto the platform wore white cotton gloves. Beforehand there was a luncheon at the home of Lt Col Roland Gwynne at which one of the guests was Dr Bodkin Adams. The lunch was a success, but matron, who was sitting next to Dr Adams, says that all he talked about was how much he had just spent on fishing rods; however, his presence was essential because it was his *Rolls Royce* and chauffeur which were used to drive Her Royal Highness from the lunch to the hospital. Mrs Valerie Reid (née Broadbent), a radiographer, recalls HRH's address to the nurses in which she told a story about the rugby player who was having his dislocated shoulder replaced in Casualty. He was shouting and making such a tremendous scene, that one of the nurses pointed out that she had just seen a petite lady deliver a baby with less fuss. 'Is that so ?' exclaimed the rugby player. 'I bet she would have protested just as much if you had tried to push it back again.'

Dr Ian Brown comments that the occasion was the only time the MP of the day ever visited the Eastbourne hospitals.

During 1953 Dr Kenneth Vickery became the MOH, and Dr Lionel H. Wilkinson took up the duties of consultant in physical medicine. Before his appointment Dr Fox was responsible for the physiotherapy clinics, with Mrs D. Kellock as the superintendent physiotherapist: she was replaced by Mr Birch.

The pathology laboratory of the day had no disposables or sterile packs. Dorothy Head sharpened the blood-taking needles and made the swabs, while "Spud" Hudson hand-honed the microtome knives and timed the processing of surgical specimens with the aid of an alarm clock. During 1953 just two pieces of equipment were installed. One, a *Histokinette* which processed the pieces of surgically-removed tissue, marked a significant advance for, as Mr A.G. Newman says, 'it represented the first step towards automation in histopathology'.

29. Nurses' Prizegiving Day 1953. It was held in a marquee in the garden and the photograph is taken at the rear of the hospital with the mortuary roof peeping above the hedge. Centre seated, left to right are Miss Sykes, Lt Col. Roland Gwynne, Miss de Pinto, HRH Princess Alice, Countess of Athlone, Mr Bowes, a Lady-in-waiting, and Mr Glegg {Harry C. Deal}.

In its way the retirement of Mr Lawrence, the head gardener at the Princess Alice, probably signalled as great a change. It was becoming difficult to cope with all the various gardening jobs, there were complaints about the appearance of the flower beds at the front of the hospital and it led to the ending of the vegetable growing which had been a feature of most of the hospitals.

The Revd Mrs Ann Cole (née Sinclair) trained as a nurse at the hospital 1953-56. While she was there the main move to Roborough occurred, 'How lovely - own room, own wash basin and own front-door key. There was no more signing in and out, we were treated as adults.' She remembers that when the West Indies cricket team were playing at the Saffrons, they would come to the Princess Alice and take the nurses dancing on the Pier. Another sport had different associations, 'We were always busy on the orthopædic wards when there was a meeting at Arlington speedway'. Among other student nurses at the time were Brenda Baldock, John Pinelli, John Salt and Sidney Cole.

The *Seaside* Convalescent Hospital at Seaford closed on 31st October 1954. Founded in 1860, it was one of the earliest of its kind in the country, caring for patients from Greater London and the Home Counties, with the aim of helping them recover full strength after serious illness.[1] It had a capacity of 102 beds, although in some years only 48 were in use. During 1953-54, with Dr J.M. Graham as the medical officer and Miss E.J. Youngman the matron, there had been 803 in-patients. The Regional Board concluded that there were sufficient convalescent beds without those at the *Seaside*.

The staff of the laboratories at the Princess Alice and St Mary's Hospitals gave a farewell dinner to Dr Geoffrey Shera on his retirement in November 1954, after 35 years in charge of pathology. Mrs Shera received a bouquet from Miss Dorothy Head, Dr Clifford Taylor presented Dr Shera with a leather wallet, and Mr A.G. Newman, the chief technician, who had replaced Mr F.C. Dixon the year before, spoke of the happy relationship which he had found in the laboratories, largely due to the lead and guidance provided by Dr Shera.

Recollection of a Dr Shera episode still brings a smile to Sheila Baldwin, Laurie Bourne, Gerald Bishop, Hugh Weavers and other members of the staff. William Bickerstaffe, the lab. porter, would collect stale bread from the kitchen, toast it and later take it to the animal house for feeding to the guinea pigs, still required to diagnose certain TB infections. On this occasion he left the toast on a plate and when Dr Shera came in early for tea he spotted the curled-up toast and promptly tucked in, just as the rest of the staff took their seats. Unable to suppress the mirth, Mr Dixon told Dr Shera that he had just eaten the guinea pigs' dinner. 'Far too good for them', was his retort. It didn't appear to do him much harm for he lived to 81.

Dr F.R. Philps, his successor, was based mainly at St Mary's Hospital after the new laboratory opened there in May 1955, as was Mr R.A. Elliston, appointed just beforehand as senior technician.

Later that year an improved mortuary entrance was built at Princess Alice and, to afford greater privacy for bereaved relatives, a small chapel for the mortuary was constructed.

Payment for on-call pathology technicians was introduced in 1955. There were only four (out of the ten non-medical staff in the lab.) who were senior enough to work the on-call rota, so they did one week a month. Not as demanding as you might imagine because most nights they were not called out. Almost three-quarters of their calls were for blood transfusions.

In 1954 Dr Ian Brown, chairman of the staff consultative committee, had suggested that a Sports and Social Club be formed, using as a basis the billiards club at St Mary's Hospital and Mr Wally Manton's cricket enthusiasts. In the event the club was inaugurated, on 1st November 1955, with a committee of Mr R.A. Elliston (pathology) in the chair, Mr M.G. Patrick (works) as secretary, Mr G.H. Cole (administration) treasurer, along with Mrs M.A. Pyne and Miss M. Hartman (physiotherapy), Mr W. Hookham (works) and Mr V. Reynolds (porter).[2] Dr Gordon Masefield, HMC chairman, became the first President.

Sister Acfield was on Arno, Tabor and Gurney, the orthopædic wards. With her were Charge Nurse Donald Wood and Sister Vigor, and in the plaster room enrolled Nurse Flora Clark, assistant Nurse George Flinders and male Staff Nurse Jeffrey Carn. They were kept busy. On Saturday, 4th June 1955, the same day as HRH the Prince Philip Duke of Edinburgh was visiting the Silver Jubilee conference of the Royal Air Forces Association in Eastbourne, a *Sunderland* flying-boat crashed off the pier, one airman was killed and three injured crew were admitted to Tabor. The following Wednesday an aircraftsman, engaged on salvage, was admitted with a broken leg and other injuries after a petrol explosion.

30. View of the front, looking south, *Taormina* and *Harberton* to the right.

About the same time the husband of Sylvia Peters, the TV personality, was admitted, and a seven-month pregnant lady who had broken her femur [thigh bone] was another event. The mother-in-waiting was treated in a Thomas splint and as Sister Ledgerwood (née Foot) says, 'On the day she had a Caesarean section, by Mr Harford-Rees in the Princess Alice theatre, there was more excitement in the hospital than in any TV program'.

The HMC Annual Report for 1956/57 states that the established posts of one house physician and two house surgeons had "been satisfactorily filled during the year", and that a new post of anæsthetic registrar [middle-grade doctor] had been agreed. The housemen still doubled as casualty officers at weekends and each did one other night a week on call. Of the senior doctors, Dr Ben Reid emigrated to Australia, and was replaced as consultant psychiatrist by Dr David Rice.

For 1956-57 the grand total of all the senior medical staff salaries at the Princess Alice, including travel expenses, was £26450. The full list of requests for equipment from the path. lab. for the year 1957-58 was:-

"one heating bath, electric @ £25/15/-;
one binocular Watson microscope 'in fitted case' @ £116;
one hot air steriliser, electric @ £75/3/-."

-items which also have an olde worlde look about them cost-wise, but by now the boilers had been replaced at £3776, new bedside lockers had been bought, and part of the hospital had been rewired. When in September 1956 Miss Mary E. Quick came from Hastings as the appliance officer, she comments, 'I was very proud of the hospital and went round taking photographs of it'. Mrs Pat Rogers, admitted to have her appendix out that year, says her main impression was of the spotlessly clean ward floors.

The 1957-58 Annual Report mentions the two chalets at the Holywell sea front (rented from the Borough Council by the hospital for use by staff) which were said to be well used by the nurses in the summer. The key had to be signed for at the hospital switchboard, but the service was a great boon in the high season for staff and families, when beach space was at a premium. They had been part of Dr Ian Brown's staff-recruiting incentives to "maximise the assets of an English south coast town". Other measures included English tuition for overseas staff, buying good-quality residences near the hospital, and promoting the Sports and Social Club. The chalets were given up in a cost-cutting exercise of the mid-1980s, by which time they had lost some of their popularity.

The mid 1950s witnessed a sad incident when Mr R.S. "Spud" Hudson, one of the senior laboratory technicians at the hospital, skilled and knowledgeable, with a great flair for his work, was seen by a cleaner to come in unusually early one morning and take 'something out of a cupboard. He seemed preoccupied and in a hurry to leave'. As was learnt later, the something was cyanide and he had hurried up to Beachy Head where he took a fatal dose, in a moment of stress.

The period 1956-57 could be described as the Dr John Bodkin Adams' years. Why happenings in a little provincial town to an otherwise ordinary general practitioner, who was also SHMO anæsthetist at the Princess Alice, should hit the world press is still a wonder. Mr Hugh Weavers, who was in the laboratory for ten years from April 1949, says that he never understood why Dr Adams' style of practice was so unlike his partners. He remembers Dr Shera calling the staff together for a confidential meeting about Dr Adams in 1954. Dr Shera asked them to be vigilant because Dr Adams might be forging doctors' signatures to procure NHS services for his private patients. Dr Shera's son, Michael, says that his father was convinced Dr Adams was a murderer and would say that the wrong victim was chosen for the trial.

Dr Adams had a cottage in the Dicker during the war, knew Sister Ruth Saunders' family, who farmed nearby, and on one occasion asked her to accompany him to a formal dinner. Twenty or more years later and miles away from Eastbourne, if she said she came from Eastbourne, hospital staff would ask, 'Did you know Dr Bodkin Adams?' And when she said, 'Yes, and I even went out to dinner with him once', they would reckon she was lucky to be alive.

On the other hand there are many people in Eastbourne who 'won't hear a word said against him'. Some believe that a certain clique "had it in for him". Many nurses emphasise that, whatever his faults, he could not have done more for his poorest patients, whom he treated as well as the richest. Always with an eye for income-generation, he practised ear-piercing for *Clements the Jewellers* as a side-line, this was when the procedure was performed solely by doctors. That he would never charge the nurses if they went to him to have their ears pierced probably has no bearing on his popularity.

In August 1956 Dr A.C. Sommerville, the coroner, held an inquest on Mrs "Bobbie" Hullett, one of Dr Adams' patients who had committed suicide by barbiturate overdosage. When the coroner commented, 'There has been an extraordinary degree of careless treatment' and, when Superintendent Hannam of Scotland Yard was identified in the courtroom, the story broke to headlines of "400 WIDOWS MURDERED" in almost every country of the world.

While the interest could be understandable by December when Dr Adams was charged with murder, it seems incredible that, as early as September, articles were appearing about the Eastbourne doctor in magazines all over Europe.

Part of the interest in the trial was that it was a rare example of a doctor being accused of murdering a patient by pursuing a line of treatment. It also achieved fame as the longest murder trial when the penalty for murder was hanging and, following the adverse publicity, it was a central reason for the Criminal Justice Act of 1967 which introduced restrictions on media reporting at the committal stage.

Dr Adams was accused of murdering a Mrs Edith Morrell in 1950. He escaped as a result of a brilliant defence by Mr Geoffrey Lawrence, in which he discredited the nurses' testimony, demolished Dr Douthwaite's half-baked theories for the prosecution, and played the masterstroke of not putting Dr Adams in the dock which saved exposing him to questioning by Sir Reginald Manningham-Buller, the Attorney General. For Dr Adams was loquacious and would almost certainly have tied the rope around his own neck when subjected to interrogation by "Bullying Manner", Sir Reginald's nickname.

At a meeting of the Eastbourne Medical Society in the Princess Alice Board Room in May 1957, and having received notice from the *White House* practice, the members pased by 34 votes to 2 the resolution:- "In consequence of the extra publicity which Dr Adams himself and his housekeeper have given to the recent case before the Courts, the Society do not consider this to be in the best interests of the Profession and to have been a very unethical procedure. We therefore call upon Dr Adams to resign from this Society".[3]   Dr Adams tendered his resignation, "I should like to clear up what is evidently a misunderstanding. May I assure you I did my utmost to avoid publicity of any kind, and all that occurred was completely beyond my control, nor have I personally benefited from it".

31. Dr John Bodkin Adams acquitted, April 1957 {photo *Daily Express*}.

Dr Adams was a champion clay pigeon shot and, despite competing in the Manx TT motorcycle race, was not stupid, but he was naïve and misguided. As Dr Basil Barkworth says, 'He could not believe that any line which he thought practical could be outside the law'.

Dr P.H. Venn succeeded Dr Adams in 1957 and also took over Dr Pollard's anæsthetic sessions.

Spring 1957 saw the gift of a beautiful ornamental garden to Princess Alice Hospital in memory of Mr A.H. Crook, by his friends. Some £600 was raised to provide this valuable amenity for the pleasure of patients and staff and as a memorial to a "Friend, Physician and Surgeon". It remains a charming oasis of peace and colour in the hospital grounds.

Visiting every day was introduced that year. Before the 1939-45 war, the visiting time was not just two hours, two days a week, but the two hours were rigorously enforced, and the number of visitors allowed at the bedside was rigidly restricted to two. Bells signified the beginning and end of visiting, and every Sunday and Wednesday queues would build up outside the entrance long before any visitors were allowed in at two o'clock (1400h). Members of a family had to take it in turn to go into the ward so as not to exceed the quota of two visitors at any one time. In 1944 Mrs Cecile Woodford and her month-old baby were classified as two persons for the purposes of the visiting allowance. On the children's wards, up to the 1950s, parents were advised to "leave the little patients" and not to visit them for the duration of their stay "for fear of disturbing them" and giving the nurses a problem in "calming them down".

Clearly, visiting times have changed for the better, but it is possible to have excessive visitors who stay too long for an ill and tired patient. Except for the immediate family, a short call to let them know you are thinking about them is often best appreciated.

Miss Phyllis Newman, the head radiographer since 1939, left in 1957. She thinks her most "rewarding case" was the cold night she was called out to X-ray a burglar who had fallen off a garden fence and broken his leg. When she returned to her digs she found her public-spirited landlord had left a bottle of rum on the stairs "to warm the cockles of your heart".

In the physiotherapy department Miss Barbara Townley, the superintendent, was a large lady who had succeeded Miss Joan Gillett. She had Miss Tonks, Miss Gillian Bishop and Miss Margaret Hartman, who was blind, as senior physiotherapists. Mrs McCutchen was also on the staff. Mr Keith Walker was now the physio. porter. Miss Naomi Fillery, secretary to Dr Wilkinson and in the physiotherapy department since 1951, worked in an office attached to the Roborough unit. Miss Joy Wright was Mr Jenkins' secretary.

About this time Miss Jean Dowden was the Home Sister, Miss E. Levack assistant matron, Miss Addey relief admin. Sister, and Miss Clarke was the night superintendent. Miss Dowden's jobs as Home Sister included running the staff clinic with Dr I.M. Brown, arranging staff medicals, and looking after any nurses with minor ailments, kept in the nurses' home.

On Monday, 25th August 1958, at 0728h, on a pouring wet day at Eastbourne station, a steam-hauled train from Glasgow passed signals at danger, came in on platform 4 and ran into a waiting electric train, the front section of which was full of Eastbourne passengers bound for London. Five persons were killed, including the driver of the local train.[4] By chance, Mr Snowball was passing the station at the time, heard the crash, and went in to help.

The walking wounded were sent to St Mary's Hospital and the seriously injured were admitted to the Princess Alice, including an unknown male, later identified as Robert Caffyn, a member of a well-known local family firm. Mr

Angus Macarthur, the Regional thoracic surgeon, drove at speed from Carshalton in response to an urgent call from Dr Lester. Within ten minutes of arrival, with Dr Venn as anæsthetist, he had opened the chest, to find it full of blood, the diaphragm ruptured and the spleen lying loose in the chest. By staunching the bleeding from the torn splenic artery and by massive transfusion of blood the situation was retrieved. Mr Newman, who rushed the blood bottles for transfusion to the theatre, remarked that at one time there was more blood running on the floor and down the walls than there was in the laboratory. Blood was pumped into the vein while it was being crossmatched by Mr Elliston and Miss Embury. Over a dozen pints [far more than the average person's total blood volume] were transfused to this one patient when the total blood bank stock at Princess Alice, of the required blood group, was only eight. Some extra came from St Mary's, and Dr R.A. Zeitlin, the director of the South London Transfusion Centre, hearing of the accident on the radio rushed ten units (pints) of blood to Polegate station. The family were especially grateful for the care and attention received. They donated funds for the nurses' library and, led by Lady Annie Caffyn, subsequently strove even more unstintingly in fund-raising for the Friends of the Eastbourne Hospitals.

In all 23 casualties went to the Princess Alice, one died the same day and the rest made good progress.[5] Mr James Gray, a local dentist, who travelled daily to his job at Guy's Hospital, escaped uninjured, although he had the dreadful experience of having to climb out of the wreckage over one of the victims. British Railways gave him £10 to cover the cost of having his suit cleaned.

The arrangements for major disasters proved effective, thanks to all the staff pulling together, especially the telephonists, but the two new theatres at St Mary's Hospital, which were ready and waiting albeit not officially open for another month, did not yet figure in the Accident Plan: so most patients were sent to Princess Alice, where there was only one theatre, in which Mr Jenkins had started his operating list. Having got there, many were too ill to be considered for transfer. Fortunately, Geraldine ward was empty, having just been redecorated, and Mr Henry Wilson came down from St Mary's and helped to sort out the casualties. The Annual Report stated, "The plan for major disasters worked well, but showed that with more cases the casualty department could be overwhelmed. The time has come at Princess Alice when only new buildings ... will satisfy."

In 1958 the consultant general surgeons (Mr Henry Wilson, Mr Peter Smith, Mr Geoffrey Estcourt and Mr Laurence Snowball) were on-call one week-end in four, with the Princess Alice and St Mary's alternating as the admitting hospital. The anæsthetists (Drs Frank Gillett, Bill Watson, Basil Kent, John Linacre and Paul Venn) did one week-end in five, and the physicians (Drs Duncan Churcher, Mark Lester and Alfred Emslie) worked a one-in-three Sunday rota.

When Doreen Acfield, the Sister of the orthopædic wards, married Miss Newman's brother in 1958 she was replaced by Sister Ann Foot (who later married Mr R. Ledgerwood, one of the chefs) and Mr Jeffrey Carn. Staff Nurses Esther Field and Anne Atkinson (later Sister Petitt) were on Geraldine ward at various times.

In April 1958 patients' records changed from being alphabetically filed in the departments to a numerical system with the records kept in a medical records library store, very much as to-day. Mr Sargant initiated this digital system and when he left, in 1959, his successor as group medical records officer, Mrs Dorothy Morris, continued the change-over. Mrs Mary Reynolds took over as medical records clerk at the Princess Alice in April 1959, when Miss Susan Trinder was about to leave on marriage. Miss Connie Lambert was the admissions clerk, followed in 1964 by Miss Josie Hemmings and later by Miss Kathleen Murphy. Either in her office near Tabor ward, or later at the District General Hospital, Mrs Reynolds was to stay for 28 years.

32. The main entrance Carew Road 1956. The foundation stone, just to the left of the figure, and the terra cotta plaque above are still visible.

Other changes included the conversion of the property 21 Upper Avenue into doctors' flats, and in the autumn of 1959 better waiting facilities were provided for visitors. This extensive reconstruction altered the front of the hospital. It included a new hospital entrance porch where relatives could be seated, and the conversion of matron's office, on the right of the front door, into an enquiry office and telephone switchboard room. One inadvertent product of the alterations was that the foundation stone, which had been displayed on the front wall, became hidden in the plaster of the new porters' room to the left of the entrance.

Matron de Pinto says that before her office was converted, it contained a floor-to-ceiling cabinet in which were kept the nurses' records and, on the top shelf, three items of special interest: a pin-cushion, said to have belonged to Princess Alice; a case containing the ceremonial trowel, used to lay the 1931 foundation stone; and a leather-bound visitors' book, containing many Royal signatures. If the hospital closes in 1994 the intention is to donate such items to the Towner Local History Museum.

The demand for beds eased a little when admissions to All Saints Hospital, newly taken-over by the NHS, commenced in October 1959. It provided 66 beds for elderly patients, although these were offset somewhat by the closure of St Luke's Home [the *Dolphin Court* site] in December 1959. The Secretary of State did not, however, agree to the full use of All Saints until 1961.

The Princess Alice continued to give full value. The in-patient costs per week remained steadily in line with inflation, for 1959-60 they were £29/11/7d [£29.58p]. This compared with £35 at the Maternity Home.

Dr Robert Moyle, dermatologist, and Norman Gray, dental surgeon, retired in 1959, the latter after nearly 35 years' service, and the former at the age of 73. Among the housemen in the 1950s who became local doctors were Dr E.G.A. Riddick (née Wylie), Dr J. Rhodes, Dr J.M. Sinclair and Dr J.H. Williamson.

Dr D.G. Churcher retired in March 1960, with Dr J.C. Linley-Adams succeeding him in the October. With the Bodkin Adams case in mind, he used a family name and hyphenated the Linley- to make a clear distinction. When he was thinking of applying for the position he asked colleagues in London whether they thought his name would count against him, to which the reply was, 'At least you can be sure of being short-listed, for the appointment panel will be mightily curious to see what this Dr Adams looks like'. In the January Dr M.F.P. Marshall had been appointed a clinical assistant to the ophthalmic department. When Miss Peyton retired, Miss Scotchmer came in as the almoner.

Miss E. Guillot, who followed Miss Clarke as night superintendent, points out that the Princess Alice was very much a busy general hospital: Crowden and Geraldine wards were acute surgical, Cavendish and Sydney Hudson acute medical, and there were the two children's wards and three orthopædic wards. Even so, at night there were only three trained staff, herself and two Sisters, to look after all the wards as well as Casualty. 'If one was off and the other was stuck in Casualty, the patients had to wait for "post-ops" and night sedations: and no amount of representations to Miss Goodland had any effect'.

That year 2462 patients were admitted into the hospital's 120 beds, and there were 41510 out-patient attendances. Among the "acute surgicals" admitted into Gurney ward for a double hernia operation in 1960, Mr John Stevens recounts that Mr Estcourt told him, 'I have done both sides and can do no more'.

The Staff Sports and Social Club held numerous functions, including a Fête in July 1960, to raise money for the building fund towards a centre for the club. As the HMC wrote in their report, "their activities continued to give a pleasant diversion to many members of the staff" - or, as the staff put it good-humouredly, 'They were always trying to wheedle money out of you, if it wasn't a beetle drive it was something else'.

There were plans afoot in 1961 for a new hospital as part of the ten-year plan by the Ministry of Health.[6] The HMC considered, 'that the most suitable site is the "island" on which Princess Alice stands'. The committee did not get carried away, however, and keeping their feet on the ground, proceeded to provide a new demonstration room and laboratory in the nurses' training school at *Harberton*, install central heating in 17 and 21 Bedfordwell Road, and put a cool-chamber in the mortuary at a cost of £912.

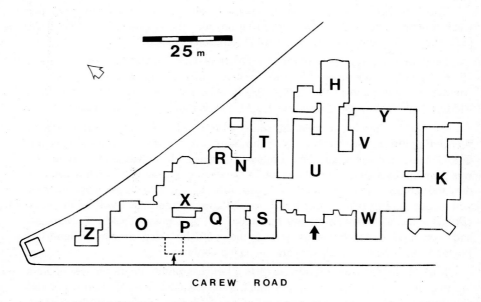

25 m

CAREW ROAD

33. Plan of the hospital 1960. **H** is the Cavendish/Sydney Hudson block, **K** the children's wards, **N** is the fracture clinic, **O** the out-patient department, **P** Casualty, **Q** Arno ward, **R** theatre, **S** Gurney, **T** Tabor, **U** kitchen, **V** Geraldine, **W** Crowden, **X** radiology, **Y** pathology, **Z** old air-raid shelter. The large solid arrow marks the main entrance; the smaller one is the Casualty entrance.

In the dispensary, soon to be called pharmacy, Miss Foxall remained the chief pharmacist, assisted by Mr J.C. Trinder, senior pharmacist since 1957, and Miss D.G. Martin, who had joined in October 1959. Miss K.A. Lomond (later Mrs Irwin-Carter) moved to St Mary's in 1959. They were assisted by Mrs Elphick and Mrs McConnell. The pharmacy porter was Mr Constable and, before him, Mr Facey. Frank Constable went on to be a pharmacy assistant. The pharmacy also supplied All Saints, the Maternity Home and the Leaf Hospital. If anything was needed for the Mat. Home after the boxes had gone, Mr Leslie Ingham, the gardener, would collect it on his bicycle.

As the pharmacy was so small, the garage next to the cottage was used as its wet store, the dry store was under Cavendish ward, and IV solutions [for injections] were kept in an old air-raid shelter. During the 1960s the pharmacy was extended to provide more work space and an office. Miss Delphine Martin was surprised by the lack of equipment, and also that before the pharmacy could purchase even a ten-litre electric mixer, permission had to be obtained from Dr A.G. Emslie, chairman of the pharmaceutical committee.

Other staff at the time included Miss Joan Biglin, Dr Fox's secretary (who was a heavy smoker and died of lung cancer), Miss Jean Hardy (later Harris), the matron's secretary (whose sister, Doreen, had been matron's secretary before her), and May, the matron's maid. Mrs Harris says that her loveliest memory is of choir-singing at Christmastime, when the nurses turned their cloaks inside out to display the satiny red lining which reflected the lantern lights.

In the catering department there was Mrs A.L. Hayward and Mrs Smith, and the telephone exchange was worked by Betty Kay, David Broomfield and, unchangingly, George Bradley. The general porters were Messrs J. Breach, S. Pilbeam, J. Wilkins and, an ever-present, the head porter Vic. Reynolds. Mr R. Harmer was the electrician, and Mr W. Clarke the carpenter, succeeded by Mr Les Feint: it was his father who drove the van which transported laundry and pharmacy items between St Mary's and Princess Alice.

There were many nursing changes in the early 1960s. Sister Coggan, who everyone agreed was a super ward Sister, left Sydney Hudson ward to look after her aged parents. Mrs Miriam Pratt says that she will never forget the kindness of Sister Coggan when her son was a patient with leukaemia in 1958. Sister Bearne followed her as ward Sister; and Staff Nurse M. Barrett (later Sister Tutt) was on the ward at the time. Staff Nurses Foord and Nulan were there around 1964.

Sister Simmonds, now Sister Hunnisett after marriage, left Casualty when she became pregnant, and Sister McIlwraith, who had been the Theatre Sister since just after the war, replaced her. As Mr Henry Wilson says, 'Sister McIlwraith was a splendid theatre Sister. She had a sense of humour, but stood no nonsense. She had a difficult theatre at PA, where the anæsthetic and sterilising rooms opened directly onto the main corridor.' Mrs Audrey Swann (née West) says that, 'Nursing in the theatre was a nightmare for me. Sister would shout her orders and if you did not understand immediately it was common to have something thrown at you. Mind you the theatres were very cramped and one wonders how so many operations were carried out successfully.' Nurse M. Browne, now with the In-Service Training Unit at *Harberton,* who met her future husband when he was a patient on Gurney ward, recalls that Sister McIlwraith would test the senior theatre nurses on the purposes of the contents of the emergency bag. It included a rubber sheet, and when nobody guessed its use, Sister would say, 'For kneeling on if the ground is wet'.

Others in the theatre at the time included Staff Nurse Janice Venn (née Green) and Staff Nurse Babbage. The theatre porter Mr Patterson married Staff Nurse Kerwin about the mid-1960s. Sister G. Foot, Sister J. Hesling and Staff Nurse V. Hanbury worked in Casualty, and assistant nurse Edwin John Porter was there for some 25 years. Mr S.E.J. Braiden, a local ambulanceman for some 23 years, says, 'I well remember Mr Porter, such an efficient man in every possible way - surely the very backbone of the department he served'.

Among long-serving ward assistant staff were Miss M. Winchester, Mrs M. Edwards, Mrs E. Clark (whose daughter Jennifer, now at the District General, started in microbiology at the Princess Alice laboratory) and Mrs Hollis, Arno ward domestic.

Sister Potter left the children's ward after 15 years to do private nursing: sadly, she was to die of multiple sclerosis in the mid-1970s. She was followed by Sister Drury, who had been at the Leaf Hospital, but came to Princess Alice from the Great Ormond Street Children's Hospital, London, and who remained Sister from 1961 to 1967. Dr Leslie Scott points out that there were children's wards and out-patients at both Princess Alice and St Mary's hospitals until the opening of the District General Hospital in 1976. 'Ideally it would have been better to have one department, but we had to keep the two wards as the children's orthopædic and ENT surgery was at the Princess Alice, while the general surgery was mainly at St Mary's, and all Eye operations were there. We enclosed the open-air balcony at the Princess Alice so that two extra rooms were made available, but over the years I tended to centralise the medical cases at St Mary's.'

After being closed for a while, part of the children's ward was re-opened in January 1961 on a five-day basis for ENT patients. During the changes Staff Nurse Dorothy Pavey found a baby's pneumonia jacket tucked away at the back of the linen cupboard, "used to prevent chill in fevers". It must have been there some time for neither she nor Sister Potter had seen one before.

In April 1961 the Revd E.L. Sporne had to retire through ill-health and was replaced by the Revd W.D. Giddey as Group Chaplain. That summer saw another great change when Miss de Pinto, the "charming and determined" matron, whose efficiency was admired by all, resigned on marriage - and became the step-mother of John Wells. Miss D.V. Lowarch was appointed in her place.

The new matron was a firm disciplinarian. According to Mrs M. Porter (née West) she insisted on nurses wearing lace-up shoes, hair above their collar, and no cardigans. She brought new ideas, but also upset some of the nursing staff. Sadly, one of the first conflicts was with Sister Lancaster who, brought up in an age when patients vomited for hours after an anæsthetic, accompanied all her patients to and from the theatre. This was not a unique approach, Sister Harrison did the same. It was true to say that possibly the most dangerous time of an operation was as the drowsy patient returned from the theatre, often in the hands of an inexperienced porter or probationer nurse, and it was far from unknown for a patient, with an obstructed airway, to be found blue and almost moribund at the ward entrance. Anæsthetics, however, were improving (muscle relaxants had been introduced in 1942) and Sisters who went to and fro between the ward and theatre could not be on the ward, which is where the matron wanted Miss Lancaster to stay. Finally, in 1962, Miss Lancaster threw her locker keys on the matron's desk and stalked out of the Princess Alice. Not that she gave up nursing, not a bit of it. She went as matron to the Bell Hostel, a Church of England Home for unmarried mothers in Salehurst Road (founded by Mrs Bell in 1886 as the Upwick Vale Rescue Home). After it closed in 1974 she went to Abbeyfield House, an old people's home in Charleston Road, where she nursed those who were far younger than herself. Eventually, she found she had an ovarian cancer, considered that she had done her life's work and refused all treatment.

Other senior nurses came to the end of their working careers in the early 1960s. One was Miss H.L. Goodland, the senior assistant matron, described as "very prim and proper", who took Mr Peter Smith to task for using the word "bum" when talking to a patient with piles. 'How can I protect nursing standards and etiquette when you use such words?' Her place was taken by Miss E.G. Carter. Another to go was Miss N. Sykes, the principal tutor of the Nurses' Training School for 18 years, who retired in July 1962 to be succeeded by Miss V.M. Watts. Mrs E.M. Childs, who had helped to launch the Enrolled Nurse Training School in July 1962, also left, to be replaced by Miss D. Hart.

Other nurses on the teaching staff about this time included Miss Knight, Miss Ashby and Mr Myers. In the first years of her retirement Miss Sykes compiled a history of the Eastbourne School of Nursing, which she produced in 1971.

These comings and goings represented substantial change, for Miss de Pinto and Miss Goodland, although different personalities, had worked in tandem, the matron being the "organiser" and the senior assistant matron, the "nurse".

Sister C. Bruff replaced Sister Lancaster on Geraldine and Crowden wards. She married male nurse Carn, but was to die tragically when thrown from her horse a few years later.

Dr Doris Rose died in 1962. She had a fall down unfamiliar stairs whilst staying with friends over the Christmas holiday. After apparently recovering, she became depressed, convinced that she could not maintain the high standards she had set herself, and took an overdose. The extra burden thrown on Mr Sydney Freedman, the remaining ophthalmic consultant, was greatly alleviated by Dr Frank Marshall, a clinical assistant in the department, who later became a hospital practitioner. Mr C.G. Tulloh was appointed in Dr Rose's place in February 1963, but left for another post that July.

In December 1962 the Staff Sports and Social Club moved into old tool-sheds and garages behind *Roborough* which had been converted into a dance hall, bar and snooker rooms by Mr Mildenhall's Works department. Such progress was only possible with the active support of the HMC, and Mr E.G. Watt, the chairman, opened the building. The cost of £3624 was shared by the club and the Friends. The club continues in good health and now also has the Sports Complex at the District General Hospital. The combined venues cater for many interests, from photography to swimming and from old-time dancing to squash. Management support has continued with Dr I.M. Brown, president from 1960 to 1976, followed by Dr B.S. Kent (1976-85), Dr S.J. Surtees (1985-91) and at present Mr D.G. Garlick. As is always the case, in such matters, it is the members who make the club; the pioneers have been mentioned, but the club would not be the success it is to-day without the hard work of members such as Mrs F. Hutchinson, Mr A. Leaney, Mr A.G. Page, and Mr L. Pain.

When Mr Page, the deputy finance officer to the Eastbourne hospital group from 1948 and treasurer to the club, died in 1962, Mr Don Smalley was a happy choice as his replacement. He remains as the Sports and Social Club treasurer after over 30 years.

Mr H. Mildenhall, the group engineer, introduced a system of "planned maintenance", a system of inspections to avoid breakdowns. It worked well, until applied rigidly by the Ministry of Health, when you couldn't get any repairs done because the Works staff were busy oiling door hinges, as strictly laid down in the maintenance schedule for the day.

Other improvements in 1962 were the purchase of an ex-nursing home at 3 Upper Avenue for use as a psychiatric clinic, and new equipment installed at a cost of £3500 in the X-ray department, where Miss B.J. Perkins was the group superintendent radiographer and the X-ray porter was Mr Arthur Biddlecombe. Miss Joan Biglin was Dr Fox's secretary; later she went to All Saints Hospital.

Not to be left behind, the Friends bought lightweight, stethoscope-type headphones for the patients' hospital radio system, and Eric Garrett, chairman of the Gramophone Society, compered radio request programs at the hospital during 1963. In turn, the W(R)VS put a tea chalet outside the casualty department.

At this time every ward had a piano for entertainment and for accompanying religious services, which were still held on the wards. The Revd Denys Giddey discovered that all were suffering badly from the ravages of moths, rust and old age, and he decided on an appeal to the public for replacements. It was just at the time that the public at large were desperate to find space for the TV set and what better way than to get rid of the unused piano? Consequently, there was an enormous response to the appeal, with two grand pianos, in the last stages of decrepitude, being deposited on the front steps of the Princess Alice Hospital without any notice whatsoever. Most of the instruments which Denys Giddey went to inspect were no better than the ward specimens, but suitable replacements were eventually selected with ease.

Between November 1962 and spring 1963, the two children's wards were extended and modernised, at a total cost of £15715. Anne Elizabeth ward, which had acted as a five-day ENT ward, was extended to make a complete paediatric unit of 18 beds. Michael Francis ward was refashioned by a prefabricated timber extension to provide 17 beds for female orthopædic patients and renamed Arno. The old Arno ward now formed part of a larger casualty department and theatre.

34. Mr S.A. Jenkins.

Sister Drury, Staff Nurse Pavey (née Elliman) and Dr Scott had planned a larger modern children's ward, with treatment room and recovery area, but to their chagrin Mr Mildenhall's finances only ran to extra bed spaces and an extra room. On the other hand, Sister Ann Ledgerwood (née Foot) says that the Arno move gave much improved conditions for the orthopædic ward patients and the adapted casualty area made a better service possible.

The extended orthopaedic facilities were largely at the behest of Mr Jenkins, who always considered himself to be a top orthopædist, but who became disillusioned when the nursing staff numbers deteriorated so badly that the beds could not be opened. He began to look forward to retirement and to play the Stock Market. He had always been rather bombastically intolerant of any slipshod approach by his staff, and he now began to berate even the patients if they did not come up to his standards. "Jenks" simply would not tolerate anyone chewing gum in his department; while any young motor cyclist, who had wrapped himself around a lamp-post, brought upon himself another lambasting if he answered "Yip" instead of "Yes" to Aubrey Jenkins' questions.

Mrs Spicer recalls a famous occasion when Mr Jenkins kept the whole clinic waiting "for what seemed hours, because the curtains of the cubicles had been changed and he refused to start the clinic until the *status quo* was restored".

His behaviour contrasted with the composure of Mr Snowball, the other orthopædic surgeon, although, as Nurse Clark says, 'They got on well with each other', and Philip Jenkins, Mr Jenkins' son and a local dentist, agrees 'They hit it off, even though they were as different as chalk and cheese'. Laurence Snowball was not only highly qualified, he was also a devout man, who prayed silently before each operation. He was not "pushy", he lived up to his evangelical ways and tended to reply to Jenks with, 'If you say so' or, 'I'm sure it is all for the best'.

Sister Ann Ledgerwood ("Footie") who worked in the orthopædic unit for 21 years from 1955 has many happy memories. 'Mr Jenkins would see any babies born with talipes equinovarus [a deformed foot] at St Mary's or the Maternity Home, and bring them to the Princess Alice the next day for their Denis Browne splints. To see their little feet made straight again gave a feeling of real satisfaction. In 1956 we had Mr Henry Wilson as a patient, with a compound fractured tib. and fib. [broken leg, with open wound] after a skiing accident, and we were all, especially junior nurse Mary Barrett, a little apprehensive about looking after him, but we had no need to worry, he was a wonderful patient.

'I found Mr Jenkins a good consultant who did a marvellous job and all those years in orthopædics were for me a pleasure to work.' Among other members of the department there was Dr Colin Barton, houseman, later Casualty Officer, Charge Nurse Donald Wood, who trained at "PA" and later became an instructor, Sister Hilda Sacker, on Arno for many years, Max Astridge, a plaster room orderly for a long time, who was exceptionally kindly and helpful to the patients, and Marjorie Winter, ward orderly, without whom the unit could hardly have managed, which could also be said for enrolled Nurse Flora Clark, "Clarkie".

Mrs Margaret Porter (née West) says 'Mr Jenkins was very supportive of his staff, his "girls" as he called us, and he encouraged me to go on with my training. I recall one ward round when he was explaining an operation and I asked, "What is fascia?". He likened it to "the streaks in what the butcher calls a silverside of beef" and he held up his tutorial while he explained fascia as a covering of the muscles, before asking permission to continue'.

It is said Aubrey Jenkins well demonstrated the not uncommon dilemma facing the 55-year-old surgeon. If techniques suddenly and dramatically change, as was happening with hip replacements with the introduction of the Charnley-type after 1962, do you continue with the well-tried methods at which you are at ease, but (we will say) mean the patient has to stay in hospital ten days, or do you retrain for a technique in which you are never quite at home and at which you will never become quite so slick before you come to retirement, but means (if all goes well) that the patient can be discharged at eight days ?

"Jenks" also behaved in an insular way with his junior medical staff, and failed to understand that they had grown up and developed since they had been with him. Having said all that, he always defended his staff - he would say, 'If they need telling off, I'll do it' - and he was also a notable plantsman with excellent specimens of *Viburnum mariesii,* and a great character with an abundance of energy who did much for orthopædic surgery in Eastbourne. In

Sister Ledgerwood's words, 'If he knew you would work efficiently and would stand up to him when he started to be difficult, in my opinion, you could not find a better man to work with'.

To return to the nursing shortage, 13 surgical beds were closed, apart from the inability to make full use of the orthopædic beds. It had been a time of many retirements and clear-outs, which possibly had a temporary adverse effect on nursing numbers, but the main reasons were a pennypinching, six-month national standstill on recruitment imposed by the Ministry of Health, and the reduction of the nurses' working week to 42 hours.

The first mature student nurse to train at the Princess Alice was Miss J. Hesling, who started her 30 years of nursing in 1962. 'I have many happy memories of nursing at the PA, although there were sad occasions; I have a vivid memory of a young lad on Sydney Hudson ward with Fallot's Tetralogy, a congenital heart disease, who was one of the few to survive into their teens. Only those who nursed him were allowed to view the post-mortem and even though I felt giddy at the time, I have never forgotten Fallot's Tetralogy and the four component anatomical abnormalities.'

35. Staff of the orthopædic department, Christmas 1967. Standing are Ann Ledgerwood "Footie" and Donald Wood; those sitting include Max Astridge and Flora Clark "Clarkie".

Among other changes in the sixties and seventies was the earlier mobilisation of surgical patients, with improved anæsthetics and easier control of anaemia, infection and pain. Even as recently as 1960, Mr Clifford Jones says he was kept in bed for three weeks, the first week at total bed rest - and this after breaking his nose and going in for a straightforward, minor ENT operation. In Mrs Pavey's words, 'No longer did hernias stay in bed for three weeks: lying flat for the first fourteen days'. The nurses' work was also eased with dipsticks for testing urines (in place of boiling up with Benedict's solution, or adding drops from bottles labelled *Tincture of Guaiacum* and *Ozonic Ether*) and more drugs were available in tablet form or as a dose-related injection (instead of doling out spoonfuls from a stock bottle, or preparing each injection by hand) - although morphine was still in tablet form and dissolved in sterile water in a teaspoon heated over a spirit lamp. Mrs Pavey says that soluble aspirin, by easing the pain of swallowing, was the greatest boon in persuading post-op. tonsillectomy patients to eat.

Mr Harry Pimm retired from the staff in April 1963, and Miss I. M. Thompson was appointed consultant dental surgeon in his place.

The 8th of August 1963 was the day of the Great Train Robbery, but for one little six-year-old it was a night of greater disaster for he was badly injured in a car crash which killed his mother and mortally injured his father. When Sister Drury came on duty she could hear him calling, 'Mummy, mummy, if you loved me you would come'. Needless to say, the whole ward loved him and spoilt him. His first smile came after Sister Drury, having heard that Billy Smart's Circus was coming to Kings Drive (later the site of the new hospital), had arranged with the Circus and the Police for the elephants to make a diversion and encircle the Princess Alice site with the ringmaster announcing, 'Greetings to Paul and all the children'. That was the start of his full recovery and Paul now has children of his own. An amazing coincidence with the train robbery was that the family were returning from their caravan which, by chance, happened to be parked near a hide-out of the robbers and, as the father was the leading member of a shooting club, the police found guns in the wrecked car.

Almost as dramatic was Robin, aged nine, knocked down by a van and unconscious for three weeks. 'We did everything for him and talked to him, but there seemed little hope until one night a young student nurse with her back to him heard him say, very slowly,"Hello", which she greeted by bursting into tears'. Robin also recovered with no ill-effects and returned regularly to the ward for a kiss and a hug until he was a strapping teenager.

Sister Drury says that being Sister of the children's ward was one of the happiest times of her life. 'We admitted ENT and orthopædic children and any overflow from St Mary's.' She was a great supporter of open visiting times for children. 'I started open visiting on my first day and, apart from the admin. complaining that I hadn't gone through the proper channels, the ward never looked back.' As one of the Records department staff remarked, 'Isn't it strange you never hear children crying on the ward these days?'

In October 1963 Mr George Cole, the deputy hospital secretary, moved from the Princess Alice to be hospital secretary at All Saints and Downside hospitals, while Mr Pumfrey continued at Princess Alice. Mr John Carden (of the Estates department) is another of those who affirm 'Ben Pumfrey was a real gentleman. One day I was doing some pipe work under the floor of matron's office, when I heard Miss Lowarch jumping up and down, yelling, "Get out! Get out!" I didn't realise she was referring to me, until Ben appeared, having crawled under the floor boards in his best suit, to ask if I would come away until the matron had finished interviewing. Sister McIlwraith, known as "Tatty", was quite a different character. When I was sent to the theatre to do a job she said I couldn't come in and that was that. So I said I couldn't wait around, whereupon she said I'd better come in. She was quite approachable after that - as I often found was the case.'

Mr Jack Boniface says 'Ben Pumfrey never hurt anyone. One day I was asked to do a repair job in the kitchen, but I couldn't get access because of the *Aga* and the cook reported me to Mr Pumfrey. When I explained the situation to him he said he would have a talk with the cook. I followed him to see what he would do only to hear him say to the cook, "I've seen Mr Boniface and it won't happen again", which I was told was his standard response'.

When Sister McIlwraith moved from the operating theatre to Casualty she had been followed by Sister Janice Venn (née Green) and, after she left on marriage, by Sister P.F. Caine who went on to be in charge of the District General Hospital theatres until her retirement in 1990. Sister Newcombe was in charge of the group theatres in the early 1970s, when Staff Nurse W.A. Fitzpatrick was at the Princess Alice theatre. Sister Venn recalls that, when she started at the Princess Alice theatre in 1955, the gas-heated sterilisers had to be turned off when Dr Pollard anæsthetised for ENT because he was still using the inflammable "open ether" technique, and Mr Cuffey continued to use a guillotine.

A new chapel, for patients and staff, was dedicated by the Bishop of Lewes on 17th December 1963. The old one was difficult of access down a narrow stair, whereas its replacement, a "semi-permanent construction", along the Carew Road frontage between *Taormina* and *Harberton,* was more accessible by ambulant patients, and enabled the old chapel to be used as part of the Eye department. The cost of £1500 came from voluntary sources. About the same time 15a Upper Avenue was bought and used as a house for the chaplain until 1980, and there was a pharmacy extension at a cost of £1014.

On 1st April 1964 Mr Norman Shuttleworth joined Mr Sydney Freedman, as Dr Rose's successor in the Eye department, replacing Mr B. Shrivastava who had acted as the locum.

Two months later Dr Richard Philps left the pathology department to join the staff of University College Hospital and was replaced by Dr John Surtees. Pathology retained part of each department (including blood banks) at both the main hospitals, although all histology preparation work was at the PA. Mr Jack Newman continued as the senior technician, with Mr Colin Alabaster in charge of microbiology at Princess Alice, and Mr Robert Elliston at St Mary's Hospital.

In the autumn of 1964 Mr R.H. Botsford was appointed deputy secretary to the group, and Mr J. Griffiths as supplies officer. Miss V.G. Digman remained the principal secretary at "29".

In January 1965 Miss D.V. Lowarch resigned and moved to a post in the north. Unpopular with her staff, rightly or wrongly, she bore the brunt of the blame for the nursing shortages, although possibly the most cogent comment on the staffing situation was in the HMC Annual Report, "... the National Health cake is shrinking and losing its sweetness, Eastbourne badly needs a slice". Eastbourne had a deficiency of 175 hospital beds, based on the Regional Board's target of 4.4 per 1000 population. On top of the deficit, nursing shortages meant there were five beds closed at Downside and 28 at Princess Alice.

Miss Carter acted-up until the appointment in May of Miss N.A. Davies, who came from Stoke Mandeville Hospital, and had experience in recruitment.

Mr J.A. (Tim) Turner, a GP in Hailsham, who had an FRCS qualification, did a clinical assistantship in the orthopædic department from January 1965 until his retirement in 1987. At first he worked five sessions a week, as he said, almost half-time and his concern was that a patient would have a heart attack while he was operating in Eastbourne; fortunately such an eventuality never arose.

Everyday, except Thursdays, Mr Turner took the large mid-day clinic, seeing as Sister Ledgerwood says, 'All the fractures from Casualty sustained since about tea-time the previous day. It has to be said that the fracture clinics tended towards crowded chaos because the patients could not be given strict times to attend. Mr Turner was very understanding and a great antidote to SAJ'.

The spring of 1965 brought quite a few accidents; the routine, as in March when two women were admitted "very poorly" after a car accident at Polegate crossroads; the local, as in May when a workman was admitted after a cliff fall at Beachy Head; and the exceptional, such as the bus accident on 22nd June near the *Lamb Inn,* when 29 people (including two pedestrians) were injured.[7] All brought more casualties to the orthopædic unit of the hospital.

There was still some mileage in playing around with the visiting times. Changing the times on the general wards to 1400-1700h and 1800-2000h daily was given a trial, but it was not a success and the times reverted back to shorter periods, with the ward Sister given discretion to allow visiting at other times. The surgical wards which introduced "unrestricted visiting" were disconcerted when some relatives turned up early in the morning with *Thermos* flasks and sandwiches, intent on camping round the patient's bed all day.

As part of the policy to encourage staff to Eastbourne and to keep them there, *Mawhood House,* a block of six flats in Bedfordwell Road, was purchased to give three flats for Sisters and three for junior medical staff.

Miss M.K. Chiverton joined the staff in 1965 as Group Medical Records Officer, replacing Mrs Dorothy Morris on her retirement. Another who retired was Col. I.C. Byrne, the deputy hospital secretary since 1949; he was replaced by

Mr C.R. Dyte, who came from Wolverhampton. Miss M.R. Stonelake also commenced in the pathology department, where agreement was obtained for the spending of £1200 to add a room to the laboratories in order to start a cervical cytology service. Despite a laudatory send-off, for its first years it was starved of funds and could provide only a restricted service.

With the reduction in the incidence of TB, the Mass Radiography Unit paid one of its last visits to Eastbourne in 1965, under the direction of Dr R.G. Rigden. Of 1414 persons X-rayed there were only 12 cases of TB, yet 14 cases of lung cancer were found.[8]

As another comment on the changing times, the medical committee at its meeting on 14th December 1965, recommended disposable syringes and needles for all the group hospitals. By 1971, at a cost of 2.1p each, 61200 syringes of 2ml size were used annually, and 14700 of 20ml size at 3.3p each.

Mr Desmond E. O'Connor Cuffey retired as Consultant ENT Surgeon in 1965, to be succeeded by Mr W.B.L. Downing. Mr Cuffey, said to be "no great shakes as a surgeon", wasn't too grand to stick to what he did well, and he took great care of his patients. He was vastly amused when, just before he retired, he heard a teenage nurse (referring to the heavy nursing load of the increasing numbers of elderly patients) express the view that, "All people over the age of 65 should be put down". She was embarrassed when she realised she had been overheard, until Mr Cuffey said, 'Yes, I can remember, just about, in my teens, when I thought anyone over 30 was past it'. The nurse in question must now be approaching retirement.

Notes and References

1. The first Convalescent Home in England was the Metropolitan Convalescent Institution in 1840. See Frizelle, GM. *The History of the Hertfordshire Seaside Convalescent Home at St Leonards-on-Sea,* (Austin, Hertford 1964), drawn to my attention by Miss Vera Hodsoll.

2. *Eastbourne Medical Gazette,* 1986; **3**: 98.

3. Eastbourne Medical Society, 21/5/1957.

4. *Eastbourne Gazette,* 27/8/58; *Eastbourne Herald Chronicle,* 30/8/58.

5. de Pinto HJ. Hospital's Emergency Plan in Action. *Nursing Mirror* 1958; 1789.

6. Eastbourne HMC, Annual Report, 1960-61.

7. *Eastbourne Herald Chronicle,* 26/6/65.

8. Medical Officer of Health for Eastbourne, Annual Report, 1965.

36. Children's ward 1931, note the rounded open-air balcony and compare with the closed-in view of 1981.

Chapter 10

The Good Old Days and New Ways

In the spring of 1966 work began on a £10020 modernisation scheme for the 60-year-old operating theatre, the main feature being an improved ventilation system costing over £2000.

This was followed on 1st June 1966 by a reorganisation of the surgical services, following an unacceptable lengthening of the waiting lists, mainly because of the increasing population. All accidents were routed to Princess Alice, the St Mary's casualty department was closed and the services centralised at Princess Alice where, over the years, the department had been enlarged about fourfold. The ambulance service would now take accidents and other casualty cases directly to Princess Alice, although poisonings still went straight to St Mary's Hospital. Another change was that on 21st June, after a rearrangement of beds and provision of an Eye clinic at St Mary's, all eye cases were treated there, so the Eye department at Princess Alice closed and all the staff, including Mr Freedman, Mr Shuttleworth, Miss M. Cartledge (the orthoptist) with Nurses Maynard and Pat Ireland, transferred.

The final stage was on 7th January 1967 when most general surgery went to St Mary's Hospital. One effect of the changes was that Mr J.M. Powley, who had replaced Mr Estcourt on his retirement in 1966, seldom operated at Princess Alice after his first few months, even though Mr Estcourt's Tuesday and Friday operating sessions had been there. John Powley does recall having to take his house surgeon from St Mary's in his car to assist at the surgical out-patient clinic, which stayed at the Princess Alice, "because my registrar was expected to hold the leg while Mr Jenkins did his hips".

As part of the alterations Sister Mavis Constable (née Taylor) moved back to Princess Alice (having trained there 1946-50) to look after Geraldine and Crowden ward patients, who were now mainly elderly medical, with a few dermatology and orthopædic cases, and a nurses' sick bay. Sister Constable was happy to look after the skin patients at Princess Alice, although the work was not popular with the nurses. The nurses disliked dermatology because they just could not believe that the cases were not infectious and they feared the disease would spread to their own skin. The two-bed sick bay, by the steriliser, was now mainly used for medical cases.

As more nursing staff became available, Tabor ward was improved at a cost of £1860 and reopened in 1966. Another effect of the new matron was that her flat became available for offices, when she moved to alternative accommodation.

The Friends started their first venture into funding day room additions at the hospital. They were to go on to provide almost every ward in every hospital with a day room. About the same time, from exchequer funds, a sun balcony was added to Arno ward, and an infamous basement area was fitted out as an X-ray film store at a cost of £950.

The year recorded the first mention of kidney units in the medical committee, and another sign of changes ahead was the provision of a staff changing room at a cost of £1300. This was to take account of the trend for fewer nursing staff to be resident, preferring to make their own arrangements, yet needing somewhere to hang their coat when coming on duty.

Among other staff changes, Miss Davies took over as the Maternity Home matron, with the retirement of Mrs Pitslow; Dr M.I. Suleman was appointed medical registrar; Dr Ashforth was given a paid clinical assistant post in anæsthetics, having worked without pay for some ten years; Dr Surtees produced a house officers' handbook;[1] a staff choir was formed under the direction of Miss A. Siggs; a group dance was held at the Winter Garden, with over 900 staff attending - and the epoch-splitting event of the year, the group medical sub-committee was renamed the group medical advisory committee.

A truly momentous occasion was when, in July 1966, the mayor, Mrs Winifred Lee asked Mr Kenneth Robinson, the Health Minister, to receive a local deputation about the need to build a new hospital. Subsequently, in March 1967, he visited Eastbourne and it was the representations of local people, especially the medical staff, which initiated the planning of the new Kings Drive hospital.

Having said that, most of the staff recall his visit to Princess Alice solely because of the intensive cleaning of the corridor lino beforehand. Throughout all the activity the Standing brothers remained steadfast as electrician and painter to the hospital.

For the year 1966-67 Princess Alice Hospital had 110 staffed beds, which were 73% occupied by 2124 patients, who had 1308 operations. Out-patient attendances were 48180 with 20162 X-ray units of work and 40707 physiotherapy units. The group pathology requests of 53242 were no longer separated into the individual hospitals.

The greatest expenditure was £97626 on admin., clerical and ancillary staff salaries and wages, with nurses' salaries next at £82505. Medical and surgical equipment cost £28853, provisions £14628, upkeep of buildings £13102, drugs and dressings £12218, fuel cost £11242, with rates of £3087, and postage, printing and stationery at £2941. There was a credit of £15101 from payment by staff for board, but otherwise the total hospital income was £1617. The average patient cost rose to £55.29p a week, but the most excitement at one of the committee meetings was caused by the disclosure that wigs were costing £4000 a year. Comments by lay members, that patients should buy their own wigs, were stilled to some extent when it was explained that many of the recipients were now cancer patients undergoing treatment, and the cost had doubled because they had to have spare ones.

At least the HMC was quite firm about its policy on TV sets, "to provide them only on long-stay wards and separate day rooms".[2]

In 1967 Sister J. Hesling started as Night Sister at the Princess Alice along with Sister Randall; she continued after the latter's retirement until 1976 when she became Night Sister-in-charge of the Accident & Emergency department at the District General Hospital, from which she retired in October 1992.

Dr Gillett retired in 1967, to continue his activities in the Society of Sussex Downsmen and the Eastbourne Rambling Club. Like his wife, Molly, he had a great interest in the work of the Friends.

Mr Downing moved to Birmingham in 1967 and, after a succession of locums, he was replaced as ENT Surgeon by Mr D.P.C. Williams in July 1969. Bill Downing had not really settled at the Princess Alice: he used to say that the hospital seemed to have a wall around it, which allowed in what it wanted of the NHS, and yet kept out any raucous elements, but his main complaints were of no cover and poor facilities[3]. What had happened, as soon became apparent, was that most of the ENT instruments had belonged to Desmond Cuffey, so when Mr Downing appeared there was no ENT equipment.

At this time Dr Ian Brown was reporting, "the geriatric position is difficult". What he meant was that there were more than 100 patients on the geriatric waiting list, and over the year 36 had died before they could be admitted.[4]

Sir Arnold France, permanent secretary to the Minister of Health, visited in October 1967 to be given full details of the state of the services. Tabor and Crowden wards were closed at the time because Miss Davies, the matron, could not staff them, although Crowden was supposed to be opening for ENT patients. As Mr Jenkins said, and not for the only time, 'I have had six beds closed for seven years,[5] and I have told the GPs not to send patients as there is little possibility of admission'.[6]

By May 1968 Miss Davies was saying that while nursing staff numbers were in excess of the Regional Board's ceiling [ie the number funded by Region], there was still difficulty in staffing the wards.[7] It would appear that the HMC had determined that the service could not be run within the funded nursing establishment and the only way out, if the people of Eastbourne were to have proper nursing care before the new hospital, was to have a gentle overrun.

It is of interest that, as part of a nurse recruitment drive, Richard Crossman, the Minister of Health, wrote to HMCs on 13th May 1970, to say that nurses should not spend time on chores, such as "sterilizing, messages or housekeeping", and that finance should not prevent recruitment. As is customary with politicians, his letter did not enclose a donation, but simply an authority to switch money allocated for other purposes to nurses' salaries. In a perverse way it supported the stance of the HMC.

As usual, the Sports and Social Club held its 1968 Summer Fête in the *Roborough* grounds, and in the medical committee there was also the regular discussion on how to stop casualties going to St Mary's Hospital, now that it had no accident service. This was in the days when people expected any decent hospital to treat all who turned up, and the situation wasn't helped by Mr Glegg (usually an effective pacifier) saying, as he tried to defuse opposition to "one central Casualty unit at PA", that 'any cases who presented themselves at St Mary's would receive attention'. Dr John Rhodes, who had been appointed consultant radiologist in place of Dr Owen Fox in October 1967, suggested changing the name of the Princess Alice "Casualty" to "Accident and Emergency department" or A&E; and this piece of public relations, coupled with two larger notices, in red, at St Mary's saying there was no service at the hospital,[8] seemed to do the trick, although a complaint was received as late as 1971.

For some years a good liaison had existed with a Bible school in Beatenberg, Switzerland, and several nurses came from there to augment the numbers. Another of the innovations of the sixties was to welcome army nurses on the geriatric wards. For their qualification they had to have experience of nursing the elderly - not easy in the services, but a quantity with which Eastbourne was well endowed, so their presence gave mutual benefit.

With Miss Josie Hughes' departure in 1968, Mrs J. Casey (née Cornish) joined the pathology office staff as the full-time secretary to Dr D.C. Taylor, the consultant histopathologist and cytologist, working alongside part-timers Mrs Jean Bedingfield and Mrs Joy Spicer.

Mr G.E. Winchester, the night telephonist at the Princess Alice, retired in April 1968 after 25 years and, in May, *The History of All Saints,* compiled by the Revd W.D. Giddey, went on sale at 2/- [20p].

A "bleep" system was tried in 1968 instead of the *Tannoy* staff-location system, and in 1971 the loud-speakers were removed and replaced by bleeps entirely.

By 1968 there were two weekly VD clinics, run by Dr W. McAleenan - women on Mondays and men on Wednesdays. They were held in the *Roborough* building with Sister Simmonds in charge. Of 78 new cases that year, eleven had gonorrhoea and three syphilis. Mr Hugh Weavers, who dealt with the laboratory specimens after Mr Dixon emigrated to Nelson, New Zealand, in 1953, recalls the juggling needed to compile the annual returns for a clinic which did not lend itself to statistical analysis. All the patients were referenced by numbers, for confidentiality, so it was not easy to be certain which were new cases and which were follow-ups (the patients often hindered rather than helped identification) and it only needed a smudge on a reference figure to raise doubts as to the patient's category and what had been done to whom. Mr Weavers recalls that he and Dr McAleenan used to spread the form out on the floor and one would work vertically and the other across and their figures never coincided in the final sum.

September 1968 was a momentous month for it saw the first meeting of the project team which was to bring the "New Hospital" into being, and it was also Mr Glegg's retirement date, Mr C.R. Dyte succeeding him as group secretary.

37. Medical staff of 1969. Seated from left Dr Lester, Mr Henry Wilson, Dr Scott, Mrs Scott and Mrs Emslie, Dr Alfred Emslie, Dr Ferguson Gow and Dr Ian Brown. Other doctors present include Drs Suleman and Baig.

The allocation from the Regional Board to Eastbourne HMC for the financial year 1968-69 was £1265238, which in the course of the year was overspent by a mere £9000. Even so, this left many good works which needed to be done.

The provisions at Princess Alice cost £1/17/1d [£1.73p] per person per week, and among the capital expenses were a fan-heater and improved doors to stop draughts in the A&E unit, and an attempt to improve the ENT facilities by joining up Crowden and the children's ward at a cost of £4500.

In November 1968 Miss R.F. McCall, audiometrician, organised an exhibition at the Winter Garden for the Hard of Hearing Association. She was later to found the charity, "Link", the British Centre for Deafened People.

The next year Mr F.N. Shuttleworth added a session and ran a School Health Service Eye Clinic at Princess Alice. In 1969 there were 195 new cases and 175 old cases, with glasses prescribed for 90. The same year 26 schoolchildren were referred to the ENT department after audiometry tests at school.

In March 1969 there was a bomb hoax at the Princess Alice operating theatre. The response of the doctors and nurses can be gauged by the HMC minute 5277 of 2nd April: " ... the committee expressed its admiration at the manner in which Mr Jenkins and staff continued working".

On Friday, 21st July 1969, Mrs M.A. Goodchild celebrated her recent 100th birthday anniversary on Geraldine ward, with a tea party arranged, together with her son and daughter-in-law, by Sister Constable and staff. This event also marked the official opening of the day room, which had been erected in 1967, and the HMC had agreed "a small party within a cost of £5" for the occasion.[9] Dr Alfred Emslie (known as "Uncle Alfred" by the nurses) said that she was his first patient to reach 100.

That month Mr D.J. Richards, from the Whittington Hospital, was appointed part-time consultant orthopædic surgeon in place of Mr Snowball, whose Wednesday afternoon operating session had run for 32 years until his retirement.

Mr J.H. Loasby was another who came to Eastbourne; he replaced Mr Mildenhall, who retired as District Works Officer in December 1969. Mr R.H. Cornish remained as deputy.

Drs Michael Cockburn, Peter Nash and Brian Steer were among local doctors who were housemen at the Princess Alice leading up to 1970. Dr Cockburn was notorious for playing "rugby" within the hospital and breaking anything capable of being knocked over by a rugby ball. Dr David Cooper, now a consultant at Worthing, was another junior doctor, and Dr Ilyas Baig was at St Mary's, 'but we had to cover the PA Casualty every other week-end, when you had a room above the theatre. Returning to the hospital I think how pleasant the wards appear - and realise that as housemen we were so rushed we didn't have time to notice them'.

Mr P.L. Brooks succeeded Mr T. Henry Wilson, who retired in November 1969, but continued in charge of the patients at *Chaseley,* a home for disabled ex-servicemen which had been opened on 28th October 1946. Mr Henry Wilson's operating session at Princess Alice was on a Thursday afternoon with Dr Bodkin Adams as anæsthetist, until replaced by Dr P.H. Venn. Dr Paul Venn did five anæsthetic sessions at Princess Alice, apart from sessions at St Mary's Hospital. As early as 1964 he was mentioning the need for resuscitation trolleys and by 1969 he had designed a "Sussex Respirator", for portable resuscitation, which was adopted in the hospitals, and the local ambulances were equipped with them.

As late as the 1950s, the standard response of doctors and nurses to a patient who collapsed and died in front of them was simply to draw the screens around the bed. Gradually, it was realised that while some patients were past saving, others could be revived, if only the efforts to keep the patient alive were started promptly. After these changes in resuscitation techniques, a smart trolley appeared in this finest of Eastbourne hospitals. He was no ordinary trolley, for he was the "Resuscitation Trolley", and resplendent in bright red livery, he was proud to be referred to, in everyday parlance, as the "Fire Engine".

One night, as Dr John Rhodes recalls, the trolley's services were wanted urgently and a message was sent for him to attend, but ...

Princess Alice Memorial Hospital, Eastbourne

Administration Memorandum No. 18/69

20th February 1969.

Resuscitation Trolley

An incident occurred in the early hours of the 20th February, when one of our night staff asked the telephonist for the "Fire Engine". The Telephonist quite rightly acted immediately and called in the fire service, when in actual fact, the Resuscitation Trolley was really what was needed.

Will all concerned make certain in future, that when this item is required, it is asked for by its proper name.

Arrangements will be made as soon as possible for a press-button system to be installed; details of which will be given out at a later date. In the meantime I must repeat that the Resuscitation Trolley must be asked for by <u>name</u>.

Ben Pumfrey

Hospital Secretary

Thankfully, the patient recovered, and for ever after the resplendent trolley was referred to in the correct manner.

Talking of respiration, even in Eastbourne the Clean Air Acts of 1956 and 1968 were bearing results. The amount of sulphur dioxide and smoke in Eastbourne's atmosphere in 1970 was a third of the levels in 1963, to the benefit of patients. While the number of chronic chest cases in the Princess Alice wards never reached the incidence of the industrial north, such factors were reducing them even further.[10]

Suitable corneas for eye grafts had been collected for years, but in May 1969, Mr Grant Williams came to talk to the medical staff about the shortage of kidneys and other organs for transplants. That same month Dr E. Millington's radiotherapy sessions were taken over by Dr Jan de Winter from Brighton, when Dr Millington could no longer cope because of his addiction. The year also saw the installation of automatic processing in the hospital's X-ray department; medical committee agreement to extend the use of identi-bracelets to all patients following a trial period, after Dr Surtees had explained the advantages;[11] and there was a complaint from Dr Brown that ward Sisters were being appointed without consultation with the medical staff as had been agreed.[12]

Obviously there were a few niggles and stretching of wings around the hospital. Mr Jenkins had arranged for his registrar and the junior doctor in A&E

to change places, but Sister McIlwraith would not accept the change, saying she had not been notified.[13] On the ENT unit, Mr Williams, faced with a six-month waiting list, had asked for more staff, equipment and alterations to Crowden ward only to be told to start with the present facilities, after which extra secretarial and audiometry assistance would be discussed.

During the winter of 1969-70 there was an influenza epidemic, resulting in over 40 nurses being off-duty at one point, so it was only to be expected when Miss Davies said "cold" admissions were to be curtailed, and that work was put in train to ensure that the heating of Crowden ward was adequate.[14]

It was in the late 1960s that Mr Colin Oliver, a senior pathology technician, experienced what must be the strangest juxtaposition of emergency call-outs. One evening he was called from home to prepare blood for someone who had "lost a leg". Naturally, he presumed it was as the result of an accident, but when he arrived at the hospital he discovered that the amputation, at the knee, had been deliberate. 'The middle-aged patient, an ex-army man, whose main occupation appeared to be writing to *The Times* on cricket matters, had been reading about self-hypnosis and, armed with a cut-throat razor, he sat on the edge of his bath and carved away the said part. Thereupon he involved his GP by hopping to the telephone. Mr Snowball, called upon to tidy-up the scene, expressed his annoyance, in his quiet way, at the selfishness of the DIY surgeon who had wasted our time and public money. Incredibly, on that same night I was called out for another unfortunate who had "lost an arm". This young girl had been dangling it out of a car, when the vehicle hit a tree and rolled. Presumably she would rather have retained the limb.'

Mr Oliver, now in Canada, was one of an intake of pathology technicians in the early 1960s who all worked in the laboratory for many years and some are still there. They included Ann Berry (née White), Ann Beere, Brenda Ashton (née Hutchinson) and David Manners.

Mr Stephen Chappell succeeded Miss Foxall as pharmacist at the Princess Alice in 1970, and went on to become group pharmacist in February 1971, on Mr Tommy Jones' retirement from the post of pharmacist at St Mary's Hospital. Miss Foxall and Mr Jones were of equal seniority, so there was no question of appointing a group pharmacist until they retired. The Princess Alice pharmacy was still sited below Cavendish ward, looking onto Bedfordwell Road. Mr R. Hackney started as a locum there in 1968 and Mr A. Howarth joined the staff after Miss Foxall left.

Miss B.J. Perkins also retired in 1970, with her place as superintendent radiographer taken by Miss R.M. Poole. Among those in the X-ray department were Miss E.A. Millen, Miss J. Hobden, Miss D. Soan and Miss M. Venus. The X-ray (or radiological) department remained near the A&E entrance, but was having trouble servicing its old equipment and at one time had to restrict work to in-patients and accidents.[15]

In physiotherapy Miss Helen Macdonald was the superintendent, with Mrs P. Budgeon, Miss J. Mcdonell, Miss Kathleen Rainsford and Mrs B. Pickney among the senior physiotherapists.

Senior nursing staff of the time included Miss I.C. Crighton, Mr W. Mikoluk and Mr H. Baguley. Sister P. Wright and Staff Nurse Nielau were on Cavendish ward, Sister Smith on Mawhood ENT ward, Staff Nurse J. Cooper on Sydney Hudson and S/N S. Silverlock was on the orthopædic wards.

As part of the 1970 spring offensive, Pay-As-You-Eat was introduced in February (instead of a standard deduction from a resident's pay); in the May the Regional Board said that "economic rent" should be charged in HMC residencies; and the portrait of Princess Alice, which hung in the front hall, was cleaned - the money for this coming from voluntary gift funds, not from the Board's exchequer. A male staff changing room near Arno ward was also agreed at a cost of £1550. In the summer Mr Alan Cosham reported on a patient satisfaction survey on Cavendish and Gurney/Tabor wards. He reported that the patients took great pride in "the PA, their hospital" and the most common complaint was a lack of information about their illness.

On 30th June 1970 there was a total of 1324 patients on the waiting list, with the waiting times for "PA clinics" varying from nil in radiotherapy to 4-6 weeks in general medicine.

From that month Dr Peter Woodbridge, a hospital practitioner in dermatology, assisted the consultant dermatologists, namely Dr Vincent Harris and, after Dr Harris' retirement in 1975, Dr D.A. Birkett for about a year, followed by Dr Keith Liddell. At first he worked in the ECG room on Wednesday afternoons. Dr Woodbridge was an enthusiastic photographer and his abilities were of great value in the dermatology ward and clinic. Dr Harris recalls that his dermatology lectures to the nurses appeared to be arranged for the time that the night nurses came off duty, for they always appeared to be more in need of sleep than "skins".

In all the comings and goings, Dr Ishaque Suleman was appointed clinical assistant in general medicine (diabetes) in July 1970, having resigned as medical registrar the previous November,[16] and the next month Sidney Pilbeam retired after over 30 years as a porter at the Princess Alice. Later in the year, Mrs H.L. Osborne succeeded Miss J.D. Newton as senior assistant matron, and when David Broomfield left the telephone switchboard to do chiropody, he was replaced by Frank Chapman. About this time the group medical committee agreed to allow senior nurses to give intravenous injections into infusion tubing, and for operating theatre technicians to do on-call, at a cost of £150 a year. The committee also discussed the need for a day hospital, although most time was devoted to "visiting hours" after Miss Tewnion had recommended 1400-2000h every day. It was decided not to recommend change "... as Sisters have discretionary powers to allow visiting whenever necessary".[17]

Margaret Chiverton, also reporting in 1970, stated that the medical records had been amalgamated at St Mary's, thus avoiding any need to create a records store beneath Arno ward.[18] This subterranean solution to the shortage of space had been proposed, but it was a far from ideal place to work. The ex-records store at Princess Alice was converted into a nurses' sick bay, and at the same time anti-static flooring was installed in the operating theatre at a cost of £377.

Mrs Reynolds took over as admissions and medical records clerk until she moved to the new hospital as admissions officer in 1976. Her assistants were Mrs Beryl Botting, Mrs Joan Bowker, Miss Carole Hollobone and Mrs Pat Tilbury.

In May 1970 two portable dictating machines were bought for the consultants at Princess Alice at a cost of £79, and the medical equipment requests for the year were:-

1 Sigmoidoscope..................	£20/0/-
1 Sphygmomanometer.........	£6/10/-
1 East Freeman Auto Vent...	£21/8/6-
2 Continator units................	£50/0/-
2 Cystoscopes......................	£120/0/-

Talking of cystoscopes [for looking into the bladder] the charge for supplying water at the Princess Alice over the financial year 1969-70 was £1876.

In December 1970 there was a further extension of the Staff Sports and Social club premises at the back of the Princess Alice.[19] One of the topical events in celebration was a Decimalization Dance. The club continued to prosper, thanks to an outstanding secretary in Mr R. Tomsett and from leadership by a succession of capable chairmen, including Mr R.H. Botsford, Mr G. Sellars, Mr H. Wells, Mr M.D. Bastable and Mr R. Sherwin. Many other staff, such as Mr Keith Marshall the membership secretary, gave years of service.

Charlotte Foord (née Phelan) was Sister of the children's ward. On Arno ward (female orthopædic) Sister Rose McGeeney who had succeeded Sister Sacker, was with Staff Nurses Whittaker, Wood and Kendrick. Sister Webster was there later. The next ward, towards Enys Road, was Geraldine, which remained female geriatric, plus a few orthopædic and skin cases, with Sister M. Constable. The male geriatric ward Sydney Hudson still had Charge Nurse Bill Bailey, and Cavendish had been converted into a ten-bed ENT ward, with Sister D. Smith (née Heineger). Along the corridor, as always, were two more orthopædic wards, Gurney (male) and Tabor (female), with the plaster room nearby, then the operating theatres on the right, with A&E opposite.

Mrs Jeanne Fry says that in the early 1970s, 'Arno was a very happy ward, even though Mr Jenkins thought nothing of "telling off" a member of staff in front of anybody, so we were terrified of him, although his heart was in the right place when dealing with patients. Mr Richards we loved as he was young and would have a few kind words for the staff as well as the patients as he rushed into the ward. The only thing we did dislike was his private patients ... because they were paying they seemed to think they could ring a bell and a nurse would run to them, when we had quite enough to do looking after the elderly patients with fractured hips, who often went quite balmy after the anæsthetic'.

The secretaries in the orthopædic department were Mrs E.E. Bath and Mrs Sue Cuthill, the A&E secretary was Miss N.M. Egan, the out-patient secretary Miss J.M. McGlasham (who had replaced Rene Wilkins) and Mrs M. Eldrett was the secretary in the social workers' office.

The 1970 World Cup was the cause of local dentist Mr J. Hyder being drawn to the orthopædic department. Playing a schoolboy game between the televised matches, he broke his left leg. The full-length plaster didn't keep him away from sport at that age, but the penalty was having to home in on the clinic repeatedly over the next nine weeks to have conservation repairs on the scuffed plaster.

Patients coming to the A&E department at night rang an outside door bell whereupon either Staff Nurse Rhodes or Brown would open the door to see what was required. Despite Eastbourne's sedate, respectable image, many of the patients were drunks who, with accomplices, were not easy to handle, especially when the only non-nursing night-staff were one porter, a telephonist and a cook. Knowing the hazards for the staff, a male orderly, Graham Butcher, from Sydney Hudson, helped out in these situations, but after a charge nurse had been knocked to the floor in a fracas, a viewing window was placed in the A&E door.

The medical staffing of the A&E department was far from satisfactory. In August 1970 there were no applicants for the post of registrar and this response was to be repeated over the years. Mr Jenkins' view was that he could not assume administrative charge, and that the department needed its own consultant. The attractions of the job were not enhanced by so much routine work; for example, in the days before GPs were paid for Immunisation Quotas, they were not enthusiastic about administering booster doses of tetanus toxoid which had been ordered by A&E, with the result that these patients drifted back to the A&E at all times for their repeat jabs.

If the GP was still an independent contractor, the organisation of medical work was under way. The pathology department had been officially renamed the Division of Scientific Services in 1969, not that anyone took too much notice, and on 9th July 1970 the Division of Anaesthesia held its first meeting.

On the other hand, the arrangements made for the exchange of mail during the postal strike in January 1971 so pleased the GPs that they asked if the system could continue. The HMC agreed,[20] and what had been a limited transport system between the laboratories and intervening GP surgeries became a series of complex van rounds linking all the hospitals and every GP practice.

Mr A.W. Briggs died that year. He had been the HMC chairman from 1965 to 1970, having ousted Teddie Watt, following the Regional Board's refusal to allow more wards to be shut, as a response to the nurse-staffing problems.

When Miss Davies moved to Ilford in April 1971 the opportunity was taken to introduce a Salmon-type nursing structure, because the grades of the 1966 Salmon Report [named after the chairman, Mr B.L. Salmon] carried higher pay scales and it was becoming difficult to fill some of these posts. Consequently, Miss G.R. Rudd succeeded not as matron, but as Chief Nursing Officer, and Miss M. Tewnion and Miss S.J. Maynard remained in post as Senior Nursing Officers, Miss Tewnion being succeeded later by Miss J.B. Compton. In November 1970 the medical committee, prompted by the pathologists, resolved that "when funds become available, further consideration be given to establishing a Control of Infection Sister".[21] As seven years was about par for the course to implement any advance if finance was involved, it is not surprising that the first, Miss V. Goddard, was not firmly in post until 1977.

Following Mr Williams' departure in the previous November, Mr K. Singh was appointed as ENT Surgeon in 1971.

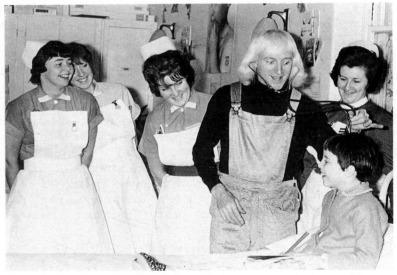

38. Jim fixing it on Mawhood children's ward 14th January 1971. Left to right: Nurses Doreen Moyse, Sheila Isted, Jean Baulcomb, Jimmy Savile, the TV personality, and Sister Charlotte Foord, with Neil Cartwright.

During 1971 over 1800 dwellings were under construction in Eastbourne, the second highest total for any town in England. Such building continued the population increase, confirmed by the census of 1971 which later showed that the population of Eastbourne town was 70715, an increase of 10000 since 1961. It was this rate of increase which was putting the health services under stress and emphasising the necessity for the new hospital on Kings Drive, apart from the need to improve standards of care, especially for the aged. The provision of nursing for the elderly was of concern, but many of the extra numbers were young families, and Dr Moira Martens, who had joined the paediatric unit in 1969 as a clinical assistant (upgraded after 1971 to medical assistant), was followed by the appointment of Dr J.L. Wilkins as a second consultant paediatrician in October 1971, although both Drs Scott and Wilkins were part-time at Hastings as well. In the child health field, it was also the year when the national smallpox vaccination of infants was suspended.

The pharmaceutical committee recommended that any medicines brought in by patients should be destroyed: this was because it was often impossible to be sure that they has been stored properly, or even that they hadn't been mixed up in the containers. The medical committee, bothered about the cost, said that they were "not wholly in favour of destroying drugs".[22]

The year brought hope for the future. On Wednesday, 22nd September, His Worship the mayor of Eastbourne, Mr John W. Robinson, cut the first turf to commence building operations at the site of the new hospital at Kings Drive, and a Regional working party, chaired by Dr W.E.R. Budd, was set up in 1971 by the Regional Medical Officer, Dr K.R.D. Porter, to report on "Services for the Elderly". By now St Mary's Hospital acted as the geriatric admission hospital, rehabilitation was at All Saints, and long-stay patients went to Downside. Dr Budd recommended extra consultants; that the long-stay service should be at Princess Alice; and confirmed the local aspirations by saying Eastbourne needed a day hospital. As a result, it was proposed that all the medical patients should be at St Mary's, and that the geriatric beds in Jevington and Wilmington wards, at St Mary's, should move to the Princess Alice. In the December Dr H.J. Elverson visited from Region to discuss the start of the program for a day hospital.

Dr Surtees was reappointed clinical tutor, and 1971 also saw the first mention of video-tape recording of patients, and of some blood products being supplied in plastic bags, although plastic tubes for certain blood specimens had been introduced by the laboratory in 1968.

Miss Linda Miller started in the X-ray department in May 1971 under Dr Rhodes, and later Dr Dexter who commenced in the following November. She well remembers 'that awful underground dungeon where we had to file the X-ray folders'. The next year she became secretary to Professor D.A. Long, when he was appointed consultant microbiologist. With all his research contacts she found the job exceedingly satisfying. She was always sorry for the pathology out-patients because they had the tiniest of waiting spaces - it could not be described as a room, more a passageway, with only a bench for a seat - which was uncomfortably cold in gusty weather, and alternately, if there was no wind, it was permeated with the most appalling smells which wafted over from the laboratory autoclaves, which had only been replaced in 1971. A regular, albeit unofficial, duty of the pathology secretaries was to notify Bill Bailey or Mrs

Cooper on Sydney Hudson ward that one of their pyjama-clad patients was about to escape, having last been seen heading past the lab. towards Bedfordwell Road.

As Miss Miller says, 'despite the lack of modern amenities the staff really loved working at Princess Alice. At the top admin. you could not imagine more "kindly gentlemen" than Ben Pumfrey, Bob Botsford and Jack Newman'.

Many staff stayed for over a quarter of a century, Mrs I. Stevens retired from the post of dining-room maid in January 1972 after 30 years, and as in most hospitals the senior porters, such as Mr Vic. Reynolds and Mr Jack Breach, had responsible jobs and were vital to the smooth running of the hospital.

Exceptions occurred, and there is no doubt that the most famous Jack of all Trades was Mr Stanley Allwright, a big, ambling, harmless man, harmless that is until "in control" of any conveyance. The description could only be "incapable in charge", as slivers of plaster were gouged out of each corridor wall and every hospital corner bore witness to his activities. In the days when the hospital could not afford special mortuary trolleys with sides, at least one other member of the portering staff, transporting a psycho-physically-compromised patient to the mortuary, had exceptionally tipped the body into the geranium beds where there was a treacherous bend. With "Stanley" the extraordinary was when nothing out of the ordinary happened. There was a notorious occasion when he was motoring to the mortuary and as he cornered round the flower beds, the flimsy sheet covering the body flipped away and the arms flopped out in full daylight. In "Stanley's" best-known exploit, his trolley somehow assumed control of itself and careered down the slope towards the pathology laboratory. It finally came to a halt only after plunging half-way through Dr Taylor's office window, giving Joe Fenwick, the pathology porter, who saw it, and the rest of the hospital who were deafened by it, the fright of a lifetime. As Mrs Joy Spicer and Mrs Dorothy Stent say, 'It could only have been Mr Pumfrey's kind heart which kept him on', although "Stanley" graced the District General Hospital for a couple of years. For some years there was general encouragement to those who might find it beyond them to hold down a job out in the hard world; and for ex-patients, part of the treatment was to help in their rehabilitation.

On 15th November 1971, in minute 4311, the HMC staff committee was informed that more than 10% of staff were over pensionable age: this might seem irrelevant, but it implies that most staff stayed to reach the top of their incremental salary range - not good news for accountants.

Apart from "Stanley's" depredations, the finance department found 1971 expensive: the Princess Alice furniture program came to £2500 (so it was paid out of voluntary gifts funds), provisions cost £1/17/1d per person per week, 17 Bedfordwell Road was bought to convert into extra residencies at a cost of £11750, flameproof curtains in Arno ward were £300, agency radiographers, at £70 per month, had to be used to maintain the on-call X-ray rota, for Christmas festivities it was agreed that each ward should receive 65p a head for crackers, trees and presents, and Dr Wilkinson requested the following replacement items for his physiotherapy department:-

1 Hanovia UV lamp	£138
1 Universette Mk II stimulator	£85
1 Impulsaphon M 55 ultrasonic unit	£195.

The only (financial) saving graces were that Sydney Hudson and Cavendish wards were closed because of nursing shortages with the loss of 27 beds, Mr H.T. Isted had been appointed only as a part-time district fire officer, and Miss J.P. Biglin did a locum as hospital secretary at All Saints without upgrading.

The final indignity was when the finance office at 29 Bedfordwell Road was burgled and all of £40 was stolen from a safe.[23]

The Sister on Anne Elizabeth ward was now Christine Pickering, to be followed by Sister Dora Smith. After Sister Ann Foot, Sister Anne Whittaker was soon to keep order on the orthopædic wards (Gurney and Tabor) with enrolled Nurse Flora I. Clark ("Clarkie"). The orthopædic ward staff, mainly Nurse Clark, also ran the orthopædic out-patients because Mr Jenkins would only have his own people. Nurse Clark - 'I had always wanted to nurse' - worked as a VAD and later in the Civil Nursing Reserve all through the 1939-45 war, and was a most valued member of the orthopædic team.

In 1971 Miss Delphine Martin moved from the pharmacy to St Mary's Hospital to take charge of the sterile products production. Of other Princess Alice pharmacy staff, Miss J. Thwaites remained the part-time clerk, but Mr Trinder retired in 1972.

The pharmacy had a trying year in 1972, through no fault of their own. In March there was a failure of sterilisation of certain intravenous fluids manufactured by *Evans Medical Ltd,* which entailed much work checking batch numbers to ensure no Eastbourne patient received a contaminated infusion, and in the August, a *Burroughs Wellcome* manager changed the formulation of their digoxin [heart] tablets without apparently considering that the potency could be altered. As the outcome was to double the clinical effect, a national policy of reviewing dosages and restabilising patients on maintenance therapy was required. One local effect was that the general porters took over the collection and distribution of pharmacy ward requirements from the pharmacy staff. Mrs M. Clive Matthews was at the pharmacy until the closure in 1976.

That year the geriatric out-patient clinic transferred to the Princess Alice from St Mary's Hospital. Mrs C.M. Andersen was the geriatric office secretary, who became the geriatric admissions officer.

The year had began inauspiciously with complaints that patients were being discharged from the orthopædic wards with bed sores.[24] It was pointed out that prevention was difficult when elderly frail patients had to be discharged as soon as possible, in view of the demand for beds. It was also the year of a Work Study which looked into the efficiency of the administrative and clerical staff. The main findings, published in 1973, were that most of the secretaries were grossly overworked, but the study concluded there were some hours spare in the chest clinic. A few hours of secretarial time were promptly deleted from the chest clinic, but there was no like alacrity to add hours to the other departments.

Sir Keith Joseph, then Minister of Health, was a visitor to the hospital on 28th February 1972. Brushing aside introductions, he said that his intention was to talk to the elderly patients.[25] It so happened that the day before, an old man, who had been living rough near Herstmonceux for years, had been admitted. He had always refused help and had been found in a confused state, living in malodorous squalor, unable to feed himself and surrounded by his only possessions - a few old newspapers and rags. By chance, he was in the first bed of Sydney Hudson ward and Sir Keith enquired of him about his health. The old man replied in a serious tone, 'While the doctors have imprisoned me here, thieves have broken into my country mansion and stolen over a million pounds of art treasures'. Dr Ian Brown, alongside the chairman, commented that if this dialogue went on Sir Keith would not discover the true state of the geriatric care situation. The chairman, Mr Lelliott, answered, 'Anyone who has been in the House of Commons for fifteen years should have plenty of experience in distinguishing fact from fiction.'

There were 37 domestic staff in post when Mrs Pessell left in March 1972 and in July Miss E. Dunstall, dining-room assistant, retired, both after long service. Dr A.K. Seeram was regraded a medical assistant that year, Dr M.J. Mynott took over one of Mr Turner's orthopædic sessions, and Miss B. French was appointed part-time dietitian. Dr A.G. Emslie also retired as consultant physician, to be replaced initially by Dr John Condon, only for him to move to the Brook Hospital in 1974 and in turn be succeeded by Dr A.M. Macleod.

When Mr Richards broke his leg skiing, he was in good company, for during April, May and June of 1972, 422 accident victims were treated at Princess Alice Hospital, of which 53 needed admission. Miss M. Hemming, home safety organiser, emphasising that many burns were preventable, said that household cloths could catch fire if placed over cookers to dry.[26]

In July 1972 the Highways and Works Committee of Eastbourne Town Council nearly put a complete stop to the work of the hospital. Mr Geoffrey Morgan, the borough surveyor, told the committee that the East Sussex County Council's proposed A22 inter-urban route would go over the hospital site, with a roundabout at Carew Road. In its response the Regional Hospital Board stressed that the services of the hospital must be given full recognition when assessment of demands was undertaken. "The hospital needs in Eastbourne include a really good geriatric service and Princess Alice fulfils an essential part of this need."[27]

Greater cooperation was now possible between the Eastbourne hospitals, and Sister D.I. Marshall recounts her "briefest of acquaintances with Princess Alice when East Dean ward patients from St Mary's Hospital were lodged there while the ward at St Mary's was redecorated".

Around the same time Geraldine ward, and Mawhood, the children's ENT ward, were redecorated, the telephone switchboard enlarged, and emergency generators installed. On completion at the end of the year, the allocation of beds was 10 ENT on Cavendish, 18 geriatric and 3 dermatology on Geraldine, and Mawhood had 9 geriatric and orthopædic. The staff sick bay was now at All Saints Hospital. During the upheaval, some elderly patients were to be found on the ground floor of the Maternity Home. Perhaps this was why the Major Accident Scheme was revised in September 1972.

The year had started with the introduction of the 80-hour fortnight for nurses and, in consequence of the Salmon Report, there were further changes in the nursing staff with many having to apply for their own jobs. Among them Miss E.G. Guillot, night superintendent at St Mary's, who now became night nursing officer, and assumed responsibility for Princess Alice, the Leaf and Gildredge Hospitals as well.

Sister McIlwraith retired from the out-patient and A&E departments in October 1972, the year it was agreed that nurses could do suturing under supervision. She was succeeded by Sister James, who soon left to marry a West Country surgeon. Sister R.M. Upton followed, and she took the A&E department to the District General Hospital in 1976. Sister M. Bowden worked part-time in the A&E for many years. It is sad that Sister McIlwraith, who must have seen the effects of many traffic accidents in her time as theatre and A&E Sister, was to die after being run over in Upperton Road.

In the November Miss G.R. Rudd, principal nursing officer, hosted a meeting of the Eastbourne Nurses' League (created by Miss Davies) at the Princess Alice Hospital. Among those present were Sister G. Beard, Miss E. Budgen, Sister M.A. Constable, and Nurses J. King, D. Knight, A. Lau, B. O'Connor, M. Porter and P. Shipton along with Miss M. Winchester, the home warden - perhaps continuing to keep an eye on them.

At the Nurses' Prizegiving that year Mr West, one of the invited fathers, pointed out to Miss Rudd that he had now given three daughters as nurses to the Eastbourne hospitals and asked, 'Does this entitle me to special treatment if needed?'. To which banter Miss Rudd replied, 'Mr West, I will nurse you myself'.

The year ended on other bright notes: the annual group dance, organised by Mr H. Wells, still had Gordon Rider as conductor, who promised, "all tastes catered for, without offending anyone"; day rooms for Cavendish and Sydney Hudson wards were built by *Lovells of Eastbourne* at a cost of £6040; the HMC suggested[28] the names *Hailsham* and *Seaford* for the general units at the new hospital, *Litlington* for the obstetric ward, and *Friston* for the Paediatric or Geriatric ward [it had not been decided which it was to be]; and Miss Gladys Rudd married Mr Sidney Lovering. The story that they met socially when he taught her how to drive, whilst possibly true, gave rise to much ribaldry about back-seat drivers. It did not stop Dr Linley-Adams drawing attention to the perennial difficulties of parking at Princess Alice.

All through 1972 the patients kept their heads down, borrowing 6080 library books, the two most popular authors being Catherine Gaskin and Dick Francis.

On New Year's Day 1973, Dr M.L. Agarwal joined the staff as consultant in geriatric medicine. He visited St Christopher's Hospice to study the arrangements there, and he extended the facilities for the elderly at All Saints.

In the late 1960s the consultant physicians at the Princess Alice had been Dr A.G. Emslie and Dr J.C. Linley-Adams, with Dr I.M. Brown gradually replacing Dr Linley-Adams as physician for the elderly. After Dr Emslie's retirement, the physicians were mainly Dr Brown and Dr Agarwal. Dr B.B. Kundu was the medical registrar until succeeded by Dr D.A. Hanraty. Having looked after the *Merlynn* convalescent home from 1956 until its closure, Dr D.A.L. Ashforth was the medical oficer of the convalescent beds at All Saints Hospital until 1973.

There was still no physiotherapy available on the wards, and the geriatricians complained that the department was too far away for many of the elderly patients to attend. The day rooms had been such a success that capital funds were found to enlarge the one on Geraldine ward.

During the year some of the first industrial action amongst ancillary staff at Princess Alice was experienced. This had an effect on the waiting lists, in that the 555 on the list in February increased to 804 in the April. By the end of 1973 the nursing situation had improved, with 660 nurses in post (although there was funding for only 630) and the waiting list for geriatric patients had virtually disappeared.

In the March Dr Surtees, as Clinical Tutor, reported that two trainers (Drs Alan Forster and Chris Savile) and a college tutor (Dr Michael Emslie) had been appointed for the GP Vocational Training Course.[29]

From 1st April 1973 giving sets [for intravenous fluids] were on Ministry contract and obtainable from the Supplies department instead of the blood bank.

On the same day, but unconnected, VAT was added to hospital meals;[30] this meant that "Spaghetti Bolognaise" cost 12p, a "Scotch Egg" 9p, and it was 2p for a cup of tea or coffee. The group costs for the year were: nursing salaries £824925, other salaries (excluding medical) £788490, drugs £207890, provisions £93450 and food £88600. Whether the figures were reliable is not easy to ascertain, for in the same month the cost of the projected day hospital was given as £174000, when it came out at nearly twice this sum.[31] The estimates were probably not helped when the Town Clerk wrote to say that the proposed A22 link road meant there was a danger the day hospital would have a very limited life.[32] In the way of the world the road was stillborn and never saw the light of day, while the day hospital looks set to pass its 20th birthday.

Later in the year Dr Kathleen Harrison was appointed part-time consultant haematologist, and when the post was made full-time in April 1977, she went to Hastings and Dr Pamela Gover took her place.

Mr C. Smith, assistant catering officer, had died at the start of 1973 and was replaced by Miss D. Collard. In June two long-serving members of staff retired: Miss D. Dyer, a domestic, who had been at Princess Alice since 1942, and Mr A.G. Newman after 20 years in the Eastbourne laboratories. Mr R.A. Elliston followed him as chief pathology technician. Miss M.B. Taylor was now one of the laboratory secretaries.

As a portent of the future, on 16th July 1973, Mr (later Sir) John Donne unveiled the Commemoration Stone of the new hospital at Kings Drive.

When Dr W.H. McAleenan left as ill-health forced an early retirement, he was replaced in October 1974 by Dr W.F. Felton, now termed consultant in genito-urinary medicine.

For the month of February 1974 the hospital had 109 beds available (including 36 orthopædic, 22 ENT, 6 paediatric and 3 dermatology) which were 81% occupied. Over the month there were 101 admissions from the waiting list, 135 emergency admissions and 40 day cases. The total number of patients on the waiting list was 772, the longest waiting time being three months for Mr Richards' patients.

The increased activity might have a connection with the 1974 request for bodies to be removed more quickly from the mortuary. It seems that with the transfer of geriatric beds from St Mary's Hospital, the tiny post mortem room was awash with bodies awaiting collection so there was no space to do post mortem examinations. There were proposals to move all the PM work to St Mary's.

Dr Hanraty relinquished his post of medical registrar on 28th February 1974 and was replaced by Dr Y.S. Fan. A long-serving member of staff, Miss N. Laird, out-patient clerk, retired the next month.

Miss Gladys Rudd decided not to apply for her own post as District Nursing Officer after the reorganisation of 1974 and retired in the April. Miss V.M. Adams continued as matron's secretary. July saw Mr Dyte and the administrative staff, including Mr B. Bailey, Mr R. Huggins and Miss V.G. Digman, transfer to *Avenue House* from 29 Bedfordwell Road.

As part of the upheaval, in April 1973, the group medical advisory committee was yet again renamed, this time as the medical executive committee, with Dr B.S. Kent as chairman, and Mr E. Harford-Rees as vice-chairman until April 1974, when Dr S.J. Surtees became vice-chairman. Since the 1920s the medical committee had met monthly of an evening in the board room at Princess Alice. Following improvements to the office of the hospital secretary it was decided not to use the board room for committee meetings, which moved to "29".

Dr Mark Lester retired in August 1974, to be replaced eventually by Dr D.G. Model. On the first of the month Miss Val Lancaster moved from Sister-in-charge, Intensive Therapy Unit, at St Mary's, to Clinical Instructor at Princess Alice; at the same time Miss I.M. Smith was appointed a qualified tutor, and Mrs L. Thomas became Sister of Geraldine, when Sister Constable moved to the day hospital. Miss S.J. Maynard, who was to take early retirement through ill-health, remained senior nursing officer for a time, a post which had taken the place of assistant matron. Enrolled Nurse J. Cooper was the Princess Alice representative for the Professional Advisory Machinery. Miss Roberts, the Nurse Training School secretary, moved to the Area Health Authority in Lewes and was replaced by Miss E.R. Connolly.

The September Nurses' Prizegiving was chaired at the Town Hall by Miss S.M. Smith, newly appointed as District Nursing Officer. Miss J.H. Taylor, principal nursing officer (education) reported that there were 142 students and 70 pupils in training and over the year 35 nurses out of 43 passed the Registration examination, and in the Enrolment exams 32 passed out of 35, with two discontinuing on health grounds. Mr L.A. Lelliott, past Chairman of the HMC, made the awards. The evening's inclement weather was cheered by Mrs Salter's cheese and wine buffet and by Miss J. Makins' flower arrangements. Nurse recruitment was as important as ever after the Halsbury Report, which recommended increased annual leave entitlement for nurses, and meant that, from 1974, Eastbourne needed ten extra full-time nurses to replace the hours lost.

Dr Wilkinson retired as consultant in physical medicine, and the next year, 1975, Dr J.A. Wojtulewski replaced him as consultant in rehabilitation and rheumatology, and was allocated four beds in Cavendish ward. Miss N. Fillery continued as secretary.

Mr D.W. Smalley, Mrs M. Tutt, Mr V. Wathen, Mr W. Wathen and Mrs J. Marshall were among the event organisers at the Sports and Social Club in 1974.

Dr W. J. Wigfield had been building up a day-hospital service since 1971, which culminated on Wednesday, 30th October 1974, with the opening, by Mr Leslie A. Lelliott, of a purpose-built geriatric day hospital, for patients recommended by their family doctor or the consultant on discharge from hospital. Mr Lelliott referred to Dr Ian Brown as being instrumental in its development, and the vote of thanks was proposed by Dr Basil Kent. The day hospital, which had been receiving patients since the July, was a single-storey building, costing £300000, in the grounds of the Princess Alice, between *Harberton* and *Roborough*. It was open five days a week from 1000h to 1600h and could take up to 40 patients on any one day. Sister Mavis Constable was in charge with a staff of six, together with physiotherapy, occupational therapy, speech therapy and chiropody staff. Staff Nurse June McPherson and Mrs Shirley Peckham, senior assistant OT, transferred from All Saints, and Miss P.K. Hall was the physiotherapist for nearly six years. The WRVS volunteers ran a shop in the day hospital and a hairdresser visited the patients. Drs Harry Desmond and W.

Doraiswarmy were among the GPs who held clinical assistant posts at the day hospital.[33]

This marked a new concept. In Mr John Evans' words, 'Without this hospital many of these patients would have to be admitted to a geriatric ward because they could not cope at home'.[34] It meant patients didn't need to stay in hospital if they required just physiotherapy, and yet all the hospital facilities, such as pathology or X-ray, were readily available. Relatives were given a respite when they could go shopping, and patients could be given a bath if it wasn't possible to manage at home. Day hospital-care reduced the length of stay in hospital for elderly patients needing rehabilitation, and avoided some hospital admissions by enabling many patients to be kept at home. The majority of patients visited the day hospital twice a week for a couple of months before discharge, but they were always missed and welcomed back as regulars, if necessary.

39. The day hospital, 1974. Ambulance bay in the foreground.

The new day hospital almost ended the days of the mulberry tree in the hospital grounds. It had been a feature since the early years, gave fruit every year and Mr Jenkins was especially fond of it. The Revd Denys Giddey happened to notice that the workmen engaged on building the day hospital were about to saw down the tree, but he managed to halt the destruction and persuade Mr Roy Dyte that the tree must be preserved. It was damaged in the 1987 hurricane, but having been tended well afterwards it is now in good shape, to give fruit for many years.

An episode not to be repeated was that of the three bathers who were admitted on Sunday, 22nd June 1975, after receiving weever fish stings on the beach.[35] Fortunately, Mr A.R. Durrani had been appointed consultant surgeon (accident and emergency) in the April, after two years as registrar.

That same April, Dr B. Steer was appointed as consultant anæsthetist, Mr H. Miller as sector administrator, Mr E.J. Thomas as part-time district personnel officer, and in June 1975 Dr A. Macleod took up his post as consultant physician.

As part of the "make-do-and-mend" efforts to keep the service going in the run-up to the new hospital, now nearing completion, Dr Brown shared the ECG room at Princess Alice with Mr Richards and his appliance fitter on Friday afternoons. This must have been a tight fit.

The Eastbourne and Hellingly Schools of Nursing combined in 1975 to form the Sussex Downs School of Nursing. In the April Miss Joan H. Taylor, who had obtained a BA (Humanities) with the Open University, was appointed director of nurse education, based at *Avenue House*. Miss P.A. Wenban was already at the school of nursing and other nurses included Mrs B.M. Watson, Mrs J. Cooper and Mr M. Burns. That year Miss E.H. Maltby retired as a tutor, Mrs S. Lemmon came to Princess Alice, and Mrs Valerie Sands started as Sister of Anne Elizabeth ward. In May 1975 Miss Pauline Wade became divisional nursing officer (general), based at the Princess Alice. A new white uniform was introduced in the mid-1970s for trained nursing staff, with a navy blue tippet for the Sisters.

Another exceptional event was the November 1975 retirement of Mr Ben Pumfrey. The Chairman of the Area Health Authority, Mr Hugh Fovargue, presented him with a portable typewriter and Mr Roy Dyte and Mr Aubrey Jenkins presented him with gifts from colleagues.

On the administrative side Mr Harry Wells remained on the staff at Princess Alice after Mr Pumfrey's retirement, with Mrs J.E. Dobson as his deputy. At *Avenue House* there was Mr Roy Dyte, the group secretary, with Mr John Evans as senior administrator, and Miss Yvonne Bullman as secretarial assistant. Miss Pauline Elliott, who was in the finance office, later became payroll manager, but Mr R.W. Robson, the finance officer, retired about the time of the change-over in the summer of 1976.

In October 1975 the Princess Alice came in for a peck of criticism when an inspector from the Good Food Guide visited the hospital, sampled meals there, and rated the food as "fair overall": which was his label for a chicken soup starter, shepherd's pie with cabbage and gravy, and a bread and butter pudding. The general staff opinion was that the Princess Alice food was superior to the other hospitals. Only 15% of patients thought the food was worse than at home and 66% of the patients said they ate the same sort of food at home. In the male orthopædic ward Mr Philip Maber said that the food was "fantastic", echoed by Mr Thomas Callis, and on the female orthopædic ward, both Mrs Emma Dalloway and Mrs Elsie Webb, recovering from broken hips, voted the food "more than enough". Mr S.A. Jenkins, the orthopædic consultant, said that he found both the patients' and the staff food invariably good, and the service cheerful.[36] Mrs Bridget Salter, the group catering manager, and Mr George Cole, now support services manager, added that when the patients had a choice of menu they were usually satisfied with their meals.

The kitchen staff were invariably pleasant and friendly. Ian cooked all the meals, assisted by "Frank the Russian", and they were served by Carmen and her team. The meals were subsidised in those days and three people could each enjoy a satisfying two-course meal followed by a cup of tea, and still have change out of a pound.

The senior medical staff of the hospitals had given a Christmastime party for nurses and other hospital staff for many years. Variously held in the nurses' home at St Mary's and the staff restaurant at All Saints, it now transferred to the day hospital at Princess Alice, as the number of those invited soared to over 300 guests. Held on a Friday night, to give Sister Constable plenty of time to clear up before the next week's patients, it was enjoyed by everyone although, as the numbers crept up, there was inevitably some loss of the family atmosphere.

The great changes of 1976 were ushered in with the closure in January of the town's oldest chemists, H.R. Browne of Cornfield Road. The firm, which had introduced X-rays to Eastbourne, was wound up after 116 years of trading. [37]

Dr Barry O'Sullivan joined the radiology department as consultant in February 1976. His appointment was funded by the Regional Health Authority only after Mr Ian Gow MP had made representations to the Minister over delays in the reportings of X-rays. Miss S. Tapscott had followed Miss Biglin as Dr Fox's secretary, along with Miss M. Anderson.

A uniform system of scientific measurement, the S.I. unit, was introduced on 1st April 1976, overseen by Miss I. Smith, Dr John Surtees, Mr George Cole and Mr Malcolm Bastable. Equally smoothly, over the following months, starting in May and continuing through the dry, hot summer of 1976, all departments were transferred to the new District General Hospital at Kings Drive. The surgical unit was among the first to go, but the orthopædic department was delayed until August because Mr Jenkins decided that the new hospital was not fully ready. Mr Singh, Sister D. Smith, Miss B.F. Funnell, the secretary, and the rest of the ENT department also transferred, although some ENT hearing-aid testing remained.

Any geriatric or general medical patients at the Princess Alice, such as those with skin conditions, went to St Mary's Hospital, while the genito-urinary medicine ("Special") clinic moved to *Avenue House.*

The staff moved with the patients, for example, Mr Bailey went from Sydney Hudson ward to St Mary's Hospital with the elderly patients, and Nurse Margaret Porter (née West) who had latterly been on Geraldine, went to Selmeston geriatric assessment ward at St Mary's, where she enjoyed working with Dr Agarwal. Of the out-patient department clerks, Miss Joan McGlasham took early retirement and Miss Margaret Apps moved to the District General Hospital.

The last Princess Alice out-patient clinics were held on 28th May 1976 after which all the clinics, apart from a psychiatric one at Roborough, transferred to the Kings Drive hospital, where Sister M.W. Tutt now ran the Eye clinic. Miss E. Guillot also centered her night-duty responsibilities at the District General Hospital. The histopathology, pharmacy and radiology departments moved over in the course of June and July, and the microbiology department about a month later. Miss Joan Taylor and most of the school of nursing moved into part of the education unit at the District General Hospital, although sadly, at the age of 60, Miss Taylor had a horrid death from cancer of the throat in the early 1980s. She was a knowledgeable and kindly tutor, and she was looked after by many nurses she had trained, who felt privileged to be able to care for her.

After the ex-Alfriston ward at St Mary's Hospital had been modified, most of the physiotherapy transferred there in 1977. What had been St Mary's dental surgery and previously the operating theatre became Dr Wojtulewski's office.

Apart from the day hospital and a few departmental areas, the Princess Alice Hospital was emptied, partly rebuilt, and prepared to receive the long-stay patients from Downside Hospital. An up-to-date central heating system was installed, new kitchens were built, and out-patient chiropody rooms provided, suitable for a hospital of some 105 beds.

The day hospital service continued and in 1977 the WRVS bought an hydraulic examination couch for the day patients. It was presented to Sister Constable, Staff Nurse McPherson and Mrs Joan Dobson by Mrs Barbara Harding (WRVS helper) and Mrs Betty Bryan (WRVS hospital organiser).

Among other shuffles, in 1976 Mrs Brenda Robinson followed Miss Chiverton as group medical records officer, and the admin. staff moved from *Avenue House* to No 9 Upperton Road, the ex-Maternity Home, in February 1978.

On 28th April 1978 the Rt Hon. David Ennals MP opened a psychogeriatric day hospital at Roborough, where part of the physiotherapy department had been housed. Welcomed by Dr Peter Linden, chairman of the East Sussex Health Authority, he met staff responsible for managing the unit including the consultant psychiatrist, Dr I.B. Raafat, senior nurses Mr L. Reinholds, Mrs F.K. Message and Mrs K. Bradley, the hospital secretary, Mr R. Ferguson, and Miss J.M. Handford, OT (psychiatry). The hospital included a clinic room, occupational therapy department, with an aids-to-daily-living section, and dining room.

In August 1978 Dr D.C. Taylor retired. Although he had transferred with the rest of pathology to the District General Hospital in 1976, his work had been mainly at the Princess Alice laboratory for 26 years. He was a competent histologist, a grower of orchids in the days when every pathologist poured out-of-date bottles of blood onto their flower beds - and a fisherman, so many tall tales were fondly told of him. One of his surgical colleagues says, 'Cliff Taylor always claimed that any private work he did was merely to be of help to the patient and the attending physicians and surgeons, "Doing this for charity, boyoh", as he would say. That is, until the day in 1970 when his secretary sent a bill in error to one of the surgeons, who discovered that for an operation in which the surgeon's fee was only £100 and the anæsthetist's £25, Cliff Taylor was asking the patient for a donation of £50 towards two pints of blood'.

The long-stay patients moved from Downside Hospital to the Princess Alice Hospital in November 1978 with most of the staff who had been caring for them.

Notes and References

1. Group medical advisory committee, 9/7/67, min. 326.
2. Eastbourne HMC, 6/9/67, min. 4908.
3. HMC Group medical sub-committee, 8/2/66, min. 3397.
4. Eastbourne HMC, 6/3/68, min. 5022.
5. Group medical advisory committee, 9/4/68, min. 534.
6. Ibid., 14/2/67, min. 249.
7. Eastbourne HMC, 1/5/68, min. 5065.
8. Group medical advisory committee, 14/11/67, min. 449.
9. Eastbourne HMC, 7/5/69, min. 5312.
10. Medical Officer of Health for Eastbourne, Annual Report 1970.
11. Group medical advisory committee, 11/11/69, min. 871.
12. Ibid., 9/9/69, min. 838.
13. Ibid., 9/12/69, min. 900.
14. Eastbourne HMC, 7/1/70, min. 5424/5.
15. Ibid. 1/3/72, min. 5958.
16. Ibid. 5/8/70, min. 5546.
17. Group medical advisory committee, 10/3/70, min. 959.
18. Eastbourne HMC, Medical Records Sub-Committee, 1/12/70; min. 94.
19. *Eastbourne Medical Gazette,* 1986; **3**: 98.
20. Eastbourne HMC, 3/3/71, min. 5696.
21. Group medical advisory committee, 10/11/70, min. 1146.
22. Ibid., 13/7/71, min. 1323.
23. Eastbourne HMC Finance sub-committee, 23/11/71, min. 2369.
24. Eastbourne HMC, 5/1/72, min. 5903.
25. Brown Ian. *A Doctor's Visits.* Gosport 1987.
26. *Eastbourne Herald,* 8/7/72.
27. *Eastbourne Herald,* 22/7/72.
28. Eastbourne HMC, General purposes committee, 21/1/72, min. 4191.
29. Group medical advisory committee, 13/3/73, min. 1766.
30. Eastbourne HMC, Catering committee, 16/4/73, min. 2906.
31. Eastbourne HMC, General purposes committee, 13/4/73, min. 4476.
32. Ibid. 20/10/72, min. 4359.
33. *Eastbourne Herald,* 2/11/74.
34. *Eastbourne Gazette,* 31/7/74.
35. Ibid., 26/6/75.
36. *Eastbourne Herald,* 4/10/75.
37. *Eastbourne Gazette,* 18/2/76.

40. Top is a view of the rear of the Princess Alice Hospital from Bedfordwell Road c. 1919. To the right is the wing containing Cavendish and Sydney Hudson wards. One of the original wards is towards the left and the extension can be surmised from the newer roof tiles. On the left are the old horse stables, which were converted into the first laboratory. Compare with the same view in 1991, with the enlarged ex-lab. and day rooms added to Cavendish and Sydney Hudson wards.

Chapter 11

A Centenary of the Princess Alice, but how much longer?

The Princess Alice Hospital embarked on its final stage, caring for elderly long-stay patients. With a resident population in 1978 of 202000, quite a few such patients could be found around Eastbourne. Long-stay by no means implied staying in till death: many patients went in and out, back to their families and homes, but in older people a relatively minor illness sometimes takes longer to settle than in the young, or there is extra need for readjustment or even to rearrange their house to overcome disabilities before they can be discharged.

Between 1976 and 1978 the wards were reconstructed. Tabor office became a small kitchen, and Miss Quick's appliance office next to Anne Elizabeth ward became the domestic supervisor's office.

In November 1978 when the patients at Downside Hospital were moved to the remodelled Princess Alice, the staff who transferred with them got down to making them feel at home. As Mrs Susan Eagan says, 'Although the move must have been traumatic for the vulnerable patients, they were much more comfortable at PA, all under one roof and enjoying every possible service to improve their quality of life'.

Among the Downside staff who transferred and who were still at Princess Alice in 1993 were Sister G. Chappell, enrolled Nurse Victor Hunte, and auxiliary nurses Mrs C. Charman, Mrs A. Chester and Mr E.G. Porras, with Mrs Fatima G. Dominques, catering assistant. Mrs Sheila Dawson, now restaurant supervisor, had been at the Princess Alice before 1976. Continuity of the medical care was also maintained; Drs Brown and Agarwal already had responsibilities at the Princess Alice, and Dr Anthony Churcher, the clinical assistant, transferred his sessions from Downside.

The night staff could be said to be the most faithful, with enrolled Nurse L. Woodrow, and auxiliary Nurses J. Grinstead, T. Grummitt, M. Lee, P. Lenahan, V. Martin, T. Pattenden, M. Pooley, V. Wallis and Mrs M.A. Porras still working at the hospital 15 years after the transfer.

There were 106 beds at Downside and 104 patients (73 female and 31 male) transferred, equally shared between Drs Agarwal and Brown. The wards at the Princess Alice were renamed after Sussex villages in line with the other hospitals. The original Michael Francis (later Arno) ward become Chichester, which received 18 female patients of Dr Agarwal from Alex. & Vic. ward at Downside Hospital. Anne Elizabeth and Crowden wards formed Arundel for 10 female and 10 male patients shared between Dr Agarwal and Dr Brown from Harding ward. Geraldine ward was renamed Kingston for 17 male patients of Dr Agarwal from Strange ward. The old matron's office on the right of the entrance was still a telephone and enquiry office, one previous telephone room opposite was a porters' room, another (on the side of the corridor away from the entrance) remained a kitchen. Mawhood ward, which had been Cavendish, became Amberley ward, with 10 beds split between the sexes and shared by Drs Agarwal and Brown, and Sydney Hudson ward was taken over for - administration. The old Tabor ward was now Ringmer with 17 beds for female patients of Dr Brown from Downside's Martin ward, while Gurney and Arno plus part of the old Casualty formed Wannock and Wannock Day Room making 22 beds for female patients of Dr Brown from Hollins ward.

As Miss Compton says, 'We tried to keep the move to Princess Alice quiet until we had the date, so as not to upset our patients. For me it was very satisfying to be associated with setting up the day hospital - a service so much appreciated by the patients - and with being involved in transforming PA from a busy surgical unit into a very happy long-stay home'. Breakfast was now at eight o'clock (0800h), dinner at noon and supper at six (1800h).

Sister Willis was on Wannock ward, Sister Channell Ringmer, and Sister O'Brien Chichester ward. Initially, Sister G. Chappell was on Arundel ward, with Sister S. Taylor (née Nichol) on Kingston. When Sister Taylor left to become a Macmillan nurse, Sister Chappell took over Kingston ward and Sister P. Milne replaced her.

The uniforms were now dark blue for Sisters, mauve and white check dresses for Staff Nurses, students wore light blue, enrolled nurses pale green, while pupils had a green and white striped dress and nursing auxiliaries a white overall coat.

In place of part of the old Casualty, out-patients, X-ray and physiotherapy, a Patients' Social Centre was opened, on Tuesday, 24th July 1979, by Walter Landauer, the famous pianist who was always ready to help any good cause. This was the year Mr S.A. Jenkins retired (he was to die in the mid-1980s after attacks of angina) to be replaced by Mr John D'Arcy whose NHS work, apart from visiting Princess Alice on request, was entirely at the District General Hospital.

The new physiotherapy and occupational therapy (OT) departments in Roborough House were geared towards rehabilitation. Physiotherapists included Miss Jill Bishop, Miss Helen Macdonald and Miss Jane Mcdonell, and the senior OT was Miss Brenda Marchant, followed by Mrs Rosalind Evans. Other OT staff included Miss Brenda Talbot and Mrs Susan Eagan (née Billings). Patients continued to be brought to Roborough for treatment along an open corridor, wrapped in blankets and sometimes waterproofs. The staff had their own hazards, however, for one morning the ceiling of OT fell down.

The Friends, with Mrs Barbara Church as chairman and Miss V.K. Podmore, secretary, and assisted by so many including Mrs H.G. Estcourt, Mrs Judy Maflin, Mrs D. Parsons, Mrs S. Pegler, Mrs M. Smart and later Mrs Milns, continued to provide those comforts that make all the difference to both patients and staff, and which included, in 1979, a piano for the Patients' Social Centre.

Unusually for Eastbourne, there was a work-to-rule from January to March 1979 as part of the national industrial action. Locally, the main impact was on the District General Hospital laundry. Mr Robert Ferguson, administrator of Princess Alice, was quoted as saying, "There has not been much at Princess Alice. The laundry was restricted, but we have not had to use disposables. The ambulancemen's strike on non-999 work is affecting the transport of patients and we are using private cars or taxis. The number of day patients is down by 70%, but staff are keeping in touch by visits and telephone calls".[1]

More in keeping, the day hospital was the recipient of £175 from the profits of the Eastbourne Football Charity Cup Final. The cheque was presented to Sister Mavis Constable by Mr Joe Angelman, mayor of Eastbourne.

Dr Ian Brown decided to retire on 1st January 1980 after almost 33 years in the Eastbourne hospitals. The appointment of a successor was delayed as various Regional bodies discussed the job description, after a failure to make an appointment. Miss Sheila Smith, principal nursing officer, who had left in December 1979 was replaced by Mr David Hay in the new year.

Between 1976 and 1980 the medical executive committee held its regular meetings in the day-hospital. It transferred to the District General Hospital in March 1980 while the day hospital was being redecorated, by which time the meetings commenced at 1845h, and apart from April 1980, never came back.

On 1st January 1981 Dr A. Karunanayake, Dr Brown's replacement, took up his post as consultant physician to the elderly; the year Dr R. Canagaratnam was appointed consultant psychogeriatrician. At the day hospital, Mrs Eve Moore was succeeded as senior physiotherapist in 1984 by Miss Roanna Mitchell and, when she retired two years later, Mrs Sybil DeGoes took her place.

Dr Joan B. Hester, consultant anæsthetist, had started a pain clinic in 1977 which had extended to a Macmillan Sisters' Home Care Service in 1979. When it became obvious that because of government cut-backs it would not be possible for the NHS to fund a continuing-care unit on the Kings Drive site, Father Christopher Spender and Canon Cyril Bess led a campaign to provide a private service which resulted in the opening of St Wilfrid's Hospice in 1981.

The projections of the 1981 census confirmed that Eastbourne's population had grown at the astounding rate of 32% over the twenty years from 1961, and that 25% of its population were over 65 years of age (compared with 14% nationally). This showed the need for greater funding and services for the district, bearing in mind that the over-65s use health-care facilities eight times more than the 15-65 age group. For 1981 the nurses' salaries at all the Eastbourne hospitals amounted to £8629758, and the hospital pharmacy costs were £570205.

The winter of 1981 saw determined opposition in the town to a Regional Health Authority announcement that a merger was planned between Eastbourne and Hastings health districts. Eastbourne won its fight, on that occasion, to remain independent.[2]

Avenida House, at 3 Upper Avenue, opened as a Mental Health Community Centre on 12th May 1982. Next door to Roborough, it had started life in 1892 as *Newlyn,* a private house in what was then Rutland Road.

41. Mr J. Angelman, Dr I.B. Raafat, Dr S.J. Surtees, Mr D.J.B. Platt and Mr D. Spilstead, left to right, at the opening of *Avenida House* {photo *Eastbourne Gazette/Herald*}.

Dr K.O.A. Vickery retired in January 1982 to be succeeded by Dr J.A.G. Watson, while Mr C.R. Dyte who retired at the end of March 1982 was replaced by Mr J.R. Sully. By April 1982 Princess Alice was part of the new Eastbourne Health Authority's "General Unit", along with the District General, All Saints and St Mary's hospitals, a staff of 2200 and annual expenditure of £15.8million. On 16th April Mr Ian Gow, Eastbourne's MP, visited the day hospital.

In preparation for national requirements, Mr Ron Lucas, Principal Nursing Officer at the In-Service and Post-Basic Training Education Centre in *Harberton,* organised courses on the psychiatric aspects of general nursing. Many of the lectures were in the marine-ply lecture hut between the Centre and *Taormina.*

Mr David Hay, Principal Nursing Officer 1980-82, was supplanted by Miss Margaret Pilbeam who, when she retired in 1985, was replaced by a Director of Nursing and Personnel, Mr Richard Ryland.

In April 1983 Sister Mavis Constable retired from the Day Hospital and Sister E.O. Francis took over. Mrs Constable was honoured by being selected to represent Eastbourne at the St James's Palace reception on 11th May to mark the General Nursing Council's change of title to the UK Central Council for Nurses, Midwives and Health Visitors.

A tougher anti-smoking policy was imposed by the Health Authority on the recommendation of Dr John Watson, the new District Medical Officer. The sale of cigarettes was stopped and a smoking ban applied to all clinical and public areas: from now on smoking would only be allowed in a few designated places. With hospitals such as the Princess Alice in mind, Dr Watson did suggest that a flexible approach be used for long-stay patients who were addicted to the habit.[3]

On 30th June 1983 the Princess Alice Memorial Hospital celebrated its centenary. The celebrations commenced with a letter of greetings from Prince Charles to Mr Derrick Platt, chairman of the Eastbourne Health Authority. A centenary exhibition was mounted in the day centre with memorabilia from the hospital's history by Mr Hugh Miller, administrator at the hospital, Miss Pat Faber, of the Health Education department, Mr Michael Robson-Salmon, medical photographer, and Dr John Surtees, medical archivist as well as chemical pathologist. A birthday tea party, which commenced with a display by the Sussex School of Dancing, ended with a cutting of the birthday cake, which had been made by Mr Roy James and members of the hospital's catering staff. Guests of honour were Mr and Mrs Leslie Mason (deputy mayor and mayoress).

At the evening reception Mr Platt welcomed the Marquis of Hartington, Sir Charles Taylor, Mr and Mrs Dennis Cullen (mayor and mayoress of Eastbourne) and some 200 guests who were either descendants of those who had attended the opening ceremony or who had close associations with the hospital.[4]

Later that year Dr Surtees suggested the institution of a Princess Alice Memorial Hospital Centenary Award, to promote research and development by staff at all the Eastbourne hospitals in commemoration of the 100 years' work of the Princess Alice, and in 1988 he proposed that this should be extended to include an award for the department of the year.[5] The awards continue to the present day, now geared to improvements in patient care and quality, the winner in 1992 being Nurse Sherrill Barrett for a project to provide patients with information on knee replacements.

In August 1983 the Health Secretary, Mr Norman Fowler, ordered that 68 jobs be cut in Eastbourne, which represented a threat to the standards of services, although "the axe", as it was termed by the local press, was reduced to 51 jobs by October and finally, after inflicting much extra work in the preparation of a response, was lessened even further.   By 1984 Mrs Vera Price was a staff representative at the Princess Alice Hospital.

Mrs Fitzgerald, considered by all as "A lovely woman", retired in 1983 and was replaced by Mr R. Hoyland, only for him to retire on health grounds in 1987.

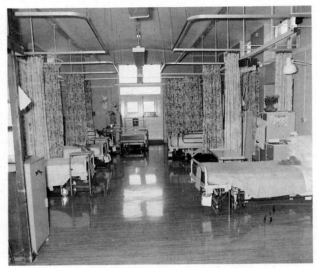

42. Ward of the hospital, 1983.

The Health Authority's ten-year blueprint of 1984 envisaged transferring 48 beds fron All Saints to Hellingly Hospital, where there was space. As this would leave All Saints with only 100 beds, that is, too few to provide a proper service, the beds could be added to Princess Alice and the services of the two hospitals neatly merged. The All Saints site could then be sold to use the money for the benefit of health services in and around Eastbourne.   The prospect of development at Meads did not engender much support from those living nearby and, as time went by, the chances of reviving Hellingly Hospital became remote.

Dr John Watson and Miss Margaret Pilbeam (Chief Nursing Officer) retired in 1985. Miss Pilbeam, who on her retirement at the age of 55 had charge of 1733 nurses in the Eastbourne hospitals and clinics, said, 'Nursing now is a tougher job mentally than when I began my career. Physically, though, I think it was a much harder job before'.[6]

The psychogeriatric day unit had Mrs J. Spicer as secretary from 1984 to 1989. She says one of her tasks was to watch out for those patients who were forever walking through the front door and rediscovering the joys of Eastbourne. Local GP, Dr G.D. Wilson, was a clinical assistant in psychogeriatrics.

A great occasion for the Sports and Social Club in September 1985 was an extension to the sports complex at the District General, celebrated by a grand opening organised by Malcolm Bastable. The club facilities at Princess Alice remained active, making full use of the large dance floor and the snooker tables.

In the autumn, on a sadder note, the 49-bed Esperance Nursing Home, as run by the nuns of the Holy Family of Bordeaux came to an end.[7] It was reopened the following year as the Esperance Private Hospital. The medical arrangements at *Chaseley* also changed, Mr Henry Wilson retiring, and Dr Iain Paterson assuming the position of GP to the unit. Mary Seiffert was the sole physiotherapist for many years.

Between 1981 and 1986 the population covered by the Eastbourne Health Authority increased by 14600 to 227000, of whom over 25% were 65 or more, compared with 17% nationally. Playing its part in catering for the elderly, by 1986 the Princess Alice site contained 104 beds for the elderly, a 40-place day hospital, and day-care facilities for 30 elderly mentally ill at Roborough House.

That year Dr M.B. Simpson chaired the newly formed AIDS Action Group, Mr A.J. Evans (Secretary to the Health Authority) moved to Tunbridge Wells, in April Mr Kevan Regan (Director of Finance and Computing) joined a local firm, T.R. Beckett Ltd, and in July Dr Peter Shave (Specialist in Community Medicine - Child Health) retired.

The Revd Canon Denys Giddey, who had retired as Chaplain to the Eastbourne hospitals in 1983, was followed by a brief chaplaincy and locums, and replaced in 1986 by the Revd Ray Morrison, from the chaplaincy staff of St Thomas's Hospital, London.

After a year of site-preparation work commencing in May 1985, Sir Peter Baldwin KCB, Chairman of the SE Thames Regional Health Authority, laid the foundation stone of Phase II of the District General Hospital on 11th July 1986. This was to contain all the medical and geriatric assessment beds from St Mary's Hospital, and some psychiatric beds and day places from Hellingly Hospital.

Following the implementation of general management, Mr John Sully was now the Eastbourne district general manager. Mr Noel Primrose was director of estates (with Mr John Fielding as estates manager), Dr Jeff Leece was director of community medicine and planning, and Mr Robert Jones was district physiotherapy manager. It was also the year when competitive tendering was introduced for catering, domestic and portering services at Princess Alice.

December 1986 saw Miss Jane Barrow (a successor to Miss Compton) reporting that the inability to recruit staff nurses continued to cause concern. The next year Mr Ryland said that the ratio of trained to untrained staff "is the worst in the Region". As usual, one suggestion was a crèche on the Princess Alice site.[8]

About this time, Sister K. Willis was on Wannock ward, Sister C. Channell on Ringmer, Sister V. Isted Chichester, Sister P. Milne Arundel, Sister Chappell remained on Kingston, and Staff Nurse B. Freakes was on Amberley until it was closed to make cost-efficiency savings.

The chapel at Princess Alice was demolished in 1987 and the services transferred to the Patients' Social Centre. Dr E.S. Searle was appointed specialist in community medicine in April 1987, and on 1st May 1987 Mrs Margaret Gooch took up the post of hospital manager at both Princess Alice and All Saints, replacing Miss Barrow, with Miss Wade remaining as Chief Nurse of the General Unit. Earlier, on 31st March Miss Audrey Balderson had retired after over 14 years as the Medical Staffing Officer, working from the District General Hospital since 1979, and Miss Elaine Wyatt took over the work. Mrs Iris Brooks was the District OT manager.

The Staff Sports and Social Club at Princess Alice continued its manifold activities with, among many other events, "Bingo" organised by Ann Wells, "Music Nights" by John O'Connor, and a Stoolball competition by Bob Sherwin.

Dr Conrad Athulathmudali commenced as consultant physician with interest in medicine of the elderly in 1987. The same year Dr Jeremy Bending was appointed consultant diabetologist. It was also the year when it was proposed to close 11 beds on Amberley ward to meet efficiency savings, this when of 39 beds closed at Princess Alice and All Saints at the beginning of 1986 for efficiency savings, eleven could not be reopened by the end of 1987.

In July 1987, Mrs Olive Francis followed Mr Hoyland as Clinical Nurse Manager for Princess Alice, which by now was the home for 96 patients, or residents as they tended to be called, whose need was continuing care. Gradually there was a change to a more home-like situation, with, as Mrs Francis says, 'the residents treated as always with dignity and respect, but now given choices as valued individuals'. Many doctors considered that smaller units nearer the patients' families were what was really needed, but that option would cost more. By now the doctors regularly looking after the patients were Drs Agarwal, Karunanayake and Conrad, with Dr Kanthi, who had succeeded Dr Churcher, doing five sessions as clinical assistant at the Princess Alice and the day hospital.

"Subjects for discussion" by members of the Health Authority's visiting panel in November included the audiometry establishment, physiotherapy staffing in the day hospital, and the heating of the hospital.[9] Now only of interest to "PA" was that A&E department recruitment, "Still presented regular problems".[10]

Training of enrolled nurses ceased at the end of the year, but the Friends continued their good work by donating £4000 for a Carter's lift and new bed curtains in Arundel ward.

A patient satisfaction survey at Princess Alice in 1987-8 found that patients thought more physiotherapy would help; that there was a too limited range of social activities, and that several patients were hungry during the night. It was decided that "action should be taken, although the inadequate physiotherapy for in-patients was from a lack of funds".

The fortieth birthday of the National Health Service was celebrated on 5th July 1988 with *Happy Birthday NHS* cakes, and the chairman visited long-stay patients at Princess Alice.

In 1988 it was estimated that the cost of a hip replacement was £2000, exclusive of the doctors' fees; expensive, but in 1948 such an operation would not have been possible.[11] Planning commenced that year for the Bourne work-rehabilitation unit to be built at the back of Roborough.

In September 1988 funds were diverted for the provision of a ward physiotherapy service at the Princess Alice, and Mrs Deidre Stark was appointed as senior physiotherapist. Later Amberley ward, which had been closed for lack of funding, was converted into a temporary physio. department within the main hospital, with Mrs Sylvia Weeks as one of the physio. helpers.

The Staff Training and Education Centre at Princess Alice held a series of training sessions on "IPR and PRP", which sound very painful even though Miss Flora Richards, the training manager, who had been at St Wilfrid's Hospice, would always do her best. Other Staff Training Courses about that time included "Resuscitation Procedures", "Nutrition Update", and "Family Planning". Mr Derek G. Keay recalls attending (as separate courses) seminars on "Trade Union Law" and "Preparing for Retirement" in the centre.

By 1988, a year after its foundation, the local branch of the NHS Retirement Fellowship, which met on the last Thursday of the month in the Staff Sports and Social Centre at Roborough, had over 200 members. It was one of the most successful branches in the country, thanks mainly to the enthusiasm of its secretary, Mrs Doreen Pidgeon, and chairman, Mr T. Henry Wilson.

Throughout 1988-92, the community midwives were based at *Taormina*. The parent education program was organised from there with regular teaching sessions in the large room on the ground floor, which was shared with OT. In September 1988 Mrs Diana Miller, a practising midwife in Eastbourne for over 35 years, and latterly the Parentcraft Liaison Sister (based at *Taormina* during 1990-92) was asked to speak at a national study on Parentcraft in Northern Ireland. She was instrumental in obtaining for Princess Alice the stained glass window, depicting *"Suffer the little children to come unto me"*, from the St Mary's Hospital chapel when that building was demolished in 1990.

St Wilfrid's Hospice had plans for expansion and on 1st April 1989 appointed Dr John Carey to the new post of medical director; up till then Dr Joan Hester had acted as medical adviser.

In 1989 came the first stirrings of the provider/purchaser concept, and the idea was floated of providing a NHS nursing home for the Princess Alice patients, which would set standards for private nursing homes. On a more practical footing, 690 out of 1940 district nursing staff (or 36%) lodged appeals against their gradings following a re-grading exercise,[12] causing a tremendous work load for the personnel department and its deputy director, Mr Colin Bowler, in particular. Mr Richard Ryland, director of nursing and personnel, said the exercise was "likely to be painful ... and there are those who will argue that the initial costing was wrong".[13]

In the September 1989 competitive tendering for Hotel Services at the Princess Alice and All Saints Hospitals, the adjudication panel of Messrs J. Neale, N. Johnson, M. MacLean and C.D. Bowler decided that the In-House tender be accepted.[14] It is of interest that the tender was £74000 above the current budget and that the only private tender was £1290000.

A sponsored keep-fit event was held on 15th October 1989 at the Day Hospital, by Mrs Pat Baker, to raise funds to adapt an ex-ambulance, which had been given to the hospital, so that it could take wheelchairs and enable more patients at Princess Alice to go on day trips.

More fine-tuning of the management structure was needed and on 1st November 1989 the units of management were reduced to two - "Community Health Services" with Mrs Stephanie Parkes-Crick as general manager and "Acute Hospital Services" with Mr Clive Uren. Fiery-tuning was in evidence on 5th November when Edwina Currie MP visited the hospitals and essentially said, 'I've changed the rules about funding, so you won't get any more'. No-one was sorry to see her get egg on her face later.

During 1989 the Friends bought a £2500 Parker bath [one side swings up allowing easy access] for Wannock ward, and Kirton chairs at a cost of £3225.

It is not often a person can do good some fifty years after their death, but Mr Arthur Beckett had left shares in his company, TR Beckett, to the Princess Alice Hospital and in 1989 the Health Authority was given permission by the Department of Trade & Industry to sell them for £3.4 million. It was by means of this windfall that a £400000 crèche and a paediatric development unit could be built in the grounds of the District General Hospital, with the Friends contributing towards a diabetic day centre.[15] Funding of new consultant posts was facilitated by reductions in the domestic and hotel establishments and a more aggressive use of the capital of endowment funds.

On 12th January 1990 a new day room on Ringmer ward was opened, thanks again to funds from the Friends, and in February a national conference on vocational qualifications was held in the Staff Training and Education Centre, organised by Alison Ridout and Margaret Browne.

The hospital stays in the hearts of local people, who give up their time for the patients in many different ways; for example Elizabeth Hale (Mrs Betty Pearce) often entertains the patients, and the East Dean and Friston Women's Institute regularly send in presents of knitted blankets and gift-wrapped parcels for Christmas. Helpers include those who have volunteered to make the morning coffee and feed some patients, other volunteers do shopping for the patients, while students from the Eastbourne College of Further Education take on tasks that will stand them in good stead for their own careers, the British Red Cross

Society provide a beauty care service, and the WRVS take a trolley round the day hospital.

These days there are many aids for the nurses and staff, such as *Mecanaid* bathchairs and overhead hoists, and many persons have provided substantial items to help the good work. The proceeds of the 1988 Eastbourne Show went towards lifting belts; Harry and Vera Sillett donated a *Sara* hoist for wheel chair patients in Kingston ward; the "Regulars of the British Queen" bought another for Arundel ward; Mr and Mrs Lewis bought a garden bench seat for Kingston ward in memory of Mrs Boston; and others have donated *Aijo* baths and chairs. Sister Chappell expresses the thoughts of the staff when she says, 'People are so supportive and help us to keep it as homely as we can'. Many of the senior sisters now wore everyday clothes instead of uniform.

For those in uniform the Sisters have a navy dress, Charge Nurses a white coat with navy epaulettes, Staff Nurses a white dress with blue belt, student nurses have a white dress without a belt, with blue bands in their caps, enrolled nurses have white dresses with a green belt, the physiotherapists have a white tunic with navy trousers and the OT white with green trousers.

Visiting is "any time on any day" and relatives are welcome to stay overnight. Meal times vary; the usual breakfast time is nine o'clock, lunch at noon and supper about six o'clock. Mid-morning coffee and mid-afternoon tea are served, with hot or cold drinks available from vending machines at all times.

In April 1990 Mr J.V. Wellesley was appointed chairman of the Eastbourne Health Authority by the Secretary of State for Health, succeeding Mr D.J.B. Platt. Later a Management Board was established for the Eastbourne hospitals, including Princess Alice. Mr Platt was the chairman and other members included Clifford Grinstead, Peter Hallam, Roy Heasman, Tony Loader, Isobel O'Sullivan, Clive Uren, Dr Peter Nash and Max MacLean.

By 1991 the district dietetic manager was Miss Jennie Starr, Mr Hugh Graham was the district health promotion manager and Mr Douglas Bailey the district catering adviser.

On 3rd November the Staff Sports and Social Club mounted the usual Bonfire Party at Princess Alice, and in the same month the new Regional Supplies Distribution Centre started at Maidstone. Staff thought a firework or two was needed at the Centre when All Saints Hospital's first order to the Centre was delivered at Chatham.

At the Friends' 1991 Annual General Meeting, Mrs Barbara Church paid a tribute to Mrs Do Parsons, who had done so much for the hospitals since 1953. The Chairman, Mrs Ann Caffyn, reported the gifts to Princess Alice and mentioned the work of those who by organising Open Gardens (Pam Alexander, Jill Churcher, Anne Cutler, Roxanne Hayes, Ailna Martin, Joanne Smith, Ethel Walters and Pam Wells), the Summer Fête raffle (Gill Garner) and the Flag Weeks (Douglas Sissons) made the gifts possible. That year the Friends bought bed curtains for Kingston ward, where relatives had provided duvets for the beds, as Sister Chappell says, 'A worthwhile advance'.

Miss P.D. Wade retired in April 1990. When Miss Gooch retired, Mrs E.O. Francis acted up for a year and in 1992 moved from Princess Alice to the District General. That year an Elderly Assessment unit was established at the District General Hospital, with Sue Wyatt as clinical nurse manager, and ward managers Sister V. Wren and charge nurses R. Gordon and M. Smith.

At the same time as the 1992 Barcelona Games, a Princess Alice Olympiad was held with each ward sending five competitors to throw the discus or race the egg and spoon. Organised by Dee Stark, Caroline Lees and Jean Barnard, who is in charge of social activities, the winners were Kingston ward.

September 9th was an Open Day for the Audiology department in Glynde ward. Audiology technicians, Sandra Freeman and Pauline Waters and others, showed how they assisted the ENT consultant Mr K. Singh, in performing hearing tests, fitting deaf aids and counselling tinnitus sufferers.

The occupational therapy team for both in-patients and the day hospital has been led since 1984 by Miss Julie Haworth. Towards the end of 1992 Mrs Florence Johnson, an OT technical instructor at the day hospital, retired, about the same time as Mrs Shirley Peckham who had worked there, although more recently at the District General Hospital. Mrs B. Powell, who had also been at Gildredge and Downside, and Mr M. Gosden, an OT technician, remained in the department, under Mrs Margaret Stirmey, the Head OT (physical disability) who was based at the District General Hospital.

On 1st October 1992 Mr Robert Jones became therapy services manager, combining physio. and OT along with other services, such as speech therapy.

Mrs Joan Dobson, an administrator since 1967, retired from the post of administrator at Princess Alice and All Saints hospitals on 2nd November 1992, when Mark Pemberton became Service Manager, Care of the Elderly.

In December 1992 Mrs Joan E. Williams, Voluntary Help Coordinator, retired after 14 years. Her office had been at Hellingly Hospital, St Mary's Hospital, and since 1989 at Princess Alice, where Geraldine Griffiths is now.

By 1993 the staff included Sister G. Chappell, with Junior Sister A. Hart on Kingston ward, Sister V.M. Martin on Arundel ward with Ros Burke as Junior Sister, Sister N. Steele (who succeeded Sister B. Cunliffe) on Ringmer ward with J. Dunn, and Sister F. Prevatt on Chichester ward with Staff Nurse D. Singh and enrolled Nurse Victor L. Hunte. Sister E.K. Page, who had been on Wannock ward, recently retired due to ill-health. Bridget Wright followed her for a few weeks until Sister M. Davies came from All Saints, working with Junior Sister M. Speigenhalter. Others included Sister B.A. Ginn, still Night Sister along with Sister M. Crowley. In the main office was Miss D.J. Meech and, until she retired, Mrs A.M. Emerson, who had worked at every Eastbourne hospital.

Miss Lyn Johnson was the clinical nurse manager for both Princess Alice and All Saints, Sister A. Hare was responsible for training, and Pam Rockingham, who had acted up as clinical nurse manager until Mr Pemberton's appointment, was now the day hospital manager with Sister V.L. Brand. Mrs Mary Perrens was the WRVS District Organiser.

In February 1993 staff learnt that the Princess Alice in-patient services would be sold off to Associated Nursing Services, who had submitted the lowest tender. If the proposal went ahead, it would mean that 1994 would witness the end of the Princess Alice Memorial Hospital.

The hospital was like one big, happy family; the visitors were now welcome to come anytime and many helped to look after their relatives. The unspoken axiom was dedication, and such show-business slogans as, "We don't want it good, we want it Thursday" had no place in the hearts of the staff, who did every clinical activity as soon as they could and as well as possible, even if no-one would ever know just how conscientiously they had worked.

One patient explained, 'In a nursing home, I was in one room and couldn't see anything out of the window. At the Princess Alice there are lovely views, and every day there is something happening at that wonderful Social Centre'.

Dr Basil Kent, who worked for some thirty years at the hospital, said 'Looking back over my professional life I have seen the virtual disappearance of the killer pneumonia thanks to sulphonamides and penicillin; nephritis [kidney disease], which was very common, has basically vanished; diphtheria has been defeated; the "fevers" no longer exist as I knew them; diuretics [drugs to remove fluid], such as *Lasix,* have totally altered the attitudes to heart failure; antibiotics have virtually emptied the children's wards, you seldom see mastoids [ear infection] or osteomyelitis; gonorrhoea and syphilis [venereal diseases] have been contained; tuberculosis has been shown the door by radiography and streptomycin; tranquillisers, such as *Largactil,* stand out as providing the opportunity to open doors in psychiatry, and as for anæsthesia, few other advances have proved more beneficial to mankind. In my lifetime, surgery has progressed more than in all the preceding millenia'.

Mr Stanley Braiden says, 'Folk were frightened of hospitals. Everything was pinstripe, starch and regimentation. Now everyone is so down to earth and so kind and understanding that fear has almost vanished and patients are relaxed before admission. ... In the old days every ward had its own band, which started its tunes at eleven at night with kidney dishes, sterilisers, and metal bedpans, now swept away with the pinstripes and starch - along with my Christian name which was changed to "Luv". I am sure that this atmosphere goes a long way towards the successful treatment of to-day's patients in all the hospitals'.

Mrs Pamela Milne (née Fillery) concludes, 'My training days were some of the happiest days of my life, the extremely long hours and hard working conditions were compensated by the comradeship of so many super nurses and the wonderful feeling of being fufilled at the end of each day'.

Dr Frank Gillett, emeritus consultant anæsthetist, who also covered for the physicians during the1939-45 war, died at the age of 90 in December 1992. He might not be expressing the views of to-day's anæsthetic establishment when, in musing about his working days, he commented, 'Chloroform was such a smooth anæsthetic', but he encapsulated the thoughts of all patients and staff when he added, 'Princess Alice was such a happy hospital'.

Miss Flora Clark, who nursed at the "PA" from 1942 to 1976, says, 'Everybody worked together and enjoyed their time there and there was good cooperation with all the services. It had a good name - even when a little cottage hospital, none talked ill of it. Improvements were needed in 1948 when there was the feeling that the intention was to improve the health of the nation'.

Mrs Wells, who was matron de Pinto from 1947 to 1961, says 'I considered it a great privilege to be appointed matron at the age of 36 and found it a happy, efficient hospital, well loved by the patients. With only 120 beds, it was possible to know every patient - and the relatives of the very ill ones - as well as the personal interests of the staff, and staff parties were like family gatherings.

'Changes have to come and it was right that the local authority hospitals, of which St Mary's was a good example, were upgraded. Now we have the excellent District General Hospital, with so many facilities that seriously ill patients no longer have to be taken to the teaching hospitals far from their homes.

'If I had my life all over again, I would happily repeat a nursing career'.

Notes and References

1. *Eastbourne Herald,* 17/2/79.
2. *Eastbourne Herald,* 10/1/81 and 21/2/81.
3. *Eastbourne Herald,* 23/4/83.
4. *Eastbourne Herald,* 2/7/83.
5. Eastbourne Health Authority, Unit Executive/Members visiting panel, 12/4/88.
6. *Eastbourne Herald,* 7/9/85.
7. *Eastbourne Herald,* 23/11/85.
8. Eastbourne Health Authority, Unit Executive/Members visiting-panel, 9/12/86.
9. Ibid., 13/10/87.
10. Eastbourne Health Authority, 15/7/86, agenda item 7.
11. Ibid., 16/2/88, agenda item 11.
12. Ibid., 17/1/89, min. 1420.
13. *Eastbourne Herald,* 24/8/88.
14. Eastbourne Health Authority, 19/9/89, agenda item 13.
15. Ibid., 18/7/89, min. 1505.

Chapter 12

Downside Hospital

(formerly the Isolation or "Fever" Hospital)

In 1885 Mr Carew Davies Gilbert leased a "site at Upwick" to the Eastbourne Corporation for "the erection thereon of a sanatorium for infectious diseases".[1] This site, which developed into Downside Hospital, was to the west of the town, on the road to Brighton, along what is now the A259 East Dean Road.

The resultant small, corrugated-iron building served as an infectious diseases hospital for Eastbourne, along with a one-storey flint building, dating from 1875, on the Union workhouse site, later St Mary's Hospital.

The building of the Union workhouse infirmary in 1889 meant that the flint building had to be knocked down, so there were additions on the "Upwick" site to supplement the old iron hut (later Breach ward) and form Eastbourne's isolation hospital. They consisted of what was later part of the administration block, Hollins & Rowe and Martin wards, the coach house and laundry.

The official title was the Borough Sanatorium for its first 25 years; the Municipal Isolation Hospital from 1914 to 1948; and for its last 30 years Downside Hospital. Most people called it "the Sanny" or the Fever Hospital.

The idea was that isolation, taking a cue from quarantine, would hamper the spread of contagious disease. This was when scarlet fever, diphtheria, erysipelas, tuberculosis and typhoid fever killed thousands every year in Britain. Even the last epidemic of cholera had been only some 20 years before, while smallpox was ever present with a terrible outbreak in 1870-73. Despite these visitations, apart from a report that a John Grace had converted a house at Seaside into a "pest house" in 1771, no provision had been made for infectious illness before 1875.

In those days if your child had a fever, carbolic-soaked sheets were hung over the bedroom door and, unless you were able to afford a private nurse, the young patient would be taken away in the fever ambulance, "the fever van", to what every town had, the "Fever Hospital", separated from the last few houses by a green field or two. In these Isolation (and isolated) Hospitals the patients were cared for by members of Miss Nightingale's disciplined nursing service, with, until antisera became available, a fairly equal chance of recovery or death. A typical stay was six weeks, no visitors were allowed and all personal possessions were burnt to stop the spread of infections.

The aim was to stop the spread to others, for there was little in the way of cure for the fevers.

Before antibiotics, and immunisations, and improved housing conditions, isolation did reduce the spread of disease, although not as much as its advocates thought, but to have any value it had to be applied widely and be harshly restrictive. So isolation hospitals were not only feared by children, but hated. Understandable, when the youngsters were not allowed to see their loved ones, the house had to be fumigated and all "fomites" [inanimate sources of infection] such as beloved books and clothes, had to be destroyed.

To ward off the possibility of catching an infection, Mrs Ann Gordon says that the children had a street chant whenever they caught sight of the fever van,

> "Touch yer collar,
>
> Never swalla'
>
> Never catch the fever ".

In 1889 the hospital was the concern of the East Sussex Medical Officer of Health (MOH), Dr E.F. Fussell. Eastbourne did not have its own MOH until Dr Reginald Dudfield was appointed the next year.

The Sanitary Committee of the Borough Council were in no haste to incur the costs of opening the new building until they had complaints from the local doctors, who reported "... Sanitary condition of the Old Building is thoroughly bad, bedding is unclean, total lack of medical appliances, the closet is offensive and the storage of food deplorable. ... Fourteen persons reside in the hospital, six infectious, and attended to by one person only. ... Four children were placed in the admin. block of the new building, one developed diphtheria and was moved to the old building. An infant suffering from typhoid fever was placed in the old building, moved to new building and back again, and died two weeks later."

The Town Hall response was, "Borough Fever Hospital. A special committee will provide proper rules and regulations and the new hospital will be furnished without delay".[2]

Admission to the "Borough Sanatorium" was at first "limited to cases of Scarlet and Enteric Fevers and Diphtheria", although one patient with erysipelas [a serious skin infection] was admitted in 1892. That year 29 cases of diphtheria, 35 of scarlet fever [severe sore throat with rash] and 10 of enteric fever [typhoid, or paratyphoid fevers] were admitted, representing 56% of cases notified.[3]

Even in those days doctors were questioning how practical it was to keep patients isolated until they were no longer infectious. On 27th May 1890 Dr James Adams read a paper to the Eastbourne Medical Society on the question of how long patients were infectious with diphtheria. He "related a recent series at the sanatorium [Downside] which appeared to show that the duration of infection is more prolonged than commonly supposed". Meetings often demonstrated larynx and trachea [windpipe] linings coughed up by diphtheritic patients at the hospital, for example, that October, a complete cast of the trachea was shown which had been removed from a 7½-year-old boy, who had died 26 hours later.[4]

Before 1890 the annual death rate in Eastbourne from diphtheria was 25.8, from a population of about 35000, but the incidence and severity of diphtheria varied from year to year. In 1890 there was an epidemic with 495 cases and 59 deaths. The discovery, that year, of anti-diphtheria serum furnished the first effective therapeutic weapon, apart from tracheostomy [surgically opening up the windpipe]. It was not always effective. Dr E. Downes related to the Medical Society the case of a "little girl aged 2½ who had nasal diphtheria" in November 1895. After six days of illness "she was taken to the sanatorium [Downside] where she was given 2 cc. of antitoxin twice a day, but she died five days later".

Medical Officer, Matron. & Nursing Staff. 1902.

43. Miss M.G. Bailey, matron, and staff of the Eastbourne Sanatorium [Downside] in 1902.

Whilst anti-serum provided merely a temporary protection, and only reduced the mortality by a third, this still meant that it saved around 1000 children a year in England and no general practitioner (GP) went out on his rounds without a syringe of anti-serum, even into the 1930s.

We now know that fomites are not an important means of spread in most contagious diseases, such as diphtheria, but 100 years ago doctors were just unravelling the ways of infection. Locally, removal of household refuse had only begun, many houses did not have piped water, and on the broader scale, it hadn't even been proved that mosquitoes were involved in malaria. Not unreasonably, some people persisted in believing that disease was spread by "miasmas", or bad smells, but gradually doctors realised the importance of carriers.

In his annual MOH report for 1893 Dr Dudfield states, "Although 16 cases of this disease [typhoid fever - a carrier-spread infection, mainly of the bowels] were notified during the last year, yet as a matter of fact, the town was exceedingly free from the disease", when to-day any case would be a matter of great concern.

In 1894 the Eastbourne Schoolmasters' Association entered into negotiations with the Council "in respect of provision of accommodation at the sanatorium for patients from the private schools of Eastbourne". Hindrance from the landowners meant that this arrangement was delayed for five years, but it would mean that many inadequate isolation sick-bays connected with private schools could be closed, not to mention the cash it would provide for the Council.

Apart from stopping spread to others, there was possibly some benefit to the isolated patients. In his 1895 report, when 72% of notified infectious cases were admitted, Dr W.G. Willoughby, the MOH since 1894, points out that for diphtheria, scarlet and enteric fever cases, those removed to the "sanatorium" had a fatality of 4.7%, while for those not in the sanatorium the fatality was 17.2%. The data is open to various interpretations: you could say that the severely ill died before admission, but Dr Willoughby was a great protagonist for isolation.

That there was resistance to providing more isolation accommodation on the site can be seen from a letter of 3rd March 1895, written by Mr H.W. Fovargue, the Town Clerk, headed "Proposed extensions to Infectious Hospital".

"The summer before last it was necessary to erect large tents in the grounds and there are at any one time at least 80 cases under treatment. The East End consists of low, marshy land and the Medical Officer of Health advises that the patients would not stand the same chance of recovery as they would in the high, breezy parts of the town. It is most undesirable to have different centres of infection ... as separate matrons, nurses and staff would need to be engaged."

The smallpox epidemic in Eastbourne between August and December that year, with 15 cases, and two deaths, demolished the opposition. The first patient who died was described as "a confirmed drunkard", which appeared to explain everything, but most of the cases were as a result of contact with clothing sent from London, where an epidemic was raging, for smallpox is one of the few infections where fomite transmission is a risk. As far as Dr Willoughby was concerned, "Two admirable results" were the speedy erection of a Smallpox Hospital and an Isolation Cottage. The hospital, costing £1250, was an 18-bed, four-ward building of corrugated iron on the Crumbles, while the cottage (*Acacia Villa,* in 357 Seaside, now a PDSA clinic for sick pets) was established for those who were not ill, but who had been exposed to the disease and might develop it.[5]

In 1896 over 80 cases of typhoid fever were notified, of which 52 (with two deaths) were "Bourne Stream cases". This epidemic started when persons drank of the Bourne Stream (from which Eastbourne takes its name) in preference to the Water Company's mains. Analysis of the Bourne Stream water had shown contamination, but as Dr Willoughby says in his MOH report for 1896, despite putting a grating over the supply on 15th August, and posting notices of the danger by 21st August, the public refused to "part with their faith in the special virtues of the water"; instead they tore open the grating, defaced the notices and sent a deputation to the Sanitary Committee to voice their protest. When the first case of typhoid fever (which has a three-week incubation period) was notified on 17th September the public mood changed and charges were made that the local authority had not acted soon enough. Apart from one or two cases who had moved away, all were admitted to the sanatorium [Downside].

On 30th October 1899 the freehold of the hospital was purchased for £3750, when the Corporation obtained compulsory purchase powers after Mr Davies Gilbert had objected to any further land being used for this purpose. Additional wards were built at a cost of £7107 and the increased accommodation was opened towards the close of 1902. The six separate pavilions, as they were called, provided 26 beds for scarlet fever, 18 for diphtheria, four for typhoid fever, and 17 reserve beds in the "iron building", later Breach ward. These figures are for adults and, as children were the usual patients, more could be accommodated.

In 1902 agreement was reached with the Principals of Private Schools for Girls in Eastbourne for construction of a separate block for the girls of these schools. This was commenced in 1904 and opened in January 1905 to provide seven beds for scarlet fever, six for diphtheria, and one observation bed. Appropriately, it was named ALEXANDRA and VICTORIA.

The hospital's seven wards were on two levels and effectively two separate units. On the lower level, nearest the entrance in Longland Road was Harding ward, followed by Strange, and furthest away Alex. & Vic. by the vegetable beds. On the upper level, nearer East Dean Road, was Hollins & Rowe ward block, behind the Lodge; Martin ward was behind the building forming the nurses' home, matron's apartments, catering department, stores and administrative offices; and Breach ward was nearby. Twenty-six beds in two of the pavilions were let off as private wards for schools.

The two levels were linked by a winding road, and centrally there was a flight of steps. Other minor, and often well-worn, paths and steps made access between the buildings.

As Mrs D.M. Bates (née Clarke) says, 'adverse weather, especially winter snow, but also heavy rain or strong winds, created difficulties in conveying meals and any goods which could not be moved easily up and down the many steps'.

The reason for the names of the wards (or pavilions) at Downside becomes clear when we learn that the mayor in 1902 was Alderman STRANGE, the chairman of the Local Authority Sanitary Committee was Dr O'Brien HARDING, the deputy chairman was Councillor M. MARTIN, and other members of the committee included Councillors BREACH, HOLLINS and ROWE.[6]

When infectious disease was prevalent and widespread, the diagnosis and treatment of these cases was a crucial part of the work of the Medical Officer of Health. Dr William George Willoughby visited the fever hospital every morning. He was, as far as the GPs were concerned, the consultant in infectious diseases. He would be called in to corroborate a diagnosis, to arrange transfer to the appropriate hospital and to treat the cases. There was a close liaison between Dr Willoughby and the GPs, and he was proud of this relationship.[7]

44. The lower wards, looking along the road towards "Rose Cottage", behind the far hedge, 1976. The chapel is to the left.

By 1893 Miss M.G. Bailey was the matron of the "Borough Sanatorium" and she continued through to the 1930s. Miss Bailey hardly ever left the place. In John Stevens' words, 'she lived as though it was a convent'. Her only close friends were Dr Willoughby and the Rector of Our Lady of Ransom Church.[8]

In 1896, for the first time, Dr Willoughby achieved his target of removing all cases of scarlet fever in the town from the household to the isolation hospital.

From 1897 to 1900 there were four deaths each year from typhoid fever. In 1900 of nine typhoid cases admitted to "Downside" one died, whereas of six cases not admitted, three were fatal. The next year of 56 cases of diphtheria, five required tracheostomy at the hospital, with success in three.

Two cases of smallpox in 1902 were isolated in the Crumbles [Langney] Smallpox Hospital, as were two contacts who refused vaccination and who "took the disease". This was the first use of the hospital since it had been built seven years before and it was only to be used once again in its 50 years' existence. Another example of a good idea being put into effect too late.

In 1904, Dr Willoughby debated whether to admit tuberculous (TB) cases to "Downside", but he decided that Breach ward was not suitable, because it had only one entrance and faced north.

The next year, for the first time since it had fully opened, there were two days over the year when the hospital was empty.

The following years, however, saw several diphtheria outbreaks. In 1908 there were 258 cases and 263 the next year, but only 14 and eleven deaths respectively, thanks to the use of antiserum. Almost every case was admitted to the hospital. In 1909 twenty deaths from influenza, one from chickenpox, two from measles, and six from diarrhoea were recorded. It was also the year that Miss R. Clark took up her post as the first school nurse. At the end of her long life, she was to come to Downside Hospital as a patient in the 1960s.

There were 37 deaths from infantile diarrhoea in 1911, and the next year saw an epidemic of 451 cases of scarlet fever, Dr Willoughby being one of the victims.

Almost all the patients were shot off to "Downside" in the "fever van", with its polished wood panels, and Mrs Doris Bates says, 'I have a faint recall of the horse-ambulance rattling along', when she was admitted with a fever at the age of three, just before the 1914-18 war.

During part of the war Dr Willoughby served in Macedonia when, in his absence, Dr Nora Smith ran the department.

In the course of the 1914-18 war, 448 servicemen were treated in the hospital and a letter was received from the Army Council expressing thanks " ... for the splendid work done by this hospital for Military patients".

In 1920 there were 254 admissions. Of 111 with scarlet fever, four died; of 75 with diphtheria there were two deaths; and ten influenzal pneumonias had two deaths. There was one case of encephalitis lethargica, which was a "new" virus infection which reached epidemic proportions in the 1920s. The average stay in hospital for the scarlet fever cases was 38 days and the cost per person per week was £6/14/0d [£6.70p].

John Stevens says, 'I had a turn at "the Sanny" in 1922 with scarlet fever, when I was carted off from home by the horse-drawn vehicle known as "the fever van". I was first in Martin ward and then went to Hollins'.

In June 1922 a soldier suffering from diarrhoea was admitted by Dr Willoughby as a possible typhoid fever. He died shortly afterwards of widespread [miliary] tuberculosis, and Dr Willoughby describes how he was misled by a blood test [Widal] which reacted to typhoid, but the test was only picking up the typhoid inoculation which soldiers were given routinely.

In the course of a meeting held at "Downside" on 26th June 1923, Dr Willoughby stated that he always liked to leave a patient for six hours after an injection of anti-diphtheria serum before tracheostomy "as the need for the operation did not arise after the antitoxin took effect". He went on to say that vomiting and suppression of urine were signs of a fatal outcome. Even so, the severity of infections was lessening, and on 1st January 1925 part of *Acacia Villa* opened as a child welfare clinic because it was not being used for isolation.

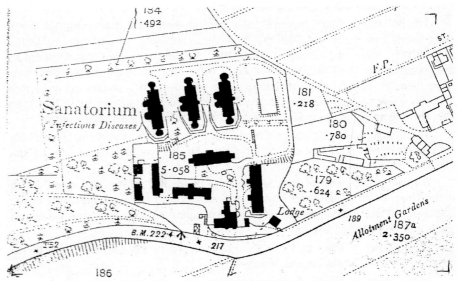

45. Plan of the hospital site, OS 1910. East Dean Road runs along the lower border. Hollins & Rowe ward block is above "The Lodge", with Martin ward to the left; Breach ward and the coach house and laundry are further to the left. The three pavilion blocks are at the top of the plan. Longland Road is to the right.

By 1928 "Downside's" bed complement had been reduced to 62, in seven separate blocks, with not more than 14 in any one block. Diphtheria was the commonest diagnosis, 113 admissions, but only four deaths over the year, followed by scarlet fever, measles, chickenpox, erysipelas, enteric fever and even two cases of scabies, for by now "any case of infectious disease of any sort" was admitted, although certain conditions, such as whooping cough, went to St Mary's Hospital. The methods of disinfection were still superheated steam for clothing and bedding, and washing with formalin for items which would not stand a temperature of 260°F, such as furs and boots. For house fumigation, formalin gas was sometimes used, but spraying with formalin or *Izal* solution, with lime-washing, repainting and repapering was preferred. Perchloride of mercury and sulphur candles had not been used since the turn of the century.

In 1929, for the first time since 1902, there was an outbreak of smallpox and the Crumbles Smallpox Hospital was in use from November 1929 into 1930. Miss Olive Poole (later Bartholomew) was one of 35 cases admitted to the Smallpox Hospital, taken there in the fever van, driven by Mr W.A. Hollobone who lived in the Lodge at the sanatorium [Downside]. She thinks she was there for about three months. She is certain she was never allowed visitors, and that the patients were kept behind high wire fencing, 'like a P.O.W. camp'. At the end of her stay she was taken to "Downside" to have all her clothes fumigated.

Despite such outbreaks, the cycle of infectious disease was changing. By 1931 Eastbourne had gone for a decade without a scarlet fever death, although the "Borough Isolation Hospital" prudently maintained 62 beds at the ready, staffed by one matron, one Sister, one charge nurse, and six assistant nurses.

In his annual report for 1933 Dr Willoughby mentioned that infectious diseases had been light in numbers recently and the 62 beds might seem excessive, when the total cost of "Downside" for the year was £4011, with each patient costing £4.30p a week, although there was an income from schools and patients of £492. He also stated that "owing to inroads of the sea, it is more than likely that the Crumbles Smallpox Hospital must shortly be abandoned".

In December 1933 Miss Bailey died after over 40 years as matron. Dr Willoughby paid a glowing tribute to her skilled and kindly care. Miss D. Sandy was appointed in her place from February 1934.

It was at a January 1935 meeting of the Eastbourne Medical Society, when Dr W. Gunn of the London County Council estimated the average diphtheria death rate at 20%, that notice was given of a new "toxoid vaccine" just coming into use for preventative immunisation.

During the year agreement was reached between Eastbourne County Borough and Hailsham Rural District Council on a payment for the accommodation of persons from the rural area suffering with infectious disease. After 1st April 1937 up to 15 beds were allocated, and use of the Borough ambulance for the transport of these patients was included in the price.

Mrs E.M. Fuller (née Walder) went into "Downside" on 5th November 1937 at the age of six with a sore throat and was there for three weeks, which 'was a short stay compared with my fellow patients. We were not allowed to have any visitors, I could only see my mother through a sash window, and I had to write notes to her because the nurses would not let me raise my voice to enable mother to hear. Those nurses were dragons. The ward had six beds, three along each wall, and they were moved into line for window visiting. We were not allowed out of bed the whole time, we were not allowed any toys and only one book, which could not be taken home'. She remembers the position of her bed quite clearly because, for three weeks, all she could see against the skyline was St Elisabeth's Church in Victoria Drive.

Under Miss Sandy's matronship in the 1930s, diphtheria cases were still nursed flat and were not allowed a pillow until the medical officer gave permission. Mrs Doris Bates remembers her fever training in 1928-30 when scarlet fever cases were kept in until all the dry skin on the hands and feet had peeled off. The nurses and patients conspired in much use of hot baths and pumice stones to pass the medical officer's inspection.

Despite 1936 having only 30 cases of scarlet fever, the lowest recorded, the pendulum swung back in 1938, with 182 cases, the highest since 1927, and two deaths, the first for decades. In 1938 the "Municipal Fever Hospital" [Downside] had 16 cases of erysipelas, with one death, 17 cases of diphtheria, with no deaths, and no cases of typhoid fever. By now the schools contributed only £167 for the use of beds, but Hailsham RDC paid a retainer of £150 plus £710 for patients as part of the 1937 arrangements.

After 45 years' service as MOH, Dr Willoughby, who wore a wing-collar to the end of his days, retired in 1939. He died ten years later. He was replaced by his deputy, Dr John Fenton. That autumn Dr Fenton wrote, "there is a rather severe type of diphtheria present in Eastbourne", and reminded doctors that the new alum-precipitated toxoid vaccine was supplied free for children. This was the active immunisation agent which gave permanent protection and which by 1945 had reduced diphtheria infections from epidemics to the exceptional.

The war furnished more cases, for in the last few months of 1939 the hospital admitted 22 evacuees with scarlet fever, and 17 with diphtheria.

The hospital continued its work throughout the war, run by the local authority. There were 226 admissions for infectious disease in 1939, 367 in 1940 and only 36 (seven diphtheria and five scarlet fever) in 1941, mirroring the evacuation of the town. Two years later there were no clinical cases of diphtheria in Eastbourne, reflecting the success of the immunisation campaign.[9]

In 1941 cases of TB on the local register totalled 173, up 21 on the previous year, so a pavilion at "Downside" was adapted and opened for 17 TB patients.

The Crumbles Smallpox Hospital had closed in 1940, although it did duty as a guard-post during the war. It was demolished in 1946, and arrangements were made for smallpox facilities to be available at Brede and Sedgwick hospitals, if required. *Acacia Villa* continued to be used for clinics, and in October 1944 four beds were made available there for contacts of infectious diseases.

In 1944, Dr Fenton was reporting that cubical accommodation was needed at the "Borough Sanatorium" [Downside] to avoid having to open up a large ward for only a few cases of a disease. In both 1945 and 1946 only one case of diphtheria was admitted to the Borough Sanatorium, although the non-immunised case in 1946 died.

After the 1939-45 war, empty beds appeared with the fall in the incidence of infectious diseases. In 1947 only 66 cases (22 of them scarlet fever) were admitted from within the County Borough, compared with 85 in 1946 and 104 in 1945. The 64 staffed beds in 1947-48 had only 102 in-patients from all sources, who spent 2171 days in the hospital: in other words a 10% occupancy.

Beds were needed for the 1947 poliomyelitis epidemic, when eight confirmed patients were admitted (Borough and County cases) and two died.[10] Among the victims who recovered was Bob Brook, the sixteen-year-old son of Mr H.N. Brook, later to be on the staff of the hospital for many years. Mr Robert Glegg says that after the 1947 outbreak of polio there was a patient in the iron lung for months.

All the beds were needed in 1948 when Eastbourne had an outbreak of paratyphoid.[11] Between 16th July and 4th September, 42 cases were admitted, many being children who had first been sent to St Mary's Hospital with pyrexia [a temperature]. As late as 1972 two children with a *Salmonella* infection [diarrhoea] were transferred from St Mary's.

Mr H.N. Brook started at the Isolation Hospital in January 1948 as porter, ambulance driver and general handyman, when it was still under the local Borough Council and managed by the MOH. Miss Dorothy M. Hateley was now the matron. There was no assistant matron in those days.

The laundry in the grounds, which coped with linen from other hospitals as well as Downside, was run by Mrs Harrison and her two daughters, one of whom, May, became the matron's maid. An old-fashioned donkey engine in the boiler room was used for fumigating the bedding and clothes, although by the 1960s a steam steriliser was in place. Alongside was a garage, which had been the stables and coach house in the days when the ambulance was a horse-drawn vehicle. Both these buildings have been retained in the new housing estate.

The mortuary was at the end of a rough track in the far west corner; the ward staff usually transported the bodies on a hand trolley. As Mrs J. Ackland and Mrs A.M. Emerson point out, it was always called "Rose Cottage" so that the patients wouldn't worry if they heard reference to it.

The gardeners were Charlie Simmons and John Martin. Arthur Cox looked after the boilers and did the fumigating of the patients' possessions when they were admitted. Bill Hudson collected the clothes and linen from the patients' houses and brought them to the hospital for disinfection.

Mr Brook says, 'There was a certain amount of friction between Mr Cox and matron and if he had any information for her he would write it down, open her office door and drop the message on the floor'.

Until the National Health Service (NHS) in July 1948, Mr Brook had to close the gates at the East Dean Road and Longland Road entrances at night and open up in the morning. He also did the window cleaning until the work was put out to contractors. Mr Brook considered that 'during the war the hospital had been let go and had become run down, but after the NHS in 1948 the place became much more civilised with beds and furnishings being renewed on a regular basis'. This is when it became known officially as the Downside Hospital.

The total beds in use varied with the epidemic state. Potentially, each of the lower wards had about 20 beds, divided into two sections, with a ward kitchen and a side-ward in the middle. Martin ward had 29 beds available, and Hollins & Rowe about the same, each with a large cubicle at each end and two smaller ones in between. During the 1950s, there was an iron lung in one of these cubicles which Mr Brook, as head porter, had to test every week.

'In those days the matron was strict and called all staff by their surnames. There were staff who would run away, rather than reply, if she addressed them, but this attitude gradually faded.' It has to be said that the matron had a very responsible position. Apart from the ward rounds and making the nursing arrangements, Miss Hateley issued all the stores for the kitchen every day (locking the rest away) - and did all the linen repairs herself. As more wards opened for non-fever cases the work became too much and Mrs H. Brook agreed to help and ended up by taking over the sewing room and linen stores. Living in the Lodge was handy, but for her husband it did mean being on-call 24 hours a day. When they retired in 1972 it became a doctors' residence.

Mr Brook adds that 'Around 1955, when the telephone number was Eastbourne 77, I received a call about two o'clock in the morning to admit a case of polio from Seaford, a Lt Commander RN on leave from the Far East. I took the ambulance, picked up a stretcher bearer from his home, brought the patient to Downside, took the bearer home, and fumigated the ambulance. The next day the matron's only comment was that the incident should not have taken the two hours which I had booked in for the job'.

At times it was the hospital porters who kept the hospital going, even if one of them did consider that his most important task was to keep the ward Sister happy by looking after her fish tank.

It was not until 1957 that the weekly hours of ancillary staff were reduced from 48 to 46, with a further reduction to 44 hours the following year.

In 1949 the Eastbourne Hospital Management Committee (HMC) agreed to open 12 beds on Harding ward for TB cases, and 20 beds on both Strange and Alex. & Vic., previously unstaffed, were also opened. The number of in-patients increased from 135 in 1948 to 182 the next year.

The VD treatment centre, or Special Clinic, moved from *Avenue House* to Downside Hospital in 1949. Cases totalled 155 in 1949, of which 44 had syphilis and 31 gonorrhoea. In 1953 the clinic went to the Princess Alice Hospital.

In 1950-51, with 63 beds, 201 patients were admitted to Downside[12] and there were 257 out-patients. An improved kitchen and a new mortuary were constructed (in that order) and Hollins & Rowe ward was extended for a sterilising room: the next year the central heating was improved. By 1952 Miss A.M. Hunt acted as matron's deputy.

As early as 1949, 76% of children on Eastbourne's school registers had been immunised against diphtheria. Consequently, there were no cases of diphtheria in 1952, and no deaths had occurred since 1946. Nationally, 1940 had 46281 cases with 2480 deaths; while in 1951 the numbers had fallen to 664, with 33 deaths.

The supervisor cook in the 1950s was Mrs Farnell, who had two other cooks and a kitchen maid, all non-resident. Mr Allan Ayres mentions that when he was a young man in the mid-1950s and attending Victoria Drive Baptist Church, it was a custom at Easter for the children to collect eggs (of both the chicken and the chocolate kind) to take to the patients at Downside Hospital.

With the conquest of TB and other infections, Downside admitted only 32 patients in 1955, with no deaths. Dr K.O.A. Vickery, the MOH from 1953, wrote in his Annual Report, "In terms of human disability and suffering this changed picture is a solid achievement. Nor are the financial savings to be despised".

46. The mayor and mayoress of Eastbourne, Sir Sydney and Lady Caffyn, with Miss Hateley, at Harding ward, 1957.

As a result of less infectious disease work the wards were gradually converted for the use of the elderly. In 1955 the Regional Board released Harding ward from use for tuberculosis patients, and made 21 beds available for elderly long-stay patients. Later it agreed that Rowe ward could also be used.

As part of the changed scene, on 16th May 1955 the Bishop of Lewes visited for the Sacrament of Confirmation, and made further visits to the new patients.

Thanks to the generosity of the Friends of the Eastbourne Hospitals, a television set was installed in Harding ward in early 1955 and was much appreciated by the newly installed long-stay patients. With the success of the televising of the Coronation and the inception of commercial ITV, television was becoming an accepted component of any ward.

In 1957 a further five beds, this time in Hollins ward, were converted from infectious diseases to use for elderly patients.

In August 1958 there was a happy 93rd birthday party for Mrs E. Parks on Martin ward, who was the oldest resident.[13]

Miss Hateley retired that year after 40 years' nursing service. Led by her, Downside staff raised £500 to build a chapel, near the Longland Road entrance, which opened in September 1958, just four days before Miss Hateley's retirement.

The matron from 1958 was Miss Ada M. Hunt, and the assistant matron Mrs M.A. Gallimore. Mrs Gallimore served as a nurse during the 1939-45 war and was in the Normandy landings. The administrative sisters were Miss H. St Quinton Severin, Mrs Doris M. Bates and later Mrs E. Field.

Miss Severin looked after the stores and, so it is said, liked nothing better than a quick "nip" to check the stocks.

Downside's beds had increased to 96 by 1959, but as an indication of how long the elderly patients stayed and how well they were looked after, only 34 were admitted over the year. In 1960 a sun lounge was built on Alex. & Vic. ward at a cost of £392, and another on Hollins for £300. These allowed alternative sitting-out places for the long-stay patients. In 1962 sun lounges for Strange and Harding wards were opened by the mayor of Eastbourne. The cost, of £1001, was met by the Friends.

The Friends and Toc H also funded "Polly" and "Polly II", which were buses used to take the old people of Downside for country drives.[14]

Around the 1960s the Sister of Hollins & Rowe ward was Miss Pargeter with Staff Nurse Sutton; Mrs Wheeler was the domestic assistant. On Martin ward the Sister was Mrs Page; and on Harding, Mrs H.C. Beecham, with Mrs Attfield as domestic assistant. The charge nurse for Strange was Mr S. Lovering, with Mr A. Flavell as staff nurse, and Miss M. Whitfield the relief domestic assistant. On Alex. & Vic. Miss A. Davies was Sister with Staff Nurse Land, and Mrs Ticehurst was the domestic assistant. The Night Sisters were Miss J.M. Campbell and later Mrs S. Delves.

Both Mrs P. Sutton and Mrs M. Land were appointed Sisters when Miss Pargeter and Miss Davies retired, with Sister Beecham on Martin, Sister Land on Harding and Sister Sutton on Hollins ward. Later Sister M. Fitzgerald was on Harding ward and Sister R.N. Andrews was on Alex. & Vic. from 1970 to 1975.

The part-time hospital secretary was Mrs H. Mildenhall, and the first extra porter to be taken on, Mr W. Wheeler, acted as Mr Harry Brook's deputy. The chef was Mr Curzon, who walked with a limp and invariably wore his tall white hat.

Staff included Sisters M.G. Locke, P.E. Dowdney, J. Bastin, G. Keating, E.D. Lunn; Nurses E.M. Moor and E.G. Pearson, with nursing orderlies D.E. Bowler, and G.E. Paine. The first male orderly was Mr L. Melluish.

Mr John Martin grew wonderful crops of vegetables and strawberries in the vegetable gardens at the lower part of the grounds, and also had plenty of work keeping the grassy banks tidy. A patient who saw Mr Martin cutting the slopes with a scythe bought him a modern mower and, with a rope tethering it to a nearby tree, his work was considerably lightened. In the 1940s and 50s chickens and ducks lived in the lower grounds and the eggs were collected daily by Walter Lower to be entered in the "Egg Book". As a hang-over from wartime austerity, Miss Hateley "pickled" eggs to last over the non-laying period. Probably for similar reasons, rabbits were bred for the hospital table. The chickens just lasted into the 1960s; about the same time the administrators decided that vegetable gardens were uneconomic and ordered they be converted into flower beds.

At one time there had been 12 separate boilers to be looked after, and until the 1960s coke-burning boilers were at the rear of each ward: the staff thought it a great improvement when they were replaced by oil-fired ones. A program of redecoration coincided with the change. Each ward chose its own colour scheme, and pictures were supplied and hung by the Red Cross Picture Library. These measures created much more pleasant surroundings for both patients and staff.

By present-day standards the wards were old-fashioned with little room for the patients or for structural improvements, but as Mrs Bates says they were homely and not too large to be impersonal - 'although, as you may imagine, quite big enough for some to complain that they were unable to see or hear the television clearly. The cricket and "Songs of Praise" were the popular programs'.

Mrs Bates recalls Harding ward had a trial run for a cage of budgerigars to interest and amuse the patients, but they had to go because "they were so noisy" for the ladies whose beds were nearest.

The House Committee met once a month in Breach ward. This ancient, green-painted, corrugated-iron building, which had been used to isolate typhoid cases in the last century, now served as a committee room, a storage place, and also as a sanctuary for birds which flew in through the roof vents. Regular members of the committee were Misses N. Bradford and E.M. Elmes, Mrs D. James, Mrs H.G. Estcourt and Messrs D.S. Maclachlan and D. Whiting.

Grass grew through the floorboards, and the hut was unbearably hot in summer and freezing in winter - except at Christmastime when it became a dining room and dance hall. At one time there were separate parties, one for the doctors and nurses, and the other for the ancillary staff. These staff Christmas dinners, held in January, had the chef cooking the main meal and the admin. staff cooking the sprouts, heating-up the soup and waiting at the table for the ancillary staff dinner. It was great fun, but as Mrs Bates points out, it needed a fine night and preferably moonlight to convey the various dishes to and fro across uneven steps and paths without mishap. Mr Tommy Jones, the St Mary's pharmacist, always brought along his band to provide the music for these "hops", which were in fancy dress. They petered out in the 1970s.

Miss Hunt disapproved of alcohol, so for the Christmas parties Mr Percy Terry, the St Mary's Hospital Secretary, would lay in a store of beer in the men's lavatory. As the Revd Denys Giddey says, 'It was only when it reached the point that there no males for dancing that Miss Hunt relented to the extent of allowing cider at the Christmas parties'.

The staff of the main kitchen, at the top end of the hospital, changed little. There was still a cook, two assistant cooks, and now Ruby was the kitchen maid. The meals for the wards and staff were cooked there and had to be carried to the wards, three times a day. At one time Mr Brook used the ambulance to deliver to the lower wards, although later two electric trolleys made life easier, despite the batteries being described as "somewhat unreliable".

Most of the staff were non-resident, having families at home, but the nursing and domestic staff were usually in post for many years and developed a strong bond of loyalty to their ward. It even went in the family. Miss Jane Traynor nursed for five years on Alex. & Vic., from 1959 to 1964, when they were still admitting the occasional case of scarlet fever, and her mother, Ann Francis Mary, had nursed at Downside for 19 years.

All the staff were long-serving, conscientious and dedicated, but the night staff were a particularly faithful troupe who reported each evening at 2000h, and if anyone was sick, they always managed to find someone to cover.

The Friends of the Eastbourne Hospitals were special friends to Downside Hospital: not only with financial assistance, but also by visiting - bringing cards and gifts for birthdays and Christmas, doing personal shopping for the patients, and a library round once a week. Toc H ladies organised strawberry teas for the patients on Alex. & Vic. each summer and would do any sewing needed by the patients. Many other groups contributed, such as the Salvation Army band, school children who would bring Harvest Festival gifts, and even individuals, such as Mr Holloway, a retired gentleman living nearby and a regular visitor to the men on Strange ward, who looked forward to having a "good old chin-wag".

The chapel, which had been built thanks to the enthusiasm of Miss Hateley, was well used every Thursday - as well as festivals - with the Revd Canon Denys Giddey conducting the services for the last 15 years until the closure.

In July 1962 the State Enrolled Nurse Training School started at All Saints Hospital, with over 20 nurses in the school. No student nurses worked at Downside, and as most of the staff were enrolled nurses or nursing auxiliaries, a local source of supply was important, especially when, as in 1964, the nurses' hours were reduced from 44 to 42 per week. The school was integrated into the general Eastbourne Nurse Training School in 1968.

June 1963 saw an "Open Day" at Downside; visitors were greeted by the staff and escorted round the hospital.

In 1966 a further nine beds were changed from "fevers" to use by geriatric patients. The conversion, at a cost of £900, was carried out by the hospital works staff, who did most of these alterations.

The Downside laundry lasted until the St Mary's Hospital laundry was reorganised in 1957, when the latter became the group laundry for all the Eastbourne hospitals. By late 1967 part of the old laundry at Downside was reduced to storing those medical records not in everyday use. Many of the group laundry staff were especially long-serving, and Mr G. Hamper finally retired from St Mary's after 43 years with the Eastbourne hospitals.

Mr Norman Gray, who had been a consultant in dental surgery to the Princess Alice Hospital for some 35 years, died at Downside in February 1967. It was an especially saddening occasion, not least because his gold denture was mislaid, inevitably raising the possibility of other interpretations.

In 1966-67 there were 100 staffed beds, 93% of which were occupied daily, but only 97 in-patients were admitted over the year, so most were long-stay, at a cost per patient per week of £19.14p. In May 1967 the Regional Hospital Board agreed the conversion of the remaining four fever beds on Hollins & Rowe ward for geriatric patients.[15] There were one or two occasions subsequently when a cubicle was used for its original fever purpose, in particular when holidaymakers returned with an obscure tropical condition, but otherwise Downside was devoted to caring for the long-stay elderly patient.

Matron Hunt was a kind and understanding lady, with much experience and a talent for getting the best out of her staff and sorting out problems. Before the appointment of catering officers in the mid-sixties she did the catering, and *Elliots the Grocers* called weekly, as did the butchers. With the chef, she planned the weekly menus for variety and seasonal choice suited for the aged family of patients, not forgetting a little extra for Christmas and Easter, and always a penny within her budget. In the days of the Star Brewery in Old Town, bottles of *Guinness* were donated each week and enjoyed by the men on Strange ward, and some of the female patients as well, although the real secret vice and great pleasure of Strange ward was a flutter on the horses. Miss Hunt's great delight was the opera and she looked forward each year to the Glyndebourne season.

Her retirement was the occasion for presentations, preparations (she bought a house in Eastbourne) and plans to visit her friends and relatives around the world. Sadly, shortly after retirement in 1968 and three weeks before the date of her planned departure, she died in St Mary's Hospital after a brief illness. As Mrs Bates says, she would have been surprised by the wealth of respect and affection expressed for her.

Miss G.R. Rudd, the assistant matron at the Maternity Home, was appointed matron at Downside on 1st July 1968, and in 1970 she became matron of both Downside and All Saints hospitals, following Miss L.E. Burleigh's resignation from ill-health. Miss Rudd went on to be appointed Principal Nursing Officer to the Eastbourne Group of Hospitals in 1971, and the next year Miss J.B. Compton took over at Downside until she became Senior Nursing Officer at St Mary's Hospital. Mrs K. Kelly was the last matron, by now called Chief Nursing Officer.

She and Sister M. Fitzgerald continued the outstanding traditions of dedicated service. It was not always easy for the nurses, especially adapting to the new pattern of nursing with the change in the age and type of patient, and in 1973 one Sister was transferred to other duties. It was also not unknown for false accusations to be made against nurses by confused elderly patients.

One unvarying support were the Friends, who in October 1968, handed over a day room which they had built on Hollins & Rowe ward at a cost of £1500.[16]

Mrs Jones, one of the night Sisters, retired in 1969, and the next year Mr Haffenden, an enrolled nurse at Downside for 23 years, retired. Around that time there were 63 nurses in post, comprising matron, an assistant matron, one-and-a-half admin. Sisters, five-and-a-half ward Sisters, two night sisters, two staff nurses, five enrolled nurses and 45 nursing assistants (auxiliaries).

Langney, the first ward of the extensions at All Saints Hospital, was opened by the Duke of Devonshire on 19th July 1969, and further wards opened the next year, relieving to some extent the pressure on the Downside Hospital beds.

The provision costs in 1970 were £1.31p per person per week. This was less than most hospitals, but by now Downside was caring for long-stay patients whose nutritional needs were simply satisfied.

During 1970 Miss Rudd discovered that certain night sedative drugs were missing from the wards.[17] The loss was thoroughly investigated and several members of the staff reprimanded. Following this episode, stocks of night drugs were made available only to Sisters.

Downside, however, was given a pat on the back by a 1971 Regional working party which reported, "the wards are bright and airy and retain the bed-spacing found in the original fever hospital. Adequate day space is provided". The Red Cross Library was also popular in 1971 when the patients at Downside borrowed 2276 books.

In April Mr R. Ferguson started as hospital secretary for Downside and All Saints, and it was the year Mrs Audrey Emerson replaced Mrs Mildenhall as part-time administrator, dealing with patients' pensions and the stationery stores, which she took over from Miss Severin. Miss A. Smith was another on the clerical staff.

Retirements abounded around 1971, including Miss N. Blythe, a ward Sister for ten years, and in the autumn, Mrs Doris M. Bates, assistant matron, who was first appointed to the group in 1955. Miss Severin followed in December 1972.

With HMC support the hospital adapted to its role of caring for the elderly. It was given an increased furniture allocation for 1971-72 of £650; the wards were signposted to direct visitors in 1972; and an additional cost agreed was the substitution of toilet paper for tow when cleaning patients after a bowel movement. No physiotherapy was available, but Mrs Shirley Peckham worked sessions as an Occupational Therapist from 1973 until the closure.

47. Hollins & Rowe ward, from near the administration building, 1978.

Appointed in 1969, Mrs Susan Eagan (née Billings) was the first unqualified OT help in Eastbourne. She covered Downside from St Mary's Hospital: 'I would load up my wheel chair with everything I needed for the morning and push it up the hill to Downside, where it was even more difficult to negotiate up and down the slopes between the separate wards - treacherous in winter and exhausting in summer. At first no storage space for me was available at Downside, until I was given a corner in the boiler house, which also doubled up as a temporary mortuary; at least no-one objected. The patients would spend the whole day in the day rooms seated in tipped back chairs, held in with a table. To break their monotony, by providing diversions and activities, was extremely challenging. The nursing staff were quite dedicated and there was no demarcation of duties; so I would help to wash and dress the patients, and the nurses would give me support. When I began some nurses would laugh at the sight of my attempts to motivate the elderly dears, but in time we all became aware of each other's aims.'

Patients at Downside came from all walks of life, some local, some who had retired to Eastbourne, but all interesting folk with memories to share. Mrs Bates says that each ward had its share of characters. On Strange there was George, quite disabled and totally dependent, and yet he was always interested in the comings and goings of his restricted world. He also had the butt of a cigarette permanently in his lips, and whenever he laughed ash spilled over his pyjamas. He greeted every nurse with a smile, and could both give and take a joke. Strange also had Jock, at the time he was there the oldest living ex-Royal Marine, and a Mr Farthing had a lovely party for his hundredth birthday. For many years in Hollins ward there was Hetty, severely crippled with arthritis, who was a "Mum" to the other patients, and Mrs Carter, a theatrical dresser who displayed signed photographs of many well-known artists from the Devonshire Park Theatre. She was also a firm believer in self-help, as far as medication was concerned, until one day she used too strong an embrocation to disastrous effect.

Mr John D. Porter, a local solicitor, remembers visiting the hospital some years ago to find that one of the patients suffering from senile dementia was the former Clerk to the Eastbourne Justices, and in the next bed was a former Eastbourne Detective Chief Inspector in an equally sad state, so much so that neither was aware of the presence of the other.

There were small improvements every year, for example, by 1973 visiting was every day, and in the course of that year five insulated boxes to keep the meals warm were bought for £65.[18] Having said that, the hot water supply to Harding ward was precarious throughout 1973 because of furring in the pipes, and repairs were not completed until the next year. Was that why in 1974 Miss H. Miles of Hollins ward wrote to the HMC to express her thanks to the staff?

Miss H.M. Harrison, a long-serving member of the domestic staff, retired in February 1974. That month Downside had 106 beds available, of which 96% were occupied, with eleven admissions over February. Staff Nurse Chappell, on night-duty since 1971, succeeded Sister Delves on her retirement in 1974. She worked in tandem with Sister Ginn.

There were seven deaths from influenza among the elderly patients on Harding ward in January 1975, so the ward was temporarily closed to reduce the spread of infection.

In the world of newspaper headlines, *Blattella germanica* is a far more heinous crime than "off" food or "hot" fridges, yet there is little evidence that the cockroach contributes to human disease. There was a little spat in April 1975 about cockroaches "overunning" the hospital, which appeared to be publicised for quasi-political purposes. Mr Alan Watson, the branch secretary of NUPE, admitted he was wrong to invite reporters to a meeting which had been arranged by Mrs Jill Carpenter, the shop steward.[19] Mr Sidney Lovering, charge nurse, denied that they had been found in patients' beds, 'Many of us have not seen a cockroach for months ... any have been promptly dealt with'. Possibly the underlying reason for the upset was that there had been two outbreaks of scabies in the hospital over the previous six months which had put the staff under pressure, followed by wild rumours that the condition could be spread by cockroaches, which necessitated reassurance from Prof. David Long, Eastbourne's consultant microbiologist. 'Cockroaches have always been a problem in old buildings which contain many patients, but they have been continuously controlled while eschewing methods which could harm the patients'.

Sister Sutton of Hollins & Rowe brought pleasure, interest and benefit to her patients by bringing her red setter *Jane* into the hospital. Both dog and the ladies of the ward enjoyed the pats and show of affection, and such therapy is now an accepted practice in many hospitals and homes for the aged and disabled.

Dr Ian Brown was in charge of Downside Hospital from shortly after the inception of the NHS, and latterly shared the patient care with Dr M.L. Agarwal. From 1960 Dr A.K. Seeram, a diabetic, who died from a heart attack in January 1985, was the registrar and later associate specialist who visited regularly. Dr D.G. Churcher had sessions there in the 1940s and 50s and later one of his sons, Dr Anthony Churcher, was the part-time doctor who visited the hospital every day for some years before its closure. Miss Andrews explains, 'Dr Churcher cared for the patients with much compassion and kindness, and Mrs Kelly was a mother to us all'.

In the 1950s and 60s the patients were heavy nursing cases, but did not have life-threatening conditions, as in the hospital's fever days. As may be imagined, the introduction of disposable materials was a great boon to the staff and patients. Few patients, if any, went home, although some would be transferred to nursing homes. One patient, Maud Wise, was there for 21 years. With the 1970s the care of the elderly showed changes; there was greater emphasis on keeping people at home with support, even if it cost more. At the same time some needed a hospice-type care, which was developed for those who required such therapy. There arose a remarkable nursing spirit devoted to the terminally-ill patients, with the case-notes locked away at night time so that the amounts of heroin, administered as required, were not broadcast. For while it is now regarded as orthodox treatment, there was a time when, for fear of addiction, the doses officially advised were quite inadequate to control severe and persistent pain.

When Phase I of the new District General Hospital on Kings Drive opened in the summer of 1976, beds became available at the Princess Alice Hospital. These were made ready for the Downside patients, because the Regional Board had decided that part of the cost of the new hospital should be recouped by selling the Downside Hospital site for redevelopment. Although the chairman of the Community Health Council, Mr John Logan, thought that Eastbourne might face a shortage of geriatric beds if Downside was closed, the Council finally agreed to closure of both Downside and Gildredge Hospitals.[20]

In November 1978 the patients were moved to the Princess Alice accompanied by most of the staff, of all grades and trades. Those who transferred included Cathy Kelly, Marie Fitzgerald, Gwen Wheeler, Mrs Attfield and Lou Melluish. Among those on the night staff who moved with the patients were Mrs J. Ackland, who had worked at Downside for some 27 years, and Sister G. Chappell, who that summer had succeeded Mrs Fitzgerald on Harding ward and been replaced as Night Sister by Sister V. Martin.

Near to the closure time, Mr A.A. Moore, one of the porters, sketched some charming views of the hospital, which were taken to the Princess Alice with the patients and staff, and are on display in the Social Centre.

In 1980 the site was sold. Over the following year the wards and the Lodge were demolished and replaced by the houses of Downside Close, although the nurses' home, kitchen, stores and office buildings, along with the coach house and laundry remain, converted into flats or garages. They can be seen from the East Dean Road, as you come into Eastbourne on the A259 from Brighton.

Notes and References

1. Fovargue, HW. Ed. *Municipal Eastbourne 1883-1939* (with suppl., Eastbourne 1933).

2. Eastbourne Medical Society Minutes, 28/8/1888.

3. Borough of Eastbourne, Annual Report, Vital Statistics, Sanitary Work etc. 1892, or Medical Officer of Health for Eastbourne, Annual Report 1892.

4. Eastbourne Medical Society Minutes, 25/5/1890, 30/9/1890 & 28/10/1890.

5. Medical Officer of Health for Eastbourne, Annual Report 1895.

6. Ibid., 1902.

7. Lester AM. *Eastbourne Medical Gazette*, 1983; 3: 20-22.

8. Monsignor Arthur Cocks was Rector 1917-30.

9. Medical Officer of Health for Eastbourne, Annual Report 1943.

10. Ibid., 1947.

11. Ibid., 1948.

12. Eastbourne Hospital Management Committee, Annual Report 1950-51.

13. *Eastbourne Herald Chronicle*, 16/8/58.

14. Friends of the Eastbourne Hospitals, 15th Annual Report 1962-63.

15. Group medical advisory committee, 9/5/67, min. 328.

16. Eastbourne HMC, 6/11/68, min. 5203.

17. Eastbourne HMC, pharmaceutical sub-committee, 24/3/70, min. 1140.

18. Eastbourne HMC, finance committee, 24/7/73, min. 2514.

19. *Evening Argus,* Brighton, 9/6/1975.

20. *Eastbourne Herald,* 4/6/1977.

48. Aerial view of Gildredge Hospital c. 1958: the cubical block crosses at an angle left centre. Below are lines of pre-fabs (temporary houses) which border Longland Road towards the right On the lower side of the trees can be seen Miss Hateley's chapel (right), the three lower pavilions and, just, "Rose Cottage" of Downside Hospital. Old Town recreation ground is top left.

Chapter 13

Gildredge Hospital

(the Eastbourne tuberculosis hospital)

Dr W.G. Willoughby, Eastbourne's Medical Officer of Health (MOH), in his annual report for 1904 wrote, "Eastbourne's south-east open aspect and bracing climate is not suitable for advanced cases of tuberculosis. ... Eastbourne has a climate for the convalescent and overworked, rather than advanced disease". In other words, Eastbourne did not want to attract tuberculous (TB) cases to the town. It goes without saying that a reputation as a town which is full of infectious cases of TB was not good for the tourist business.

Such aspirations did not stop TB from occurring in Eastbourne, whether called phthisis or consumption. In 1904 there were ten cases and ten deaths from TB meningitis alone, and the 53 deaths from TB in 1908 well outnumbered the 48 from cancer.[1]

Even so, the only accommodation for patients with lung TB in the Eastbourne of 1910, when TB caused 10% of all deaths,[2] was in part of one ward at what was called the "sanatorium", later Downside Hospital, although some terminal cases were admitted to St Mary's Hospital.

When an anti-tuberculous service was established by the National Insurance Act of 1911, one consequence was that central and local authority could combine to build sanatoria especially for the hospital treatment of TB cases. Infectious cases were not usually accepted in general hospitals.

As early as 1905, Dr Willoughby had submitted a report on the provision of a "Sanatorium for Consumptives in Eastbourne". His decision was that a site, near to "Downside", but more airy and facing south was required. The initial mention of a special TB hospital on the local medical network was in September 1910 when Dr Willoughby set out the pros and cons of a "Rate-Supported Sanatorium for Local Consumptives". The first TB sanatorium had opened in Silesia as far back as 1859, so sufficient time had elapsed to accumulate knowledge about sanatoria. The advantages were that suffering was reduced, there would be less expense to the Poor Law, and the isolation of infectious patients would present less danger to the community. The disadvantages were the expense (estimates ranged from £25 to £1000 per bed), the possible damage to Eastbourne's reputation as a health resort, and the questionable value for money: bearing in mind that the curative effect of sanatoria was problematical, and that the TB rate had fallen by 40% in the previous quarter of a century without a sanatorium, thanks to improved social conditions.

In 1912 the Corporation went ahead with a dispensary for the treatment of persons suffering from TB, while negotiating with landowners to acquire a site for erection of a TB sanatorium. Plans were finally approved in 1913 for a TB hospital on a site purchased from the Davies Gilbert estate for £1250.

This tuberculosis sanatorium, later Gildredge Hospital, was opened by Dr (later Sir Arthur) Newsholme, Chief Medical Officer, on 27th July 1914. It provided accommodation for 22 patients, at this stage, and cost £2143 to erect.[3]

Dr W. Muir-Smith (father of Leslie a local GP, and Tony a local dentist) was appointed part-time medical officer-in-charge, called the clinical TB officer.

No made-up roadway adjoined the hospital, which was approached *via* what is now Upwick Road. Its remoteness, with only the Old Town recreation ground nearby, made it suitable for TB patients.

At the time of its opening no school or street escaped the ravages of this most forbidding malady. The average expectation of life after a diagnosis of pulmonary TB was five years, and just to obtain the prize of a bed in a sanatorium meant months of waiting.

Even in 1923 there were 127 new cases of TB in Eastbourne, with 47 deaths, many of them teenage girls.

There was always some uncertainty about whether Gildredge was a "hospital" or a "sanatorium". Any confusion was not helped by the fever hospital, later Downside, being referred to as the sanatorium before 1914; the implication in the nomenclature was that sanatoria were to isolate long-stay patients or convalescents, whereas a hospital treated patients aggregated together for that purpose.

In the 1920s and 1930s, when Miss A. Strugnell was matron, its official title was the Gildredge Tuberculosis Hospital, although John Stevens, who lived in Old Town for over 80 years, says that in his young days it was always referred to as "the consumptive hospital".

The accommodation at the Gildredge consisted of twelve cubicles, six in a line, on each side of a central suite of rooms which formed the Sister's office, treatment rooms, ward kitchen, and a nurses' changing room. Cubicles 1 to 6 were for female patients, 7 to 12 for males, two to a room. Toilets, a bath and a sluice were at the far end of each row of cubicles.

The cubicles, which faced south, had french-windows opening onto a terrace pathway, for which an overhanging roof provided trifling protection. As Staff Nurse Eileen M. Howe says, 'Before the terraces were enclosed nurses and patients had to brave all weathers'. Miss Elizabeth Brockhurst says that the french-window doors (which split to open like a horse-box door) were bolted open and she recalls snow coming on to the foot of her bed when she was a patient there in January 1953.

The hospital was built when the beneficial effect of fresh air had been fused with romantic ideas about the healing powers of nature. Dr Henry McCormack argued that the windows must be thrown open day and night. "Neither driving winds nor damp are to be as dreaded as much as confined air", and Dr George Bodington stated that "breathing over and over again diseased effluvia converts a slow consumption into a galloping one".

Fresh air was about the only weapon against TB in the 19th century and, while greater use of it might improve to-day's ventilation systems, it does appear that in many sanatoria the concepts of "Open Air" went too far. At Gildredge not only were the french-windows always open, but the windows on either side, looking onto the terrace, were also kept open at all times.

In front of the terrace a rockery fell away to the level of the grounds. At the back of each cubicle, the recreation-ground side, a large door opened onto a walkway with a corrugated-iron roof. This backyard gave easy access to the mortuary. The kitchen had a crockery steriliser and hence there was no need to barrier-nurse infectious patients, apart from exceptional circumstances.

To reach the male cubicles from the staff area in the middle, nurses had to mount several steps, so a metal trolley was left up there permanently - and it was useful for giving out teas. This didn't solve the problem of negotiating the steps with a laid-up sterile trolley, when two nurses and four steady hands were required to ensure nothing slid off.

Chest aspiration was the usual procedure which needed a trolley and, as there were no resident doctors, sometimes by the time the doctor reached Gildredge all the trolley contents had to be boiled up again - a situation completely overcome by the introduction of sterile packs from the Central Sterile Supply Unit. When Dr Surtees visited Gildredge in 1972 to perform a sternal-marrow puncture on a patient with myeloma [cancer] all the sterile tray items were from the CSSU. He hasn't forgotten the occasion because when gathering-up the instruments at the finish, Sister Halsall, who had assisted, rammed the contaminated marrow needle into her hand, fortunately with no untoward effects.

Firm rules were laid down for the TB patients. Each had a chart showing the grade of activity allowed, which ranged from strict bed, sitting out of bed, to walking in the garden for increasing distances. A large recreation hut in the grounds had various games facilities, including a grand piano which had an inscription inside the lid stating that it had been donated in 1916.

Miss Hurst emphasises that great care was taken so that patients of similar age and interests shared cubicles, and no TB case was ever with a non-TB patient.

At first, most TB cases could not gain admission. In 1924, of Eastbourne's 118 new cases, only 54 could obtain institutional treatment anywhere, with only 34 admitted to the Gildredge, and of these 17 died.[4]

The next year was much the same. Twenty-one patients were in the hospital at the beginning of 1925, during the year 47 were admitted, 17 died, and 30 were discharged, leaving 21 in the hospital at the end of the year.[5] The hospital costs were £2.65p per person per week, of which food amounted to 59p. This cost was reduced to £2.27p after deducting charges.

After Dr Muir-Smith's death in March 1928, Dr D.G. Churcher was appointed the part-time medical oficer. By now Dr A.G. Shera, at the Princess Alice Hospital, did most of the sputum tests for TB bacilli, and Nurse M.L. Richnell was the main out-patient TB nurse.

For the next decade the beds stayed at 24, looked after by the MOH, assisted by the clinical TB medical officer, the matron, one Sister and three nurses. Mr H.C. Wilkins was the gardener during the 1920s and 30s.

In his annual reports as MOH during the 1930s Dr Willoughby repeatedly stressed that "the accommodation at Gildredge is just equal to Eastbourne's requirements". These remarks were possibly made knowing that the councillors had received electors' comments about having to wait for a bed, because he routinely went on to emphasise that it was "strictly a hospital, not a sanatorium".

It is true that by 1934 there was practically no waiting list and it was possible to admit all males without any wait. It has to be said, however, that this was partly brought about because 23 cases were initially admitted to St Mary's Hospital, where six died and whence 12 were transferred to the Gildredge.

A real, if slight, improvement was apparent by 1937, when admissions reached 50 and there were only 13 deaths. The cost was steady at £2.75p per patient per week, although the income from the patients had dropped to £37.

The one thousandth patient was admitted to Gildredge in 1938, and it is a sobering exercise to examine the figures for the 25 years. Of 1008 admissions (520 females) by the year end, 366 had died in hospital, 171 had died from TB after discharge, and of those followed-up only 40 were known to be working.

The next year the hospital was assessed as 24 beds available for casualties, as part of the wartime Emergency Hospital Scheme, but on 12th September 1940, with the Battle of Britain raging overhead, the hospital was closed, and the patients dispersed inland, mainly to Darvell Hall, a 104-bed sanatorium at Robertsbridge. Gildredge continued in reserve as part of the EHS,[6] until it was withdrawn from the scheme in 1941, after which it remained empty until reopened for TB cases in September 1945.

There was a strange happening on 29th December 1942, when a bomb landed near the hospital. Perhaps fortunately, because demonstration phosgene gas cylinders were stored in the grounds, the bomb ricochetted over Longland Road and passed through 62 Victoria Drive before exploding.

Initially, after re-opening, Gildredge was used for chronic cases of TB while the more acute ones still went to Darvell Hall. Dr Shera continued to do the TB sputum tests; in 1945 of 316 examinations, 105 proved to be positive for TB. Over 1946, the first full year after the war, there were 24 deaths at the hospital.

Shortly after the 1939-45 war, temporary houses or "pre-fabs" were put up in the grounds, and the hospital entrance became the access to the estate, so the Longland Road gate to the hospital was moved towards the north. In September 1952 there were complaints that the hedge between the pre-fabs and the hospital had grown thin and permission sought to "buy some shrubs". The pre-fabs were knocked down in the 1960s and replaced by the Barcombe Close flats.

During 1947-48, when Miss Toyne was the matron, the official 24 beds had 21 in-patients, who spent 6435 days there (in other words, most were in for the whole year) and there were 484 out-patient attendances.

In 1949 Dr A.H. Ferguson Gow succeeded Dr D.G. Churcher as medical officer, although Dr Churcher remained on the House Committee until 1960, other long serving members of that committee being Miss I.B. Brooker, Miss V. Moore, Mr P.S. Muddell and Mrs V.I. Watt.

Dr Ferguson Gow was appointed jointly by the Regional Hospital Board and the local authority as a whole-time chest physician. Like similar appointees, he was to preside over the revolution in TB treatment which did him out of a job. Miss B.M. Halsall, a Sister at St Mary's, who transferred to Gildredge as departmental Sister in July 1950, says that streptomycin treatment was already in use for TB cases when she went there.

Miss F.E. Shire was appointed matron in 1951. It is obvious food was important at Gildredge for she was soon reporting to the Hospital Management Committee (HMC) that there were insufficient funds to buy both a second hen-house and soft-fruit plants.[7] The following year she wrote, "The hens have started re-laying and I will re-erect a corrugated tin-hut, thus affording temporary accommodation"; so the catering committee made £10 available for fruit plants.[8]

In 1953 the hospital roads were resurfaced in concrete and the next year the first day room was built for the women patients at a cost of £404.

Around 1955, two TB huts were assembled in the grounds, having been moved from St Mary's Hospital.[9] They could be rotated to face the sun and were in use until 1963. The patients - one per hut - often lived there for weeks at a time, and Elizabeth Brockhurst says that they were really comfortable.

Miss Florence Powell, who had been matron of a hospital in South Africa, was the administrator in the 1950s, when Mrs Kathleen Hall (née Thorpe) was Dr Gow's secretary, and Sister Dunhill was on night duty. Staff included Nurses Moor and Tarrant; Mrs Grooms was the cook and Mrs Morrow a domestic.

Elizabeth Brockhurst describes the patient's life-style at that time. 'Most patients were on "strict bed", but everyone had to be in bed for an hour before lunch, an hour after lunch and an hour before supper. There was no day-room then, so when you were up you could only sit in an arm-chair beside your bed. Since TB was associated with poor conditions, the food at the Gildredge was good, although it could be cold for the end-cubicle patient. To even matters out, the meals were served from alternate ends each day'.

Gildredge grub, produced by a staff of one cook, one assistant cook and a kitchen maid, was special, and cost more than the other hospitals. In 1952 Gildredge spent £1.22p per head per week on food, compared with £1.10p at the Princess Alice Hospital.[10]

Miss Brockhurst continues, 'At Gildredge there were two patients to each cubicle. Each had an ancient cupboard, a light, a radio and a chair. The beds had green or pink bedspreads and they had very high backrests, with two or three pillows. There were radiators below each window. In the bath and wash-rooms there was no heating in the early days, and they were cold even with a radiator. The back door to the corrugated-iron covered walkway was never seen open, and was used only to remove bodies, whereas the glass doors at the front were always open. Visiting was Sunday and Wednesday afternoons only.

'Quite a few of the staff had been treated in other hospitals for TB, but remained surprisingly strict, firmly believing that the Spartan regime aided recovery.

'Dr Ferguson Gow was a tall rangy South African, who had lost the function of one lung himself. I liked him, but he was unpopular with a lot of the patients because he smoked along the veranda, whereas patients were not allowed to smoke. It must have been hard for a chest physician before streptomycin's worth had been proved, with one patient getting better and the next dying.

'I received strep. injections about once a week (Dr Gow tended to give daily streptomycin for only six weeks in case of side-effects) and later I started PAS and INAH daily.[11] I have never tasted anything so revolting as PAS, universally known as "sewage". Later, an artificial pneumothorax [designed to rest the lung] did not work so I had a pneumo-peritoneum. Air was put in once or twice a week for thirteen months, mostly at *Avenue House,* where about twelve patients assembled, brought in by ambulance, for an X-ray scan and to put up with witty remarks, such as "I see you had shepherd's pie for lunch", before being blown up like a balloon by Dr Gow's cannula.'

Pneumo-peritoneum was usually supplemented with a "phrenic crush" when the nerve to the diaphragm muscle [which helps to move the lungs] was interrupted. 'Don't let anyone tell you that it is painless', adds Miss Brockhurst.

After the war, any chest surgery was carried out by Mr R.S. Pilcher, from the Thoracic Surgical Unit at St Helier Hospital, Carshalton. It was Mr Pilcher, operating at University College Hospital, who carried out the first pneumonectomy [removal of lung] on an Eastbourne patient, a Mrs Robinson, who survived thanks to the help of an oxygen tent and the transfusion of about a gallon of blood. Mr A.M. Macarthur who worked from Carshalton, UCH and the Brook Hospital, Woolwich, followed as thoracic surgeon until 1971. Between 1971 and 1979, by which time local chest work had been transferred to the

District General Hospital in Kings Drive, Mr R.R. Burn acted as the thoracic surgeon, also working from St Helier. After 1979 patients were sent to Mr N.S. Hooton at the Brook Hospital. All the thoracic surgeons visited Eastbourne about once a month to review patients and to perform bronchoscopies. If it was decided to operate, the patient was transferred to the Brook Hospital.

Miss K.M. Hill, the matron from July 1955 to September 1961, recalls Gildredge as a small hospital with a loyal and contented staff. She left on marriage, becoming Mrs Partington, and she points out that she had to leave because her contract stipulated a residential post. She considers the greatest achievement during her stay was the enclosing of the veranda terrace along the south side of the cubicles. While these covered corridors were not heated and were, to say the least, airy, they were a great improvement in comfort for patients and staff, compared with the previous open terrace path. The final part to be enclosed was the front of the female block in 1960 at a cost of £358. There was further betterment when, in 1959, space was found for a hot food trolley.

49. Staff at Gildredge Hospital in the 1960s. Back row, Daisy, cleaner, S/N Lance, S/N Knight, Sister Halsall, S/N Wilcock and Valerie, cleaner. In front Mr Terry, the cook and Nurse Traynor. Behind is the enclosed terrace, with the patients' cubicles visible through the glass.

As early as 1957 the Eastbourne HMC Annual Report stated, "it is noticeable that the length of stay is less", and with Miss Hill's departure, and the declining amount of TB work, the post of matron was discontinued. The admin. merged with St Mary's Hospital and Miss D.V. Lowarch assumed the mantle of matron.

In practical terms, Sister Bertha M. Halsall who had acted as deputy matron, took over the running of the hospital, without extra help. Being actively involved in the nursing meant that she invariably joined the doctor's ward round, rolling down her sleeves and putting on her cuffs, having just come from a patient.

With the decline in the incidence of TB, more patients were admitted suffering from chronic bronchitis and emphysema, and patients with lung cancer were taken in for terminal care whenever possible. With these changes more male beds were needed and it sometimes happened that cubicles 5 and 6 (those nearest the central rooms) were used for men.

While the in-patient cost per week had risen by 1960-61 to £22.52p, this was only in line with inflation.

No student nurses worked at the Gildredge, although they would visit as part of their training. The staff were mainly state-enrolled nurses or nursing auxiliaries.

Between 1959 and 1966 Staff Nurses E. Knight and A.V. Guy nursed at the hospital. Other staff, at one time or other, included Staff Nurse, later Sister, H. Neuman, Staff Nurses Rattue, Hutton and Wilkins, enrolled nurse R. Day, with nursing auxiliaries Bartlett, Romero, K. Smith, and P. Bunting. Night staff included nursing assistants Moon, Ogilvie and J.K. Surridge. Mr A. Butcher was administrative officer to the consultant around 1960, and Mrs Baulcombe, Miss Berlyn, Mrs Selfe, Valerie Rogers and Daisy Castle were on the domestic staff for many years.

Many of the staff recall that there were no locks on any of the doors and occasionally a freezing tramp would knock to ask if he could come inside, when he would usually be found some sustenance to tide him over. Gildredge had a more exact meteorological association in that for some years the official rainfall recorders for Eastbourne were situated in the grounds.

The number of admissions increased as the length of stay became shorter, and in 1960, for the first time, more than 100 patients were admitted over the year. In 1966-67 Gildredge still had its 24 staffed beds, which were 67% occupied by 140 patients over the year;[12] however, the cost per patient per week had risen to £29.90p. At least there was a firm cap on the furniture allowance at Gildredge; in 1971-72 it amounted to all of £50.

Miss J. Makins was the Unit Nursing Officer, 1970-77. Sister M.F.F. Brunt (née McGarry) worked in the Eastbourne hospitals from the 1950s until she retired in 1987. She was at the Gildredge 1971 to 1976 and married whilst there.

Nurse M. Hastings, there from 1959 to the closure, says, 'Gildredge was a happy hospital because the patients were with us a long time. I recall one jape when a patient, David Palmer, made a hot-air balloon out of coloured paper and sent it up by means of burning cotton wool soaked in surgical spirit. It came to a halt near Matron Hill's room and she was not at all pleased, saying they could have had a fire'.

It was not all fun; at times it was more than hard work. On one horrific day, a patient with chronic TB died of a massive haemoptysis [coughing up pints of blood from an eroded lung artery] and Nurse Hastings was one of those who got to work and cleaned up the cubicle to make it spick and span again.

The out-patient chest clinic before 1959 was at *Avenue House,* in the centre of town. In 1958 the HMC bought 12 Vicarage Drive, next to St Mary's Hospital, for £4463 to accommodate the clinic. It opened in March 1959, with access through the grounds of St Mary's.

The chest clinic stayed in this semi-detached house until 1978, and acted as the admissions office for Gildredge Hospital. The staff consisted of Dr A.H. Ferguson Gow, the consultant in diseases of the chest, Miss Jay Hurst, higher clerical officer, with a secretary and a nurse. Chest clinics always kept their own case-notes and chest X-rays, and locally they followed the patient to Gildredge, if admitted. When it was decided to close Gildredge and transfer the chest clinic to the District General Hospital, Dr Kenneth Vickery, the Community Physician, was concerned that all the necessary tuberculosis procedures should be maintained, so Miss Hurst was designated the TB Information Coordinator to liaise between Dr Vickery's public health department, Dr Douglas Model (who had taken over the chest work) and the community at large.

In 1971 Miss E.L. Post, the chest clinic nurse, retired, and took up painting in oils. She had been associated with the TB service for 30 years.

Mr Edwards, the cook who made Matron Hill's wedding cake, was followed by Mr E. Terry. During the 1960s catering came under Miss Gladys Smith (catering officer at St Mary's Hospital) with Mr Terry as cook. He went to St Mary's Hospital after the Gildredge closed.

Mrs L. Jefferys, who was the assistant cook for twelve years, says she has many happy memories. 'Half my time was concerned with the welfare of patients and staff. The main kitchen block, or bungalow, was just below the hospital towards Longland Road, and consisted of kitchen, store room, nurses' home and dining-room, with a resident staff of about half-a-dozen. The surroundings were green and pleasant: we faced the playing fields and we backed on to the Downs. On an early shift the bright eyes of foxes were almost a guide to the kitchen. Although it was a hospital for the very sick, all was not gloom and doom, thanks to the Sisters and nurses. This was especially so at Christmas when the wards were decorated and patients and families were joined by all the staff for carols and festivities on Christmas Day. Everyone, and I particularly recall Dan, one of the porters, attended to the patients with deeds well beyond their actual duties.'

When, in the mid 1960s, a patient left £3000 to the hospital, this was used to enlarge the centre block and install central heating in the nurses' home.

The small nurses' home in the grounds consisted of matron's flat, a sister's bedroom, four staff bedrooms (either nurses or domestics), two bathrooms, an office and the nurses' dining-room, with kitchens. When the post of matron was discontinued her office was changed to a domestic staff dining-room and her lounge became a nurse's bedroom.

Miss E.M. Howe adds, 'In the nurses' home kitchen Mr Terry, the chef, and Mrs Jefferys, the cook, produced the lovely meals for patients and staff'.

It was a regular hospital routine, and quite an up-hill push, to move the metal food trolley from the kitchen to the wards at midday and back, although usually a porter would help; for the evening meal the chef brought it and ward staff would assist. If it snowed, the nurses collected the fare from the kitchen on trays.

Among other routines the dispensary-box was collected by Mr Alan Trusler, Monday to Saturday at 0900h and returned the same day, with any requirements made up at St Mary's Hospital; the laundry was collected and returned from St Mary's by Mr Brian Hancock, or on occasions by Mr Richard "Dick" Hassell of the Works department; Miss Joan Rodda came weekly with the Red Cross Patients' Library service for nearly 30 years, from 1947 to the closure; an occupational therapist came on a regular basis to Gildredge; and the hospital sewing was done by a lady who came to the hospital, until all such work was sent to the sewing room at St Mary's.

Religious services were held in the chapel throughout the year and at Christmas. When the chapel was demolished, they moved to the male recreation hut. They were conducted by the Revd L. Sporne, and later the Revd Canon D. Giddey, and sometimes by a lay reader, Mr F. Sewell. The organist for many years was Mrs S. Weir. Denys Giddey describes how he replaced the veteran harmonium, and in poor health, with a harmonium from a disused chapel. 'This was a success until, around the demise of the hospital, the bellows succumbed to a combination of asthmatic wheeze and destructive airways disease.'

Out of the routine was Christmas itself, always a busy time, but enjoyable. A few patients could be allowed home for a day or two, but for the others every attempt was made to make them feel at home. Coloured lights were strung up along the balconies, usually by the porter or gardener, although as the safety regulations became stricter, Mr A.E. Solly, the electrician from St Mary's Hospital, supervised.

Even at Christmas, children were not allowed on the wards for fear of infection unless, as Miss Halsall put it, 'We opened our hearts to allow them in for a terminal case'.

Sister Halsall's deputies in the 1960s were Staff Nurses J.E. Wilcock and H. Lance. Other Staff Nurses over the years included V. Brown, Cooper, Knight, Turner, Wilkins and male S/N Thompson.

Sister Halsall recalls the discharge of one patient, 'A Mr L--, who came to my office to say farewell and, as he went out, the catch of his case came undone and out fell a red blanket. We had a good laugh as he was one of our regulars.

'The inside walls of the cubicles were painted pink, cream or green, and there was a patient who was so superstitious that she just would not go into a green one; eventually other patients had to be moved around to accommodate her.'

Miss J.E. Wilcock, who worked at the hospital from 1962 to 1969, says that it was one of the happiest times in her professional career. The care of the TB patients by that time was "first-rate". Dr Ferguson Gow and his houseman did a ward round twice a week to change treatment, read X-rays and check on progress. 'As the treatment began to take effect and the patients felt better, much good humour prevailed and the staff were frequently teased by the patients.

'With the passage of time the incidence of TB dropped and the hospital took in other patients, at one point many with lung cancer. This had a stressful effect and staff needed to make adjustments to cope with the different type of patient.'

Mrs Susan Eagan (née Billings), the first unqualified OT help in Eastbourne, thought that the Gildredge site was in a lovely spot beneath the Downs, and with each room opening out onto a green area it had a bright and friendly atmosphere. She remembers an elderly blind gentleman who had to be supplied with a constant flow of occupational therapy materials to weave and trays to cover.

When S/N (later Sister) Veronica M. Kendrick started at Gildredge in February 1970, she naturally found a great contrast to her previous hospital, the Brompton, London. She comments that on occasions they were still boiling up syringes and forceps in ward sterilisers, and the ward telephone was an extension from St Mary's Hospital, but she came to find the work of rewarding interest.

Eastbourne's first year with no recorded deaths from TB was 1968.[13] By the 1970s there were few TB patients, and Miss Kendrick found it all the more sad on perusing the beautifully bound admission books to read of the many young patients who had died of TB in the past. Miss Brockhurst says that in 1952, before the drugs were known to be effective, most patients did not expect to recover, and even in 1970 patients remembered this reputation and would admit to the fear that the only way they would leave would be by the back way in a box.

Apart from Sister Halsall, the thirteen nurses in post during 1969 included Staff Nurse V. Brown (who was to succeed her), enrolled nurses E.M. Thorogood and J. E. Brewer, nursing auxiliaries Coleman, Platt, and Mr Monk, while Frances Lyons was another part-time nursing assistant. Night staff included Sisters Hibberd and Ware, charge nurse Pinelli and assistant nurse Ogden.

Mr S. Fellowes now acted as gardener, the porters were Mr Ledsome and Mr Prodger, and among the domestics were Mrs Edwards, Mrs Buchan, Mrs Buckland, Mrs V. Laye, Mr Romero, and Miss Diane Knott, who worked on the domestic staff between 1967 and 1976. Miss Knott recalls working a rotational duty between the hospitals in 1967: Monday at Princess Alice, Tuesday at the Leaf, Wednesday at Downside, Thursday at Gildredge and Fridays at St Mary's.

Members of the Gildredge House Committee in the 1970s included the Revd George Cumming, and Messrs H.A. Riddick, N. Proudler and F.C. Solly.

Although in 1971 the Red Cross Library issued 952 books, by the next year the number had fallen to 664. The most popular titles were Joyce Strange's *The Lakeland Vet* and Derek Tangye's *Cottage on the Cliff.*

Gildredge continued to have 24 beds available, even though in the month of February 1974 only 66% were occupied, with 16 admissions. By now the hospital had visiting every day.

Miss B.M. Halsall retired on 30th September 1974. Over the years 1950-55, when she had been resident on-call, she received an annual TB allowance of £20-£25 for the work with infectious cases, as well as her departmental Sister's allowance. Both were discontinued when nursing salaries were reconstructed. Until 1960 salaries were paid in matron's office, and after that date on the wards.

As Miss Halsall left to begin her retirement, Mrs Jefferys rang the handbell which had signalled the beginning and end of hospital visiting times. Miss Halsall says that her most frightening moment was when a 19-year-old tuberculous girl threw a knife at her. 'We later became the best of friends. More than most, I can well understand the frustrations of a teenager under the restrictions of the treatment, frightened at what lies in store, and seeing the best years of life pass by.'

From his appointment in March 1975, Dr D.G. Model had a few patients at Gildredge and, when Dr Ferguson Gow retired in October 1978, he took over. As a contrast to the wasting away of TB patients, some of Dr Model's patients came to undergo intensive weight-reduction diets for obesity, and at least one lady was admitted because it was thought the peaceful environment would benefit her high blood pressure. In the Gildredge Hospital's last year of existence only six cases of TB were admitted.

The Gildredge had been very much a "family" hospital, with the patients often staying a long time and frequently returning. At weekends, one of the nurses' duties was to renew the Birthday List, for when a patient had a birthday the cook baked a special cake.

Some of the long-stay patients had unusual hobbies. One made bows and arrows, another who had been a glass blower on Eastbourne pier gave all the staff presents of glass animals for Christmas, and Miss Billings' blind man worked at making wickerwork trays. He was so breathless that he stood over his bed to work, because he could not get up if he once sat down.

Over 1977-78 the last ten patients moved to Cuckmere ward, St Mary's Hospital, as that ward was made ready for them. Sister Sheila Sayers, in charge for the last few months at Gildredge, also transferred to Cuckmere ward.

Miss McCall's Link Centre for Deafened People used the nurses' home buildings on a temporary basis, but as the value of the site for redevelopment had already been set against the cost of the new District General Hospital, the hospital was eventually vacated and demolished in 1979. It was replaced by the flats of Bodmin Close. In 1993 there remains the brick wall along the recreation ground boundary, and a telephone kiosk marking what was the Gildredge Hospital entrance from 1946.

In Staff Nurse E.M. Howe's words, 'To some the memories may seem sad as many terminally-ill patients were nursed in the Gildredge - all someone's dear ones, but every one of the staff did their utmost to make their time as cheerful and comfortable as possible'.

In essence, as soon as effective treatment for TB was available there was no need for the Gildredge. Would that it could be so for all hospitals?

It must have helped a few patients, giving them a better chance of recovery by improving their general condition, but its real value was to reduce the spread of disease within a family, by removing a source of infection. What was the Gildredge Hospital is now a housing estate, and while we hope that its like will never be seen again, the worthy efforts of the staff should not be forgotten.

Notes and References

1. Eastbourne Medical Officer of Health, Annual Reports 1904 & 1908.

2. Eastbourne Medical Society Minutes, 27/9/1910.

3. Fovargue HW. Ed *Municipal Eastbourne* 1883-1939 (with suppl., Eastbourne 1933).

4. Eastbourne Medical Officer of Health, Annual Report 1924.

5. Ibid., 1925.

6. Ibid., 1941.

7. Eastbourne HMC, catering sub-committee, 10/12/1952, min. 574.

8. Ibid. 14/1/53, min. 585.

9. Surtees John. *Barracks workhouse and hospital, St Mary's, Eastbourne, 1794-1990.* (Eastbourne Local History Society 1992); 49.

10. Eastbourne HMC, catering sub-committee, 12/11/52, min. 561.

11. PAS was para-aminosalicylic acid, and INAH, isoniazid. They were effective anti-tuberculous drugs, especially in combination and could be taken by mouth, although PAS was dispensed in cachets in an attempt to mask the unpleasant taste. PAS was isolated in the early years of this century, but its value in TB was not realised until 1948 and INAH was introduced in 1952. Both have side-effects and have been replaced to some extent in TB therapy, but they were life-saving in the 1950s. The main therapeutic exercise was to establish the "cocktail" of drugs which gave fewest side-effects with the least chance of developing resistance.

12. Eastbourne HMC, Annual Report, 1966-67.

13. Eastbourne Medical Officer of Health, Annual Report 1968.

Chapter 14

The Leaf Hospital

In 1884 Carew Davies Gilbert leased No. 1 and 2 Marine Road, near the seafront, to the Misses Jane and Julia Leaf. They were the daughters of William Leaf, who had financed the building of the nearby Leaf Hall 20 years earlier, "to promote the social, moral and spiritual welfare of the working classes of Eastbourne" in other words, "to keep the working man off the drink".

The Leaf sisters lived in No. 1, and started a dispensary for the poor in the adjoining house, where four years later they founded the Leaf Homoeopathic Cottage Hospital.

In 1902, having moved to Worthing, they assigned the lease of 1 and 2 Marine Road to trustees. The original trustees were Mr F.C.S. Roper and the Revd J. Howard Palmer, who acted as the honorary treasurer until his death, when he was succeeded by Mr R.C. Lambert.[1] Others involved in the management included Mrs Robertson and Miss Cooper. The treasurer in 1913, Mr A. Tabor, bought next-door, No. 3 Marine Road, for £500 and gave it to the hospital.[2]

Now 1-3 Marine Road, it was described as a "free Homoeopathic Cottage Hospital for the treatment and relief in sickness of poor persons living at Eastbourne or within 15 miles from the Town Hall, but if there is no such person desiring admission, other poor persons can be admitted. The treatment shall always be in accordance with the purposes of homoeopathy".

Not everyone was allowed in. As set out in the Annual Reports, "Patients are admitted by a 'letter of recommendation', which can be obtained from subscribers, who are entitled to recommend one patient for each guinea subscribed. 'Letters' are available for one year from issue and entitle patients to treatment for a period not exceeding one month". To modern ears these rules sound more like a corn-flakes packet offer than matters of life and death.

Dr A.H. Croucher, a bearded giant of a man, was the Misses Leaf's doctor and he became the honorary physician and surgeon to the hospital. Said to have "a wonderful name for curing TB" (this was before BCG and antibiotics), he lived at *Onslow House* in Burlington Place and most days cycled into the hospital. When he retired to Oxford in the 1930s he was replaced by his son.

Mr C.E.(Ted) Dobell, mayor of Eastbourne in 1980, believes he owes his life to the elder Dr Croucher. On bonfire night, 1921, he developed a pain in his stomach, and the local GP, having said it might be an appendix, gave him medicine, but over the next week he slowly deteriorated until his mother went to the Leaf Hospital in Marine Road. Later that day Dr Croucher came to see him and, as soon as the doctor saw how low the lad was, he lifted him into his car, took him to the Leaf and operated to drain an abdominal abscess. Mr Dobell's life hung on a thread for two nights and in all he had three operations, including removal of the offending appendix when he was fit enough, and another to remove all the drains and stitches. 'I was in the hospital for three months recovering. I can remember mother bringing in an egg for me, which had to have my name written on it. The treasurer and a trustee of the hospital, Mr E.H. Black, thought he saw a likeness in me to his son who had been killed in the war, and arranged for me to have three weeks' convalescence at St Luke's Hospital, the children's Convalescent Home of All Saints, where *Dolphin Court* stands to-day'.

Mr Harold Spears' experience at the Leaf was not so happy. Following a tonsil operation, he developed septicaemia and he always had some ear trouble afterwards, although living well into his eighties.

Old Dr Croucher's reputation for curing tuberculosis (TB) rested on his espousal of Spahlinger's anti-tubercular vaccination, which he first used in 1913. Alas, it was one of many spurious TB cures peddled over the centuries, which has to include the great Robert Koch's tuberculin of 1891. Such false dawns explain the medical profession's cautious acceptance of the claims for new therapies.

Miss Bevis, who had been matron of the Leaf since the opening in 1888, died in 1911, and was replaced by Miss P.E. Tucker. That year a Sale of Work, organised by Mrs Mortis, raised £179.75p for the hospital.

Miss Julia Leaf died in 1913, when her hospital treated 197 in-patients and 450 out-patients, of whom 102 were dental.

The No. 3 Marine Road extension opened on 27th August 1914. This gave six additional beds, making a total of 14 beds and two cots, and the opportunity was taken to install X-ray apparatus,[3] although Dr Croucher did his own X-rays at home. Of the year's total of 123 admissions, tonsil and adenoid operations (Ts & As) accounted for 53.

The next year Miss Brattan, who had followed Miss Tucker as matron, left and was replaced by Miss I.L. Jones.

The hospital continued to function during the 1914-18 war, and Dr M.V. McKechnie was anæsthetist at the Leaf from 1914 to his death in 1926.

In 1920 the Leaf Hospital receipts were £1962.82p while the expenditure was £2109.03p, despite receiving £119.23p from the mayor's Sunday Hospital Fund. The cost per patient per week was £3.55p. The overspend was probably due to the post-war inflationary state, but it was put down to £250 spent on much needed redecorations.[4] By now Mr Tabor had resigned, Dr J.A. Martin had replaced Mr H.T. Hedley as secretary; the matron was Miss Smith and the Sister Mrs Jeffreys.

Over April 1921 there was an average of 14 patients in the hospital each day. While the hospital provided a range of services, the operations were mainly dental or Ts & As. In 1923 the local authority paid for five children sent up for tonsil operations.

That year Mrs Alice Brockhurst found it a grim hospital, but she had been put there by Dr Pirrie for a plaster jacket, which could hardly be welcoming.

At this time the patroness was Her Grace the Duchess of Devonshire, the president the Earl of Dysart, and Mr W. Macfadyen Scott was the hospital chairman, having replaced the Revd H. von E. Scott in 1920. By the end of the 1920s the honorary medical staff were Dr A.H. Croucher, his son Dr A.T. Croucher, Dr H.J.A. Pollard, and, as anæsthetist, Dr H.R. McAleenan until he was appointed to St Mary's Hospital in 1930; Dr R.M. Barron eventually succeeding him. The consulting dental surgeon was Mr H. Turner, the consulting surgeons Mr D. Liget and Mr J. Eadie, and the gynæcologist (described as the "physician for diseases of woman") was Dr E.A. Neatby. Miss Edith Tanner was now the matron and the Sister was Miss E.E. Hedley.

In 1929, with the accommodation for 16 patients unchanged, although now apportioned to six males, seven females and three children, the number treated in the year was 397 (of whom 220 were out-patients). Since opening, the hospital had attended 11177 patients. That year the receipts were £2593.41p, and expenditure £1948.68p. The medical expenses, which presumably included drugs and dressings, came to only £235.59p, and X-ray repairs amounted to 17/- [85p].

Following the example of other hospitals, Mrs Jethro Robinson formed a Ladies Linen League that year, which worked from the Angles Hotel [later the Majestic]. The League solicited gifts of material and made it up into bed linen and uniforms, to save having to buy such necessities.

Money was always accepted with alacrity from anywhere. Of the many fund raising events, the Jumble sale realised £57.81p; the Pound Day £47.42p and 1130 pounds in kind; the grant from the Penny-a-Week Fund was £158.80p; Alderman Miss Alice Hudson opened the Annual Sale of Work at the Town Hall on 22nd October which raised the handsome sum of £481.07p; and the matron's Christmas fund received £5 from the mayor. A box of chocolates from Miss Rolleson and a box of tangerines from Mr and Mrs Benz were Christmas gifts.

Of 26 pages in the 1929 Annual Report, 17 were devoted to finance - donations, gifts and lists of subscribers. Details of what benefits had been achieved stretched over only three pages. Of the 177 in-patients, of whom four died, 80 were Ts & As, four were varicose veins, four had pneumonia, there were two operations for ovarian cyst, one appendix operation was performed, one patient had a fractured humerus, and one managed "extractum dentium".

It is said that Drs Croucher, Pollard, Barron and Gordon-Wilson used to meet at a cafe in Cornfield Road, after their GP surgeries, to discuss and arrange the hospital schedules.

In 1930 the receipts from Hospital Boxes varied from £22.90p at the Victoria Hotel, Latimer Road, to 5d [2p] at the Willingdon Laundry. That year the new building fund opened with a target to raise £25000 [£750000 in to-day's money]. The 1931 Annual Report, stressing the need for a new building, commented "...Visualise the difficulties under which the hospital carries on - narrow passages, inconvenient wards, different floor levels in the converted houses - in which such splendid work for the sick and suffering is being done".

Dr A.H. Croucher retired in 1932 after 44 years, while Miss C.F. Adams commemorated her retirement as headmistress of Eastbourne High School the same year, by presenting a theatre instrument trolley. Among other gifts that year were a sewing machine (from Miss Draper), honey (Mrs Campbell), flowers (from the Ex-Servicemen's Club), 50 eggs (East Dean school); a quart of milk daily from the Sea View Company, and Mr and Mrs Hemsley's wedding bouquet.

50. The original three-gabled house section of the St Anne's Road hospital. Part of the 1934 extension is to the right.

There had been proposals for a new hospital "in keeping with the twentieth century" since 1902 and when it was decided that a new hospital had become essential, the original intention was to build on a site in Ringwood Road. Planning permission was refused, however, so the hospital moved elsewhere. The site chosen was originally leased in 1881 for the building of a dwelling house, *Ivymount,* which by 1933 had become 33 St Anne's Road, and on 2nd June Mr H.B. Grylls transferred the freehold to the Leaf Hospital trustees for £4000.

Messrs James Bodle were selected as contractors, and the firm of B. Stevens as the architects. The original house became the entrance and residencies, while the considerable additions, south towards Arundel Road, included a north-facing operating theatre and a block of wards, with many single cubicles.

Dr E.A. Neatby did not live to see the foundation stone laid by the local MP, Mr John Slater, on 11th October 1933, who was himself to die soon afterwards.

Fund-raising continued apace. Under special donations were £7.50p from the Anderida Lodge of Freemasons, 1/8d [8p] in farthings from Anon., 2/6d [12½p] from the Eastbourne Corporation Slate Club, and a gift of gramophone records from Mrs Astley Roberts. It might be thought that she was simply disposing of household rubbish, but Mrs Astley Roberts was a formidable lady, so it can be presumed that no-one voiced such a suggestion.

The highlight of 1934 was the opening, on Friday 12th October, of the new Leaf Homoeopathic Cottage Hospital, in St Anne's Road: the ceremony being performed by the Rt Hon. Viscount Hailsham. The hospital now had accommodation for 30 patients, "24 public and 6 paying", with a dozen bedrooms for nurses and domestics on the top floor. The "Bun Penny" collection, organised by Mrs J. Robinson and Miss I.J. Dodd, purchased the operating table, and there was almost enough for the operating theatre shadowless lamp.

Throughout the 1930s the patroness remained Her Grace the Duchess of Devonshire, with the Earl of Dysart as president. The "Hon. Sec." was Mr G.A. Hewson, the "Hon. Treas." Mr C.A. Rolleson, and the nursing staff consisted of the matron, Miss E. Tanner, one Sister and four nurses.

During the 1930s the medical staff included Dr R.M. Barron, a GP in Seaside, who gave anæsthetics mainly for ENT cases, and Drs G.F.A. Caldwell and B.S. Kent, both local GPs. Any surgeon could use the private rooms for a patient, but he had to look after the patient, because there were no housemen [junior doctors], the GPs acting as duty doctors. Dr J. Gordon-Wilson, a GP who lived in The Goffs and a well-known mountaineer, joined in 1936, with Mr D.E. O'Connor Cuffey, the ENT surgeon, following in 1937, when the list of operations consisted of 45 appendicectomies, 38 Ts & As, 13 circumcisions and 12 haemorrhoids [piles].[5]

When Mr T. Henry Wilson came on the staff in 1938, he did most of the surgery, which that year included ten mastectomies [removal of breast], 16 hysterectomies [removal of womb], 73 appendicectomies, and only 22 Ts & As. Dr H.J.A. Pollard, a voluntary medical officer at the Leaf, who had come to Eastbourne in 1923, continued to do a certain amount of homoeopathy, and gave anæsthetics at the hospital into the 1950s.

Mr Henry Wilson, an enthusiatic member of the TA, was known to turn up at the operating theatre in full Mess dress, black tie, Blues trousers, half Wellingtons and spurs, if called out from a regimental dinner.

By 1936 the Local Authority made a yearly donation of £15.75p. In addition, for each child referred from the local authority for a tonsil operation, the hospital was paid two guineas [£2.10p]. Perhaps the reason why most children were sent to the ENT hospital was that their charge was only £1.37p.

Before the 1939-45 war the Leaf was a small, sound, cottage hospital, where a private room was £4.50p a week. This was when the surgeon charged about 20 guineas [£21] for an appendix operation [BMA Guidelines in 1990 were £500].

51. The south aspect of the "new" Leaf Hospital in 1934.

Dr Paula Gosling, as a child in the 1930s, remembers waving to her mother, who was in the Leaf for an operation, and who had been brought to a window by one of the nurses, 'No question of actually visiting, of course'. Even when in later years the visiting hours were more accommodating, it was said that the Leaf put the clocks forward, so that visitors wouldn't hang around after visiting time.

In 1939, the hospital joined the Emergency Hospital Scheme, scheduled to provide 31 beds for casualties if necessary. Many of the staff joined the forces, including the nurses, with Sister Roseveare joining the QAIMNS. The year showed a deficit of £1243, and even worse was ahead because the hospital faced paying back the £7500 received in 1936 from the Caleb Diplock inheritance.

During the 1939-45 war the hospital proved its worth for general civilian use and for war casualties, especially after Dunkirk, with Mr James Eadie, now retired to Seaford, remaining on as surgeon and doing good work. Apart from air-raid injuries and victims of traffic accidents in the blackout, a casualty of the war was surely the elderly air-raid warden who, one night in 1941, fell into a bombed basement and died at the Leaf of a fractured skull.

When, in 1940, one of the town's First Aid Posts was damaged by enemy action, it transferred to the Leaf Hospital and remained there for the year.

Mrs Eileen Goldsmith (née Gillam) was in the Leaf during the war and remembers assisting another patient to slide under the bed when the local air-raid siren sounded.[6]

In 1941 the hospital treated 269 in-patients and 147 out-patients. Dr E. Owen Fox joined the staff that year and Mr G.A. Hewson resigned. The next year Miss Tanner resigned after 20 years as matron. Her successor, Miss K.G. Mackenzie, appointed in 1943, proved to be the last matron. Mr A. Lucas Young became the hospital's ophthalmic surgeon in 1944, when there were still 24 general beds and seven private beds.

Services slowly returned to normality, and over 1947-48, there were 494 in-patients in the hospital's 31 beds, who stayed 7889 in-patient days. There were also 527 out-patient attendances. After the war the private fees were advanced to "an outrageous" seven guineas [£7.35p] a week.

With an excess of expenditure over income of £3217 on a total expenditure of £12600, it is perhaps no surprise that the name of the "Hon. Treas." was P.S. Muddell, but the real reason was that, with developments in medicine, private hospitals could no longer depend on donations to pay their way.

The hospital secretary was now Mr E. Haigh and the assistant secretary from 1946 was Miss E.F. Dawes, who was to give devoted service until her retirement in the 1960s. She says, 'The Leaf continued to receive donations and gifts in kind long after the National Health Service started, demonstrating the tremendous goodwill enjoyed by the hospital in the town'. Miss Dawes also explains the origin of the "Bun Penny Brigade"; they were supporters who collected Victorian "Bun" pennies in red-painted cocoa tins scattered throughout the town.

The Duchess of Devonshire was still the patroness in 1947, but the president was now the mayor of Eastbourne. Sir Robert J.S. Dodd was chairman of the committee of management, and the "Honorary Consulting Medical Staff" formed quite a magnificent list, namely Sir John Weir GCVO, Mr David Ligat, Sir James Purves-Stewart KCMG, Dr Alva Benjamin, and Mr James Eadie.[7] Miss Eileen Dawes says that, 'Sir John, a Physician to the Royal Household, took his responsibilities seriously and was a regular and interested visitor'.

Among the "active medical staff" was the ENT surgeon Mr D.E. O'Connor Cuffey, returned from the war, and Dr E. Owen Fox who stayed on as radiologist. The tiny X-ray department also remained until, as Mr Harford-Rees puts it, 'the machine was declared unsafe'. Mr McSwiney, who had come to Eastbourne in 1936, continued the gynæcology service he had started when he joined the Leaf staff in 1939; beforehand, gynæcological surgery had been the province of the general surgeon. Dr B.S. Kent, one of his partners, was anæsthetist at the hospital until 1948. Cmdr G.R.D. Hankinson was now the dental surgeon and Mr W. Shortis the ophthalmic surgeon, after Mr Young emigrated to South Africa.

In view of its financial position, the Leaf was in no position to do other than to welcome the NHS. The Annual Report for 1947 says, "It was felt that no other course could be taken but to agree ...it is our hope that [the hospital] may be allowed to take a worthy part in the new ... scheme".

When the NHS started in 1948 Drs Barron, Caldwell and Gordon-Wilson had their contracts terminated by the Regional Hospital Board. The next year, at a sub-committee of the HMC, the question was raised of just what was meant by being a private patient in the NHS. The official response stated that the emphasis was on equality for private and general patients; they "only pay for privacy".[8]

Sister B.P. Drury recalls a private patient admitted from the Grand Hotel after a heart attack. He recovered, and the staff thought it such a luxury when he went back to London in a limousine ambulance.

Sister Drury attended the same local infants' school as Mr C.R. Brooks who, starting at the Leaf in 1948, became an operating theatre technician (now ODA) and worked there until he moved to the Distict General Hospital in 1976, where he assisted Mr Harford-Rees at the first operation in the new theatres. Above the Leaf operating theatre door was a plaque with the inscription, "This Theatre was furnished and equipped by the Bun-Penny Brigade"; the notice has been saved from destruction by Mr Brooks.

On 1st February 1951, in implementation of the Regional Plan, the Leaf became a gynæcological unit and a component of the Eastbourne Nurse Training School, along with Princess Alice and St Mary's hospitals. Sisters Bevan and Elphick were in command, with Sister Belsey in the operating theatre. That year the Leaf catering staff consisted of Gladys Simmons, the head cook (who was resident), one assistant cook and two kitchen maids.

The same year Mr McSwiney retired and was succeeded, as consultant obstetrician and gynæcologist, by Mr E. Harford-Rees. At that time, there was just Mr Harford-Rees and one junior doctor to look after the Leaf Hospital and the midwifery beds at St Mary's. The next year Dr Bill Watson joined the Leaf anæsthetic staff as the first consultant anæsthetist.

With the NHS, the work became more intense and, in 1953, Miss Mackenzie was persuaded to retire on health grounds. The hospital was absorbed into the Princess Alice administration, with Miss de Pinto matron of both hospitals.

Miss Levett acted as senior Sister at the Leaf and was in charge at night. Sister Levett always did a "tucking-up round" the night before operations when she would say to the patients, 'Now just rest quietly and put your trust in God'.

After the matron left, her flat became vacant and when funds permitted, a resident Senior House Officer was appointed, who covered the gynæcology work and shared the on-call with the other junior doctor.

Sister Betty Drury worked there 1952-58, along with Sister Rudd. Sister W.G. Dupree followed Sister Drury, as ward Sister, and was at the Leaf until its closure. When Sister Betty Belsey resigned on marriage, Sister Gwen Beard took over the running of both the operating theatre and the out-patient clinic.

As Sister Levett's cat often accompanied her to the hospital and Sister Dupree always brought her dog to work, animal life was well represented at the Leaf. Sister Drury mentions the one instance of euthanasia at the hospital, when a pigeon, mauled by a cat, was painlessly "put to sleep" in the operating theatre.

Dr H.J.A. Pollard died of a heart attack, when hand-starting his car in October, 1956. His anæsthetic sessions were taken over by Dr Paul H. Venn, and his sessions at the *Merlynn* convalescent home by Dr D.A.L. Ashforth.

For the Christmas tour of the hospital by the mayor of Eastbourne in 1957 the operating theatre staff laid out the instruments with humorous labels, a case of extraordinarily large needles being marked "Guided Missiles". The issue of the *Eastbourne Herald* for the 28th December carried a photograph of Mr Harford-Rees carving a turkey at the hospital.

The Leaf Hospital made a practice of admitting patients around Christmas; they could be an old lady who would otherwise be on her own, or a hotel proprietor who could not afford to miss the summer season.

In June 1958 Mr Harford-Rees reported that a male nurse had recently been posted to the Leaf theatre, 'an arrangement he did not find satisfactory',[9] but otherwise the Leaf Hospital continued serenely on its way, caring for the gynæcological problems of Eastbourne.

Mrs Grace Taylor thinks of it as, 'A dear little hospital. Mr Harford-Rees said I had to go in for "just a little Spring cleaning"; that didn't stop me being kept in for seven days'.

There were still 31 staffed beds in 1966-67 which were 80% occupied by 725 patients, who had 718 operations. Out-patient attendances were 4078. A WRVS canteen, for use by staff and patients, was opened at the Leaf by Mrs E. Haddon-Carter in March 1968.

Mrs E.M. Fuller (née Walder) says, 'Night duty at the Leaf was lovely compared with the general hospitals. You were able to sleep for an hour on a bed in an empty side ward, and the cook was like a mother to the young nurses'.

Mrs E.M. Thorogood recalls being sent to do her theatre stint at the Leaf, rather than the general hospitals, because she was a little nervous. She says that Mr Harford-Rees was so kind and encouraging; 'He used to sing in the theatre and I think it helped us all'.

While the work was mostly gynæcology there were a few single rooms for private patients. Assistant Nurse M. Hastings remembers she was washing a titled private patient when Dr Bodkin Adams came in to visit. Afterwards, the patient said he was such a nice man and Nurse Hastings was not to believe all those awful things people said about him. 'When he went out he left behind a parcel for the patient, but it was only a box of paper tissues.'

Mr Harford-Rees, with Dr Linacre as his anæsthetist, did his private patients and terminations first thing in the morning before the main list was due to start.

Mrs M. Neal-Edwards provided some consultant cover for ten years from 1960, and among Mr Harford-Rees' assistants over the years were Miss E. Coates, Miss P. Black and Mrs M. Khan. Dr Mary Simpson took over the sub-fertility clinic from Mrs Neal-Edwards, until Mr Shardlow joined the staff.

Dr M.I. Baig, a senior house officer at the Leaf in 1971, comments that when he was resident he was the only male in the hospital.

Around 1970 Sisters Dupree and Ginn were the night sisters, and other nurses included Staff Nurses Greenish, Thorpe, McGarry and Holden. Mrs W.M. Woodward had taken over as the admin. assistant on Miss Eileen Dawes' retirement, and Miss Pallot was secretary to Mr Harford-Rees. She was succeeded by Miss Margaret Somerfield who, still there when the Leaf closed, moved with the unit to the District General Hospital in 1976. Mr Harford-Rees points out that the Leaf secretary had to, 'liaise with the GPs, act as almoner, admission clerk, and returner of returns, apart from doing all the typing and anything else needed'. Miss Somerfield adds that she arranged convalescence for patients and also paid the weekly wages for the domestic and office staff.

There was just the one X-ray room at the hospital, with a radiographer attending once a week on Thursday mornings for routine requests. A radiographer called each day for any urgent cases.

In 1970 the cost of provisions was £1.81p per person per week. That year a new telephone switchboard was installed in the board room, thus releasing the waiting room for use entirely as intended, and the following year the Leaf was given £200 out of voluntary gifts funds for its furniture allowance. Perhaps it was the new, comfortable chairs that were responsible for the number of library books issued to patients increasing to 786 in 1972.

In most of the Eastbourne hospitals regular religious services on the wards diminished in the 1950s and 60s, but ward services lasted at the Leaf into 1973.

Mrs Shirley Peckham, occupational therapist, looked forward to visiting the Leaf and viewing the flowers, while the patients welcomed the visits of squirrels through the french-windows. 'The Leaf had a fortunate site, with a lovely garden, full of trees for the birds, which the patients enjoyed in summer, plus the first-rate catering by Mrs Simmons and her team. It was a happy unit.'

Up to the closure the hospital continued with 28 gynæcological beds and three private beds. In February 1974, from a waiting list of 573, there were 75 gynæcology waiting-list admissions and three private admissions.

Sister G. Beard, the operating theatre Sister for many years, retired in January 1975. Mrs Marie Brunt (née McGarry) recalls that "Tiny" (as Sister Beard was called) delighted in hearing Sister McGarry mimic her laying out the theatre trolleys for the next day's operating list, 'Now let's see, two tummies, one repair and two D & Cs'. Mr Cyril Brooks remained the ODA.

In October 1975 Mr Julian Shardlow was appointed as an additional consultant obstetrician and gynæcologist. Mrs Khan left a year afterwards and Mr D.N. Roychoudhuri took her place. Until the closure of the hospital the custom continued of the consultant carving a turkey on the wards at Christmas.

The last gynæcological out-patient clinic at the Leaf closed on Friday 28th May 1976, and the in-patients were transferred to the District General Hospital. The empty hospital was maintained on a care and maintenance basis - which even so cost £8500 a year. The envisaged use was as a geriatric hospital, until the CHC proposed a chiropody school in Eastbourne on the Leaf site. In December 1979, following talks with Brighton Polytechnic (now University), the go-ahead was given for the Regional Health Authority to spend £500000 converting the Leaf Hospital into the Sussex School of Chiropody[10], although the final cost was £1303000. This was opened on 23rd November 1983 by Sir Peter Baldwin KCB, with Mr M.F. Whiting as Principal Lecturer and Mr P.A. Shenton as his deputy.

Following recent changes in further education, the building has been renamed "The Leaf Hospital, Department of Podiatry, of the University of Brighton" with Professor Michael Whiting as head of the department.

So the Misses Leaf's name and their "Cottage Hospital" will keep on into the twenty-first century.

Notes and References

1. Wright JC. *Bygone Eastbourne.* (Spottiswoode, London 1902); 252.

2. Leaf Homoeopathic Cottage Hospital, Annual Report, 1913.

3. Ibid., 1914.

4. *Eastbourne Gazette,* 9/3/1921.

5. Leaf Homoeopathic Cottage Hospital, Annual Report, 1937.

6. With Eastbourne directly facing the enemy-held coast, the regular air-raid warning often sounded long after the German planes had come and gone. After representations, Eastbourne was allowed to sound its own air-raid warning - called "The Cuckoo" by the local population.

7. The Leaf Hospital, Annual Report, 1947.

8. Eastbourne HMC, catering sub-committee, 9/2/49, min. 60.

9. Eastbourne HMC, Group Medical Committee, 10/6/58; min. 1854.

10. *Eastbourne Herald,* 1/12/79.

Chapter 15

The Maternity Home

Up to 1919 Eastbourne did not have a maternity home. A few nursing homes catered for the affluent, there were a few beds at the workhouse (later St Mary's Hospital) for emergencies, otherwise midwifery cases were attended at home. If a doctor was called out for an emergency delivery case it was not easy to obtain admission to St Mary's out of hours and, if he did manage to arrange it, the voluntary ambulance service was not at its speediest in the middle of the night.

Dr G.D. Sherwood describes being called to an exhausted mother whose baby was stuck with a hand presentation, and having to do a "podalic version" [turning the baby round] by a mixture of antiseptic and aseptic techniques, while the midwife dropped on the anæsthetic. "With the danger of infection, was I glad, at the end of ten days, that both mother and child had survived."[1]

Childbirth was still risky, for after the immediate improvement in maternal mortality with the introduction of antiseptic techniques in the mid-nineteenth century, there was surprisingly little further change. Maternal mortality was around 1 in 200 births in 1850, was 1 in 250 in 1906 and almost the same in 1934, and if there was any concomitant condition, such as rheumatic heart disease, it could be much higher.

Mothers died from infection, exsanguination and exhaustion. Puerperal (childbed) fever [described by Hippocrates 2500 years ago] caused half the maternal deaths. Eastbourne had five cases in 1902, two of which were fatal. It was the cruellest of tragedies, and a family disaster, if the mother, having survived the ordeal of labour, died of infection a few days later.[2] Hence it was not until the "sulpha drugs", blood transfusions, and improved Cæsarian sections became easily available in the 1930s that the maternal mortality rate (and the baby's prospects) improved to such an extent that nowadays a maternal death is a most exceptional happening and an occasion for review.

There was little educational or preventative work in maternity and child health until the end of the 1914-18 war, when the Maternity and Child Welfare Act of 1918 gave an opportunity for regular welfare work.

Dr W.G. Willoughby, the Medical Officer of Health, realised the need for hospital beds and looked around for suitable accommodation. In November 1919, at his instigation, No. 9 Upperton Road was bought for £4179 from Miss Minnie

Davies Gilbert and conveyed in March 1920 to the "Mayor, Alderman and Burgesses of the County Borough of Eastbourne", for use as a Municipal Maternity Home.

The first building on this site had been in 1865 when the plot was leased to James Dexter by Charles Glyn Prideaux Brune and John Samuel Enys. The premises were named *Woodlands,* and faced New Road [now Upperton Road] with, at the rear, the "road from Eastbourne Old Town to the seaside" [later Water Lane and now Southfields Road]. By 1902 the house was called *Enfield,* when an extension was agreed by the landlord, Carew Davies Gilbert, and it was known as No. 9 Upperton Road from around 1914.

In October 1915 it was leased for use as a Voluntary Red Cross Hospital, and in 1917 a sectional building was erected in the grounds for use as a recreational hut by the convalescent troops. A doorway was made which led down steps so that hospital and hut could be connected by a covered way.

By 1920, owned by the local authority, it was Eastbourne's Maternity Home, with six beds, for married mothers only. The patients were, by and large, under the care of their general practitioner, although after the first year Mr A.H. Crook provided a consulting obstetrical service. Miss C.B. Macintosh was the matron. It was funded by the Borough Council, with the aid of fees and a government grant, and patients paid two guineas a week [£2.10p]. In 1925 of 146 mothers, full charges were paid by 134, part charges by eight, and four failed to pay.

Meanwhile, in 1918 a maternity and child welfare clinic had been started at the Town Hall. The ante-natal clinic was held twice a week at the town hall, but "special cases were seen at the Maternity Home". In 1930 *Avenue House* in The Avenue, which had been the Union Guardians' headquarters, became the site for welfare clinics. In 1934 it was extended to take the maternity clinic.

In 1920 there were 993 births in Eastbourne, with 16 stillbirths and an infant mortality (that is, the number dying from birth to 12 months old) of 59.8 per1000. In other words about 60 babies died in their first year of life, one reason why Dr Willoughby was keen to use part of "No. 9" as an Infants' Home.

Mr Eardley Holland told a local meeting in 1923 that 50% of stillbirths were due to complications of labour and 15% were due to syphilis. "The foetus was killed by too quick a delivery and half the deaths could be prevented".[3]

The first blood transfusion at the Maternity Home was in 1924, and it was around the mid-twenties that there occurred the first, and possibly only, instance of a male being admitted and put to bed in the Maternity Home. One of the mothers needed a blood transfusion, which in those days had to be provided from friends and relatives. Her husband was bled to provide the blood and in the course of the donation he fainted, fell, cut his head and was put in a bed to recover.

By 1924 the Maternity Home had 144 deliveries (20% of births in the town) of which 13 died. There were two stillbirths and one Cæsarian section during the year. With 120 attendances at the ante-natal clinic and a long waiting list, an extension to the Home became essential. During the alterations the Infants Home, also at "No 9", was reduced to eight cots, but nominally it had 16 beds, or 18 cots, a number which was exceeded for short periods.

The extensions, completed in May 1925, provided four extra maternity beds, facilities for ante-natal and post-natal clinics and bedrooms for the staff.[4]

In 1925, when there were 147 deliveries, doctors delivered 48% of the mothers, and midwives the remainder. The main reasons for midwives seeking medical assistance were contracted pelvis, delayed labour, breech presentation, prolapsed cord and adherent placenta [afterbirth]. The average duration of stay was 17½ days. It was the year that the Maternity Home was sanctioned as a Training Centre for Midwives, and of the seven nurses accepted for training, four sat and obtained the Central Midwives Board examination during their stay. Unfortunately, 1925 also saw an outbreak of "summer diarrhoea" in the Infants' Home with two deaths, which was ascribed to infected milk.

Councillors Miss A. Hudson, Miss D. Chamberlain and Miss E.M. Thornton had been instrumental, with Dr Willoughby and Dr H.E. Coghill, in establishing an Infants' Home, or baby care unit, at No. 9 Upperton Road. It opened on the same day as the Maternity Home - 10th March 1920. At the beginning the unit's 18 cots were designated for "ailing infants without definite disease, permanently or temporarily deprived of a home with their own parents; infants suffering from prematurity or malnutrition are also received". In its first nine months 115 cases were admitted; they included two of marasmus [failure to thrive] and two of prematurity - so most of the cases must have been "deprived". They had an average stay of 26 days, and ten deaths occurred.

Mrs Doris M. Bates (née Clarke) was only fourteen when she started there. She had always wanted to nurse and when she left school, 'Miss Macintosh, the small, dark and Scottish matron, agreed that I could start in a month's time at nine o'clock. I was there at eight o'clock and one of the nurses said, "You're not expected till nine, but as you are here you can do the brasses". I said, "I haven't come to do the brasses, I've come to look after the babies," but I soon found out that as the youngest nurse I was there to do the brasses. We cared for sick, premature, rickety and marasmic babies from a few days to a year old, when they were returned to their homes or went for fostering. We had basic lectures in anatomy, physiology and the nursing care of sick infants from Drs Hester Coghill, Daphne Dear, Ethel Downing and Bodkin Adams. The training was for two years, followed by an examination and a certificate of proficiency in the feeding and care of infants. There were up to 16 babies in the main building and on occasions another 12 in an old army-type hutment in the grounds [this was the ex-recreation hut, described as an "open-air building" by Dr Willoughby]. Apart from Sister Dare who was in charge, all the nurses were very young, but they cared for those infants wonderfully and dressed them beautifully in clothes we made from materials supplied by the three lady councillors. Those infants received "Tender, Loving Care", they were massaged with olive oil - cod liver oil for the tiniest - and they thrived and grew bonny. Mrs Cottingham, whose daughters, Dorothy and Lily, were maids, coped with the huge amounts of washing, single-handed, hanging it on big airers before being mangled - it was not ironed. She was an extremely thin lady, who wore a sacking apron and heavy soled boots, but she always had a smile for us nurses.

'Our salary was £1 per month. Our parents bought the uniform and with three tucks it lasted well. As an outdoor uniform we wore blue coats and veils. One bonus was the bathing tent rented for the staff on the seafront and we bathed until October.

'The feeding methods in vogue were those of Sir Truby King, the New Zealand doctor who pioneered mothercraft. Raw milk was delivered to the kitchen daily, the feeds made up and pasteurised in a large fish kettle. The milk was then stored in an icebox. On summer evenings we collected vegetables from the garden and started the next day's supply of veal bone broth.

'Once a year there was a Summer Garden Party, so-called "Bun Struggle Day", when all the eminent people came to swell the funds. On Twelfth Night there was a Christmas dinner and dance. One year I danced with Dr Bodkin Adams, all I remember was that his dinner jacket smelt strongly of moth balls.' Mrs Bates especially recalls Christmas 1926 when at Miss Macintosh's instigation, the midwives and nurses Clarke, McDowell and Neall, as well as Sister Dare, dressed up as flowers.

'In the 1920s Dr Bodkin Adams lived opposite the Maternity Home and, as he never drew his bedroom windows, the on-duty midwives, if they wished, could watch his preparations for bed from across Upperton Road'.

Mrs Bates goes on to say, 'There was a selection of lovely old prams in which the infants were given an airing in the Mat. Home garden, and a massive *Dunkley* pram in which we proudly wheeled them along the seafront, often in our off-duty time'. The day staff were non-resident, but became resident for night duty when the hours were 0800 to 2000h. There was no break, you just asked one of the midwives to keep an eye on your charges while you had a rest. When on nights you coped with both wards, kept an eye on, and stoked if necessary, the boiler, and kept the meals warm for the midwives. Nurse Collyer, the midwife, who lived in the Maternity Home, was often called out at night by the face of an anxious father appearing at the basement window of the milk kitchen to appeal for "Nurse to come", and off into the darkness would go the midwife and pupil midwife, with their bags, on their bicycles, in all weathers'.

Mrs Bates did fever nursing at Hove sanatorium (later Forelands Hospital), her general training at St Mary's, was also a health visitor in the 1950s and, from 1960-71, assistant matron at Downside Hospital - apart from raising her family.

With the passage of time, the numbers of ailing infants decreased and, as the demand for maternity beds increased, the Infants' Home was abandoned in 1929. An occasional infant would still be admitted, but after 1932 such cases tended to go to St Mary's Hospital.[5] The closure of the Infants' Home gave space to increase the number of maternity beds from ten to 16.

The Maternity Home continued as a midwifery training school, with pupils coming from as far as London for the statutory six months' experience.

By 1932 Miss H.A.G. Collyer had been succeeded by Miss L.M. Smith as the municipal midwife for external work. The municipal midwife attended over 50 midwifery cases annually on the district, that is, outside hospital.

That year the number of deliveries in the Home was 252, which represented a third of the births in Eastbourne. The staff for the 16 beds comprised the matron, one Sister, two midwives, five pupil midwives and one probationer.

When, in 1935, Miss P. Bavington succeeded Miss Smith as the resident municipal midwife, 107 district confinements were attended in the Borough.

During early 1936 the Maternity Home received the St Mary's Hospital maternity cases while alterations were carried out there. Later, in 1936 and into 1937, the Home itself was enlarged to enable it to cope with the number of cases applying for admission, and to provide accommodation for the domestic staff.

The 1937 reconstruction extended the capacity from 16 to 25 beds, although at one point during the building work only 12 beds were available. This extension was opened by Sir Arthur S. MacNalty, Chief Medical Officer at the Ministry of Health, on 3rd June 1938.

In 1938 Mrs D. Dougall (née Funnell) was a nursery nurse at the Home, and she recalls, 'If Mr MacQueen was called in for a case everyone stood to attention, whereas Dr Bodkin Adams didn't stand on any ceremony and would just want to be shown to the patient'.

As part of the preparations for war, under the Emergency Hospital Scheme (EHS), the ten-bed St Mary's Hospital maternity unit was closed in July 1939, and the Maternity Home capacity increased from 25 to 45 beds, by boarding out the resident staff at 1 The Goffs. The aim was to cope with the predicted expectant evacuees. Of the 164 expectant mothers evacuated to Eastbourne in September 1939, all did well and 93 were successfully delivered before Christmas.

When the Germans reached the other side of the Channel, in June 1940, Eastbourne changed from an evacuation area to a front-line town. The resident staff returned to the Maternity Home in the July, but on 14th September it was closed. St Mary's Hospital opened a seven-bed unit for emergencies, and routine midwifery was sent inland to Langton Green, Tunbridge Wells or East Grinstead, with a few going as far as Stratford-on-Avon, Oxford or Woking. In 1943, volunteer car drivers took some 129 expectant mothers inland for delivery.

The Home remained part of the EHS, holding in reserve 25 beds routinely, and a maximum of 45, ready for casualties, until 1941 when it was withdrawn from the scheme. Despite requests from general practitioners for an early re-opening, the Maternity Home stayed closed for most of the war.

It opened again on 6th March 1945, with 23 beds, and within a year had 320 confinements (188 by midwives and 132 by doctors). The average stay was 14 days. By now Mr S.A. McSwiney was the on-call doctor for consultations, but he was not involved in the running of the home and for that matter was not often consulted about the midwifery. The matron was Miss Rowe, whose 13 midwifery staff shared the deliveries with general practitioners. When Mrs H.J. Murphy, physiotherapist to the orthopædic clinic, returned from the armed forces, she gave the mothers post-natal exercises.[6]

In 1947-48 there were 25 beds, with 477 in-patients who stayed 6124 in-patient days. Including the *Avenue House* clinic, 3738 out-patient attendances were recorded.

When the National Health Service started in 1948, the Mat. Home reached the peak of its popularity, with two-thirds of local babies being born there. Mothers wanted a rest, and aimed to avoid the laundry involved in a homebirth. In the course of 1949 there were 550 births at the Mat. Home, 201 home births, 64 in private nursing homes, only seven at St Mary's, and just one at the Princess Alice. For the first time all expectant women attending the ante-natal clinics were routinely tested for the rhesus factor [a cause of jaundice in the baby], as well as other blood groups, and WR and Kahn tests [for syphilis].

With the NHS, ante- and post-natal clinics for domiciliary deliveries were transferred from the Maternity Home to the local authority clinics.

One unchanging medical and lay obsession remained "The Bowels". Costiveness over two days warranted castor oil, neat, in a tumbler rinsed in cold water so that the oil flowed turgidly. This appalling draught continued to be on standard issue when admitted for labour into the early 1960s.

In 1951 Mr S.A. McSwiney retired, to be replaced by Mr E. Harford-Rees. Mr McSwiney had been ultra-conservative in the management of childbirth, and he was so irascible that colleagues took no notice of his short-fuse antics and just laughed at him, but he was knowledgeable and before he came to Eastbourne the speciality of obstetrics had been entirely in the hands of general practitioners.

It was also the year that the Mat. Home stopped keeping chickens, although the vegetable beds stayed for a year or two. The catering staff consisted of one head cook, one assistant cook and two kitchen maids.[7]

In 1953 there was some concern about the incidence of infections among the mothers. After discussions and meetings a protocol was agreed whereby Mr Harford-Rees visited every day and did a clinic on Saturdays and any cases needing consultant care were to be transferred to St Mary's Hospital.

The Regional Board, in 1954, arranged a system of cover for Mr Harford-Rees by Mr J.F. Foulkes from Hastings. It wasn't of much practical help but being single-handed in his speciality, he was otherwise effectively permanently on-call. The arrangement only lasted to April 1960. Later that year Mrs M. Neal-Edwards was given three half-day sessions for on-call at the consultant rate of £5.75p per half-day session. This arrangement was also not entirely satisfactory as Mrs Neal-Edwards lived 25 miles away in Hove, but it lasted until she resigned in 1970, having reached retirement age four years earlier. At least approval had been given for a Junior Hospital Medical Officer and as a result, over the years Mr Harford-Rees received some help from Miss E. Coates, Miss P. Black, and Mrs Muzzafar Khan, who was graded medical assistant in 1966.

Mrs Judy Baker hasn't forgotten that 'If you had a day or so to go before labour, Mr Harford-Rees would declare, "Mother Nature isn't ready for you to-day". Not that you didn't soon know when Mother Nature was ready because, just beforehand, you were given a concoction of dry bread, an orange and castor oil'.

Sister Mary Bridger (but always known as Jane) was at the Maternity for twenty years from 1955 and reckons she must have delivered about 1000 babies there, apart from assisting at many more births. She says, 'The hospital was a lovely place. The wards were bright and the whole place was so clean. The routine was strict: the babies were kept in the nursery in neat rows and went out to feed precisely every four hours - and the Dads were only allowed to view them through the nursery window. In the 1950s we had a matron and an assistant matron, and matron even had her own maid. Gradually it was whittled down to just an assistant matron.

'The GPs looked after their own patients and Mr Harford-Rees did a clinic once a week for any problems. Sometimes a mother in labour had to be transferred to St Mary's Hospital, which was traumatic for all concerned.

'I have known a GP turn-out three times in a night, each time immaculately dressed, and I have even seen Dr Bodkin Adams wielding a pair of forceps.

'The gardens were beautiful, Mr Read, Mr Binns and Mr Leslie Ingham, the gardeners, producing lovely vegetables for the patients' meals. And, like many hospitals we had a resident cat, Jimmy was the name of the one in my time.'

Mr Ingham, who started at the Mat. Home in 1949, says, 'We had a wonderful bank of blackcurrant bushes and we kept a few apple trees and vegetables almost to the end'.

Mrs S. McCrindle, who as Sylvia Hinde started her general nurse training at the Princess Alice in 1952, comments 'The food for mothers and staff was cooked on the Mat. Home premises and staff meals were taken at a communal table, with as many as work allowed sitting down together with the matron. Mrs Visick came in to wash all the baby clothes and on a good day these were hung out to dry in the garden. The staff embroidered flowers on all the baby-gowns, even taking them home to complete if there hadn't been a spare moment, and bootees were made for every baby.'

After the war there were many changes of matron. Miss D.E. Charles, there through the early fifties, was followed by Miss F.W. Mosley. Miss Charles was a noted breeder of poodles. When Miss D.M. Furse, matron 1956-59, resigned on marriage, she was replaced by Miss R.K. Hobart and in turn Miss E. Mickle, who came from the army. The matron from 1962 was Mrs W. Deans who resigned in November 1963 and Mrs M. Pitslow succeeded. When she retired in 1966 she was not replaced, and the general hospitals' matron, Miss Norah Davies, took over with Miss Gladys Rudd acting as assistant matron at the Maternity Home.

Gradually the pattern of obstetrics changed and the call on the Maternity Home beds diminished. The maternity clinics, which were overcrowded and at St Mary's Hospital mixed up with other clinics and staff medical examinations, were transferred over the years from *Avenue House* and St Mary's Hospital to the ground floor of the Maternity Home. The two labour wards upstairs were preserved for deliveries, but from the mid-1960s most births were at St Mary's Hospital, where by now the facilities were handier for blood transfusion or Cæsarian section.

52. The frontage of No. 9 Upperton Road in 1993.

In 1966-67 the Home had 27 staffed beds, 67% occupied daily by a total of 646 patients. There were now 3962 ante- and post-natal out-patient attendances.[8]

Fortunately, the Eastbourne hospitals were always well supported by generous gifts, and the Eastbourne Round Table presented an incubator to the Maternity Home in February 1968. In October of that year the HMC agreed that

10 Mat. Home beds could be used for gynæcological conditions, but "to save embarrassment to single women it should be known as the convalescent wing".[9]

By the spring of 1970, when the cost for provisions per person per week remained only £1.61p, the nurses in post totalled 20 and comprised the assistant matron, one night Sister, five midwifery Sisters, one Staff Nurse, four Staff Midwives, five nursery nurses and three enrolled nurses.

Later that year a running battle commenced about husbands being present at the birth. In December 1970 the HMC considered a request for husbands to be present at their wives' confinements, but on the advice of Mr Harford-Rees the request was refused due to lack of adequate facilities at the Maternity Home, although husbands could be present at the first stage and facilities would be available in the new District General Hospital at Kings Drive.[10] The next year Mr Lelliott, the HMC chairman, received a petition containing 1013 signatures calling upon the HMC to permit husbands and wives to experience the birth of their child together.[11]

In 1971-72 the Maternity Home was allowed to spend £200 on furniture, and there were proposals to use 10 beds on the ground floor for elderly orthopædic patients, on a temporary basis. The ground floor still housed clinics and a few gynæcology patients. The following year the last of the St Mary's ante-natal clinics transferred, the use of two rooms by the commissioning team for the new Kings Drive hospital was agreed, and once again the question of husbands being present at births was discussed at length by the HMC.[12]

Otherwise, visiting was now on Wednesdays, Saturdays and Sundays between 1430 and 1530h, and husbands only were allowed every evening.

Miss L.W. West became nursing officer with overall responsibility for the midwifery services in 1974, and had an office at the Maternity Home with Mrs J. Holding, her secretary. The assistant matron was Miss E. Vine and Sister P. Merrell was her deputy. Other staff included Sister S. McCrindle, who went on to be clinical midwifery manager at the new Litlington ward in the District General Hospital, midwife A. Huggins (née Stone) and nursery nurse P. Hughes (née Harvey). Mrs R.E. Alce, who had been at "29", was the hospital clerk, assisted by Mrs M. Knight (née Charie). There were 17 GP beds and 10 other beds available in 1974, which saw about 30 booked admissions each month.

After 1974, the ambulance service became the responsibility of the East Sussex Area Health Authority, and when it was decided to locate the headquarters in Eastbourne, a prefabricated construction was built in the grounds of the Maternity Home, facing onto Southfields Road. This ambulance control centre opened on 1st April 1977. As a consequence almost all the gardens were covered by buildings, or tarmac for car parks.

At least the Maternity Home avoided the indignity of the St Mary's Hospital Maternity unit where, for a short time before it closed, admin. affixed a wire-mesh rubbish basket in the entrance wall, which displayed the instruction, "Place your litter here".

At last in October 1975 an extra consultant obstetrician and gynæcologist was appointed, when Mr J.P. Shardlow joined Mr Harford-Rees.

Over 1975, the last full year of the Maternity Home, live births at all the Eastbourne hospitals amounted to 1831 plus 15 stillborn. Even with Eastbourne's increasing population, the good traditions of the Mat. Home are being maintained, for while the hospital births had increased to 2158 by 1986, there were only seven stillbirths, although one of 15 domiciliary births was a stillbirth.

Perhaps the best compliment is in Mrs McCrindle's words, 'So many of the midwifery staff, including myself, had their own babies there and remember it with affection'.

The Maternity Home closed in May 1976, when the patients and staff were transferred to the District General Hospital's Litlington ward and out-patient unit. The building became an administrative block for the Eastbourne Health District, and also housed the offices of the Community Health Council. In 1982, after refurbishment of the plumbing, and some tarting-up, the conception was to use it as the headquarters of the Eastbourne Health Authority. In 1992 it became heavy with the Financial Services of the Eastbourne NHS Trust, but is soon to be delivered into ecclesiastical hands.

Notes and References

1. *Eastbourne Medical Gazette,* 1976; 2: 25.

2. Loudin I. *BMJ,* 1987; **295**: 485-90.

3. Eastbourne Medical Society, 30/1/1923.

4. Medical Officer of Health for Eastbourne, Annual Report, 1925.

5. Ibid. 1933.

6. Ibid. 1945.

7. Eastbourne HMC, catering sub-committee, 10/1/51, min. 320.

8. Eastbourne Hospital Management Committee, Annual Report, 1966-67.

9. Eastbourne HMC, 7/8/68, min. 5151, and 2/10/68, min. 5172.

10. Ibid., 2/12/70, min. 5636.

11. Ibid., 3/3/71, min. 5691.

12. Ibid., 3/1/73, min. 6144.

INDEX